NEUROPSYCHOLOGY: THE STUDY OF BRAIN AND BEHAVIOR

CHARLES M. BUTTER

The University of Michigan

BROOKS/COLE PUBLISHING COMPANY
Belmont, California

A Division of Wadsworth Publishing Company, Inc.

To Irene, Pamela, and Noah

BROOKS/COLE PUBLISHING COMPANY
A Division of Wadsworth Publishing Company, Inc.

L. C. Cat. Card No.: 68-21883.

Printed in the United States of America

SERIES FOREWORD

Basic Concepts in Psychology was conceived as a series of brief paperback volumes constituting a beginning textbook in psychology. Several unique advantages arise from publishing individual chapters as separate volumes rather than under a single cover. Each book or chapter can be written by an author identified with the subject matter of the area. New chapters can be added, individual chapters can be revised independently, and, possibly, competitive chapters can be provided for controversial areas. Finally, to a degree, an instructor of the beginning course in psychology can choose a particular set of chapters to meet the needs of his students.

Probably the most important impetus for the series came from the fact that a suitable textbook did not exist for the beginning courses in psychology at the University of Michigan—Psychology 100 (Psychology as a Natural Science) and Psychology 101 (Psychology as a Social Science). In addition, no laboratory manual treated both the natural science and social science problems encountered in the first laboratory course, Psychology 110.

For practical rather than ideological reasons, the initial complement of authors comes from the staff of the University of Michigan. Coordination among geographically dispersed authors seems needlessly difficult, and the diversity of points of view in the Department of Psychology at Michigan makes the danger of parochialism quite small.

Each author in the Basic Concepts in Psychology Series has considerable freedom. He has been charged to devote approximately half of his resources to elementary concepts and half to topics of special interest and emphasis. In this way, each volume will reflect the personality and viewpoint of the author while presenting the subject matter usually found in a chapter of an elementary textbook.

AUTHOR'S FOREWORD

The study of neural processes mediating behavior has taken rapid strides in recent years, and in this book I have attempted to document some of these advances. Inevitably, the size of the present volume has required that a selection be made from the voluminous material in this field. The selection I have made includes samples of the various areas of research dealing with the neural regulation of behavior. The focus of this volume is on the analysis of functional neural systems which mediate behavior at a level of complexity of interest to psychologists. Thus, the term "neuropsychology" is used here in the original sense of Lashley's—a joining together of the neural and the psychological. Moreover, wherever possible, I have emphasized the manner in which neuropsychological investigations have contributed to our understanding of behavior. The material dealing with neuroanatomy and neuron physiology, which presents stumbling-blocks for the psychology student, has been kept to the minimum necessary for understanding the more complex neural processes.

I take this opportunity to express my gratitude to the several people whose services have contributed to this book. Karl Pribram and Daniel Kimble offered many suggestions and criticisms of an initial draft of the entire book, and Merle Lawrence, Mathew Alpern, and Rudolph von Baumgarten provided critical evaluations of the chapters dealing with the sensory and motor systems. Edward Walker and Charles T. Hendrix provided valuable advice and suggestions at all stages from initial planning to final production, and Robert Mann added considerably in the final editing process. Donna Adler and Laura Smedley helped with the editing and typing of the manuscript, as did Irene Daniel, who helped organize some of the material. Finally, Leslie Thurston was responsible for most of the figures which appear here; the remainder were drawn by Jean Koelling.

CONTENTS

INTRODUCTION

1

". . . the small gland which is the principal seat of the soul is suspended between cavities containing . . . animal spirits in such a manner that it can be moved by them in as many different ways as there are sensible differences between objects . . . and conversely . . . the soul . . . impels the surrounding spirits toward the pores of the brain, through which they are conducted by the nerves into the muscles, by means of which the soul causes them to move our limbs . . ."

Long before the advent of neuropsychology, men grappled with the problem of how the body governs behavior. The quotation above shows that the philosopher Descartes attempted to explain behavior by means of "animal spirits" acting on the pineal body, a small structure within the brain. Although contemporary descriptions of brain functions are markedly different from those offered by Descartes, modern science does uphold the historic view that the brain is the primary organ controlling thought and action.

In fact, modern science has greatly strengthened this view by providing more complete knowledge of how the brain operates. In their efforts to understand how behavior is determined by activity of the brain, today's investigators are reaching the point where they can envisage some of the neural events associated with states such as hunger, sleep, and even dreaming. But before we turn to the findings of neuropsychology, we should consider certain fundamental views neuropsychologists share with other scientists who study psychological problems.

THE SCIENTIFIC APPROACH TO PSYCHOLOGICAL PROBLEMS

THE BEHAVIORISTIC VIEW

According to the behavioristic view, one knows what an animal (or a human) senses, what it can learn, and what it likes and dislikes only by observing the animal's responses—the activity of its muscles and certain glands. In short, by this generally accepted view, psychological events are described objectively in terms of observed behavior. Thus, in order to tell whether an animal can hear a particular sound, one must observe whether the animal consistently responds to the sound in some way, perhaps by pricking up its ears or turning toward the sound source. Likewise, one can determine an animal's food preferences only by observing what it eats when it has the choice of several foods.

Behaviors such as ear pricking, turning, and choosing a food are all public events in the sense that one person can observe them and others can check and validate the observations; by contrast, thoughts are private events that cannot be directly observed. Thus, in order to study thinking, a psychologist observes its overt consequences–behavior in problem-solving situations. The behavioristic approach, then, provides an objective basis for the study of all psychological events.

DETERMINISM AND THE MECHANISTIC VIEW

A basic working assumption of behavioral science is that the behavior of organisms is like all other material events in that it is determined by physical events and can be predicted when all relevant conditions are known.

A physical event that evokes a response from an animal is referred to as a stimulus. For instance, one may consider the presentation of food to be a stimulus when it evokes the response of eating. Moreover, according to the mechanistic view, a stimulus evokes a response only if the stimulus produces some physical effect on the central nervous system, which consists of the brain and spinal cord. In other words, the central nervous system (CNS) provides the mechanism whereby physical events become effective stimuli for evoking responses.

This mechanistic view may be better understood if we consider two closely related concepts of biological science: structure and function. The way in which the organs within our bodies are built (that is, their structure) determines the way in which they operate (that is, their function). Thus, for example, the structure of the heart—its chambers, valves, and its connections with blood vessels—determines its pumping action and the way in which blood is circulated. Likewise, the structure of the CNS—the connections between sense organs and muscles—determines how it operates and thus how we behave. Information is conveyed from sense organs via nerves to the CNS, and responses are produced by messages emanating from the CNS via another set of nerves. The CNS, then, provides the connections for linking together stimuli and responses.

Here is an illustration of the way the CNS provides this connection. When sense organs inside the mouth are stimulated by food, nerves carry "messages" about this event to certain brain centers; these centers then send messages to other centers, from which, in turn, nerves travel to muscles which perform chewing and swallowing movements. On the other hand, if some unpleasant or inedible substance enters the mouth, sense organs send different messages to the brain; then certain brain centers are activated so that a pattern of muscular activity producing rejection of the substance takes place. In both of these cases, the brain receives a message on the basis of which it signals a particular set of muscles to perform appropriate movements—ingestion in the case of edible substances and rejection in the case of inedible substances. Appropriate movements such as these are adaptive in that they contribute to the survival and to the integrity of the organism.

Of course, chewing and swallowing are not single responses; rather, they consist of a series of smoothly coordinated muscular activities. This coordination, a fundamental feature of all bodily movements, has two important aspects: temporal integration and spatial integration. First of all, muscular movements take place in a particular sequence. Chewing and swallowing, for instance, do not accomplish their functions if they are not properly ordered. This sequential organization is referred to as temporal integration. Secondly, there is the coordination of muscles which act simultaneously, as in two legs in the act of walking. This spatial integration, like temporal integration, is essential for the performance of adaptive movements. According to the mechanistic view, the CNS is responsible for coordination of muscular activities. We will examine some of the ways in which the CNS provides integrative functions in the following chapters, after we consider the goals and techniques of neuropsychology.

It should be pointed out that the mechanistic view of behavior presented here is not a matter of belief; the scientist does not profess it as an article of faith. Rather, he uses it as a working assumption. That is, the investigator is willing to accept this view, at least for the time being, in order to conduct experiments. If the results of his experiments suggest a close relationship between brain activity and behavior, then he is more willing to accept the assumption. If, on the other hand, his experiments consistently were to fail to show any such relationship, then he would have to reject the assumption and adopt a new one. Thus, skepticism and pragmatism are fundamental features of the scientific attitude.

GOALS OF NEUROPSYCHOLOGY

Neuropsychology is the study of the relationship between brain and behavior. A neuropsychologist attempts to find out how the brain regulates and controls behavior and psychological processes. For instance, a neuropsychologist might try to determine what regions of the brain are critical for solving problems, or for perceiving sounds, or for regulating food intake. Once he has some knowledge of the brain regions that are critical for a particular behavior (no small task in itself), the neuropsychologist may then attempt to find out how neural mechanisms accomplish that behavior. By analogy, knowing something about cylinders, spark plugs, and gasoline might enable one to understand how an engine works.

Moreover, the neuropsychologist believes that increasing our understanding of the mechanisms that underlie behavior will increase our understanding of behavior itself. Pursuing the analogy, once we know how an engine works, we should be able to explain how a car moves. As we shall see in later chapters, there are numerous examples of ways in which our thinking about psychological processes has benefited from a knowledge of neural mechanisms. For now, let us turn to the methods of neuropsychology—the several different techniques the neuropsychologist has available in studying neural mechanisms of behavior.

THE METHODS OF NEUROPSYCHOLOGY

ABLATION

One technique the neuropsychologist makes use of is ablation. An investigator can ablate (that is, remove) a particular part of an animal's nervous sysem and then study the resulting impairment or alteration in behavior. An important adjunct to this method is the study of behavioral changes in humans whose brains have been damaged or are diseased. By means of this technique, it is possible to determine what parts of the brain are necessary for a particular kind of behavior to take place in a normal manner. If, for example, following ablation of a particular region of the brain, an animal does not respond to visual stimuli, one may conclude that this region of the brain is necessary for vision.

ELECTRICAL RECORDING

Another method which the neuropsychologist uses is recording the electrical activity of the brain. According to current views, the brain is a complex communication system in which the units of information are electrical pulses. These electrical signals are extremely weak in comparison to the electrical potentials in lamps or household appliances. However, the brain's electrical activity may be measured by placing probes, referred to as electrodes, on the surface of the brain or within the brain itself, and then amplifying the weak signals by means of conventional electronic amplifiers. This method has provided information concerning the physical characteristics of neural messages and the pathways they follow through the nervous system. Moreover, by observing the behavior of animals while the electrical activity of their brains is recorded, it has been possible to infer what events occur in the CNS when animals are in various states, such as sleep or waking.

ELECTRICAL STIMULATION

Electrical stimulation of the brain is another method used by neuropsychologists, since the brain not only generates electrical signals which may be recorded but is also responsive to electrical stimulation. An electrical current passed through an electrode implanted in the brain may cause the animal to respond in a particular manner. Depending on the site of stimulation, the behavior may be a simple muscle twitch, or it may be a complicated series of movements such as those seen when an animal is aroused, fearful, or searching for a mate. Electrical brain stimulation is thus an important technique for determining what areas of the brain control motivational processes.

OTHER METHODS OF NEUROPSYCHOLOGY

Ablation, electrical recording, and electrical stimulation are the three major techniques used by neuropsychologists to investigate brain-behavior relationships. However, there are still other techniques that neuropsychologists have borrowed from the neural sciences.

For instance, they use methods developed by anatomists in order to study microscopically the fine structure of the nervous system. By means of anatomical techniques one can, for example, trace the pathways over which sensory information is conducted into the CNS and determine the parts of the brain to which these pathways lead.

Another set of techniques involves the use of chemicals. A number of biochemical events take place within the nervous system, as in other body systems. Some of these are related to metabolic processes common to all body tissues. Other biochemical events which take place in the CNS reflect its own unique functions, and are important factors in the regulation of behavior. Consequently, the study of normal CNS biochemistry is a valuable approach to the study of the CNS. Moreover, the analysis of biochemical changes associated with different behavioral states and the effects of biochemical alterations on behavior are important research tools in the study of brain-behavior relationships.

The neuropsychologist also uses the techniques of the behavioral sciences. These involve various procedures developed in psychological laboratories in order to study processes such as learning, memory, and perception. Many of these procedures are described in another volume in this series (Walker, *Conditioning and Instrumental Learning*, 1967).

It is apparent from this discussion that neuropsychology, unlike most fields of psychology, is not restricted to the study of any one particular process. Rather, it is a way of approaching a broad range of psychological processes. In the following chapters we shall be concerned with the neural events underlying such diverse phenomena as motor skills, perception, motivation, and learning.

BASIC NEURAL PROCESSES 2

Neuropsychology, like other areas of psychology, is concerned with behaviors that involve the whole organism, such as building a nest, flying an airplane, or planning a trip. Behaviors such as these are referred to as molar responses to distinguish them from the actions of particular muscles, or molecular responses. In order to understand the complex neural machinery that controls molar behavior, one must first become acquainted with the simpler neural mechanisms which regulate molecular behavior. Thus, in this chapter, some fundamental neural processes underlying behavior will be discussed.

STAGES OF NEURAL CONTROL

What kinds of processes occur in the nervous system when a simple response takes place? When the paw of a dog is pricked, the paw, as well as the whole limb, is quickly withdrawn. Other responses may also ensue—the dog may yelp and back away—but the limb withdrawal is a highly consistent response which all animals show under these circumstances. The neural processes underlying this behavior may be divided into several stages (see Figure 2.1). First, the nervous system must receive information concerning the painful stimulation of the paw. The reception of stimuli is the function of sensing devices called receptors. Receptors are sensitive to particular stimuli and translate these stimuli into the electrical signals that the nervous system uses as information. Receptors that are sensitive to environmental stimuli are referred to as exteroceptors (see Figure 2.1). In Chapter 4, we shall discuss the variety of different receptors on the surface of the body and within the body. The signals generated in receptors in the pricked paw are conducted by neural pathways, called afferent nerves, to receptive portions of the central nervous system (i.e., the spinal cord and brain). Thus, the function of the receptors in the stimulated paw and their afferent nerves is to inform the CNS of the stimulating event so that appropriate action can be taken.

In order that the appropriate response (i.e., withdrawal of the limb) be made, electrical signals must be transmitted from the receptive portions of the CNS to executive centers (motor or effector areas) controling movements of the limb (see Figure 2.1). The internuncial process, that is, the linkage between sensory and motor processes, is one of the main functions of the CNS. With regard to this function, we

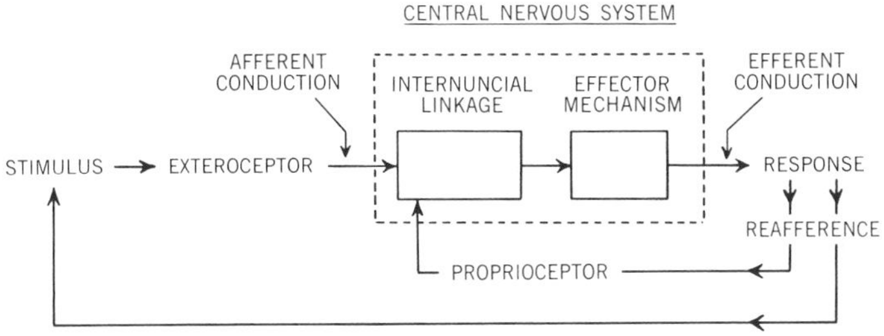

Figure 2.1

Diagrammatic representation of neural processes involved in behavioral integration. (See text for explanation.)

may view the CNS as a complex communication system within which information is conveyed from one region to another. The motor areas of the CNS give rise to efferent nerves. Via these efferent pathways electrical signals are sent to the flexor muscles of the stimulated paw and to other muscles in the leg, causing them to contract so that the limb is withdrawn.

So far we have mentioned three processes which take place in the nervous system when an animal responds to a stimulus: (1) reception and conduction of information to the CNS, (2) internuncial linkage with motor mechanisms, and (3) effector mechanisms. In addition, there is another process which plays a crucial role in the regulation of behavior, response "feedback" to the CNS, whereby the CNS is informed whether the response has taken place and what its outcome is. This process is called reafference (see Figure 2.1). Regarding the example of limb withdrawal, receptors in the limb (proprioceptors) send afferent signals concerning the movement and position of the limb to the CNS, informing the CNS whether and to what extent its executive orders have been carried out. In addition, the CNS is informed whether the limb withdrawal was successful in terminating the painful stimulation. If it were still to receive pain messages after the limb has been withdrawn (as it would if a thorn were lodged in the paw), then it must issue new commands to the muscles to terminate the painful stimulation. Reafference then, plays a crucial role in determining whether behavior should be terminated or continued. Through this process the system becomes self-regulatory.

GENERAL PROPERTIES OF CELLS

The nervous system, like other systems in the body, is composed of cells. These cells are the basic units of structure and function in living organisms. Each cell is a structurally separate and integrated unit within which the vital processes of growth and metabolism occur. The chemical reactions involved in these processes take place partly in the protoplasm, a watery substance which contains a number of different chemicals, granules, and other structures. Also present within the cell is an area of differentiated protoplasm called the nucleus, which is responsible for regulating the processes taking place in the rest of the protoplasm. In addition, the nucleus contains the chromosomes, structures which are involved in reproduction and heredity. Surrounding the cell and forming its external boundary is the cell membrane. This limiting membrane regulates the movement of nutritive substances into the cell and waste products out of the cell. Furthermore, the membrane's electrical properties are responsible for the cell's irritability (responsiveness to external stimuli). We shall discuss the chemical and electrical events underlying irritability later in this chapter.

SPECIALIZED FUNCTIONS OF CELLS REGULATING BEHAVIOR

RECEPTORS

While all cells share the features mentioned in the previous section, different kinds of cells tend to specialize in particular functions. Moreover, each kind of cell is structurally modified to carry out specialized functions. Thus, receptor cells play the role of detecting stimuli and converting these stimuli into electrical messages. The body contains various kinds of receptors, many of which are sensitive to rather specific kinds of stimuli. These specialized receptors act as "stimulus filters,"

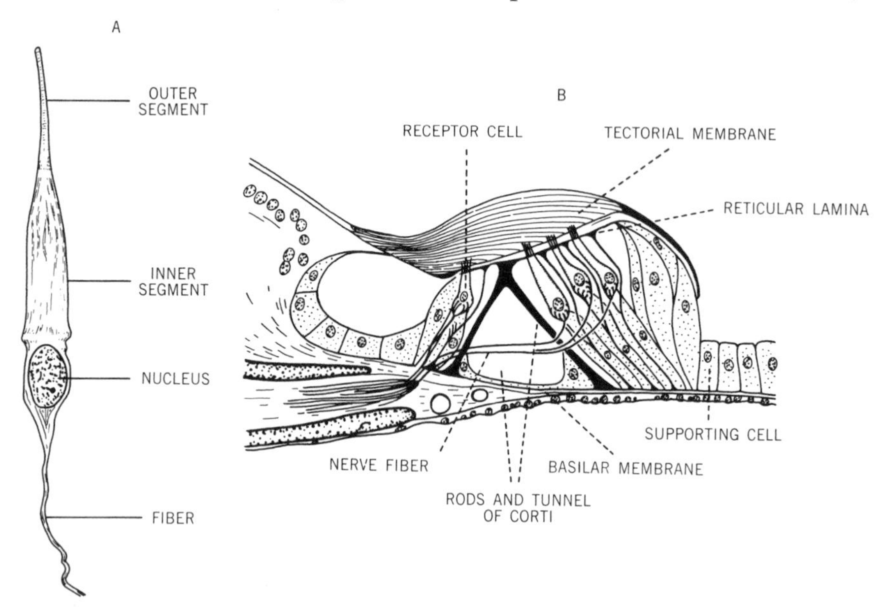

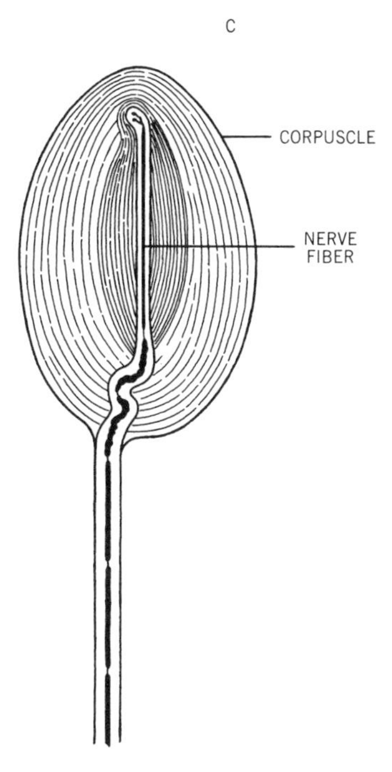

Figure 2.2

Examples of different kinds of receptors. **(A)** *A visual receptor from the primate eye. The light-sensitive portion of the receptor (the outer segment) is long and narrow, thereby offering a large receptive surface for the light entering the eye. From Polyak, S. L.,* The retina, *Figure 45. By permission of the University of Chicago Press, 1941.* **(B)** *Auditory receptors in the inner ear of the guinea pig. The cells have fine hairs which protrude through the reticular lamina and are embedded in the tectorial membrane. Pressure waves in the surrounding medium cause these structures to move, thereby bending the hairs of the sensory cells so that they generate electrical signals. From Davis, H., A model for transducer action in the cochlea, Figure 7, page 186. In* Cold Spring Harbor Symposium on quantitative Biology, 30, *1965.* **(C)** *Pacinian corpuscle found in skin and other tissues of mammals and sensitive to touch and pressure. The terminal of the afferent nerve fiber is compressed and possibly stretched when the corpuscle is compressed by external forces. The fiber generates an electrical signal when its terminal is compressed. From Goldman, D. E., The transducer action of the mechanoreceptor membranes, Figure 4, page 60. In* Cold Spring Harbor Symposium on quantitative Biology, 30, *1965.*

readily allowing some forms of energy into the afferent channels but not others. Examples of different kinds of specialized receptors are shown in Figure 2.2 It will be noted that each has a unique structure appropriate to its particular function. On the other hand, there are some receptors, such as those provided by free nerve endings in the skin, whose sensing properties are not revealed by their structure. The functions of different receptors and the way in which they convert stimuli into electrical signals are discussed in more detail in Chapter 4.

EFFECTORS

Another class of specialized cells regulating behavior are the effectors. These cells are directly engaged in the production of responses, and they are innervated by the efferent nerves. In general, there are two kinds of effector cells: (1) those which specialize in the secretion of substances regulating internal bodily processes, and (2) those which specialize in contraction. The secreting cells form the glands, whose functions will be discussed in Chapter 7. The contractile cells, or muscle fibers, form muscles. Two kinds of muscle cells—striped and smooth—may be distinguished (see Figure 2.3). Striped muscle fibers owe their appearance to alternating dark and light fibrils. Since the striped muscles are attached to bones, their contraction has the effect of either moving portions of the body or of exerting tensions so as to counteract other forces, such as loads on the body or gravity. Because of their attachment to the bones, striped muscles are often referred to as skeletal muscles. Smooth muscles which lack the striations found in striped muscles, are found in the walls of many internal organs as well as the blood vessels. Their action produces effects such as movements of the stomach and contraction of blood vessels. Unlike striped muscles, smooth muscles show intrinsic rhythmic contractions independently of the influence exerted by efferent nerves. Cardiac muscle (forming the heart) also has this characteristic. In addition, cardiac muscle fibers are folded and interdigitated so that they form a kind of network. This unique structural arrangement is responsible for the synchronous contraction of large areas of the heart, an action which aids in the smooth pumping of this organ.

NEURONS: STRUCTURAL FEATURES

Neurons are cells that are found in the nervous system. Like cells in other body systems, neurons are structurally modified in a number of ways appropriate to their functions, which include the reception and transmission of electrical signals. A neuron consists of a cell body, or soma, which contains protoplasm and a nucleus, and one or more fibers attached to the cell body (see Figure 2.4). Relative to the soma,

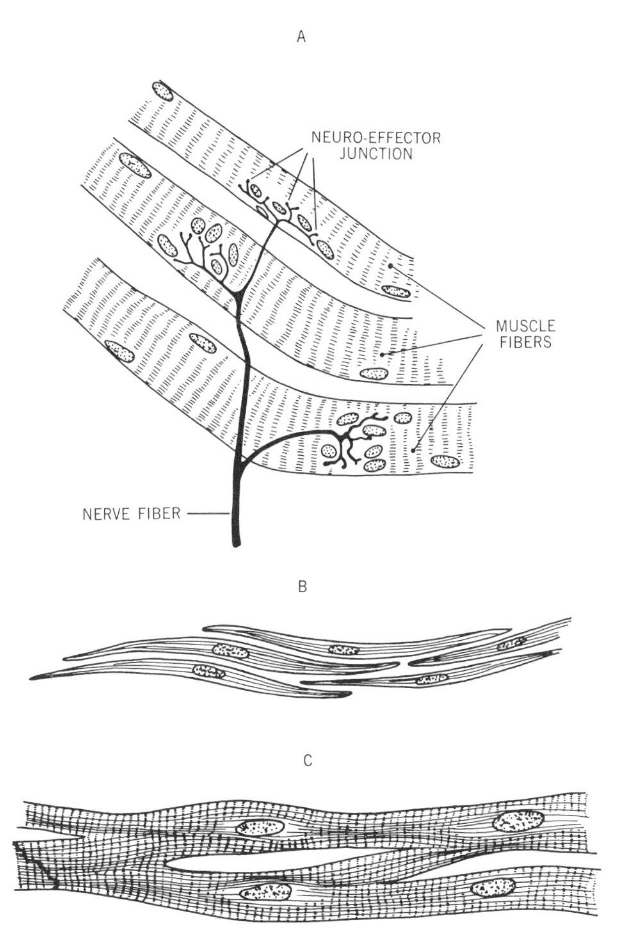

Figure 2.3

Effector cells. **(A)** *Striped muscle fibers. An efferent nerve fiber is shown terminating in muscle fibers. The site of termination is called the neuro-effector junction. The oval structures in the fibers are nuclei. From Gardner, E.,* Fundamentals of neurology, *3rd ed., Figure 79, page 139. Philadelphia: Saunders, 1958.* **(B)** *Smooth muscle fibers.* **(C)** *Cardiac muscle fibers. From Gardner, E.,* Fundamentals of neurology, *3rd. ed., Figure 80, page 140. Philadelphia: Saunders, 1958.*

some of these fibers may be short. Others may extend as much as several feet—an immense distance considering the small size of the soma. Some neurons have only one fiber—these are called monopolar neurons. Bipolar neurons have two fibers, while those with more than

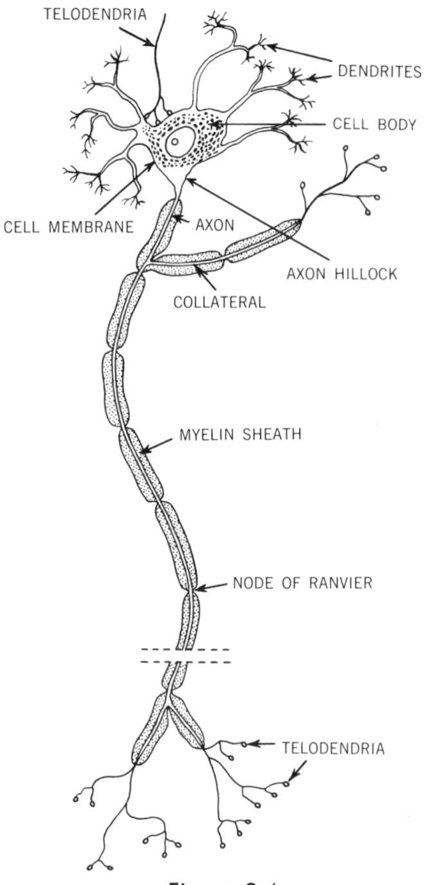

Figure 2.4

Diagrammatic representation of a motor neuron from the spinal cord. Relative to the cell body, the axon is many times longer than shown here, as indicated by the broken lines interrupting the axon. The telodendric endings shown at the top of the figure are not a part of the neuron in the figure, but are from another neuron. From Brazier, M. A. B., The electrical activity of the nervous system, *2nd ed., Figure 1, page 2. New York: Macmillan, 1960.*

two fibers (such as the one shown in Figure 2.4) are referred to as multipolar neurons. Fibers which terminate close to the cell body are usually called dendrites. Dendrites frequently divide into a number of small branches before terminating, like those shown in Figure 2.4. Another kind of fiber is called an axon; it is sometimes longer than the dendrites, and it is attached to the cell body at a region called the axon hillock. Each neuron usually has but one axon; this axon, however, may give off side branches, or collaterals.

A sheath of fatty substance called myelin is frequently found surrounding the membrane which forms the wall of the axon (see Figure 2.4). This myelin is thought to serve as a kind of insulation against the leakage of electrical messages. The myelin is not continuous, but is interrupted at regular intervals called nodes of Ranvier. As we shall see in a subsequent section, these nodes play an important role in the conduction of electrical messages. In addition, fibers outside the CNS are encased in a sheath called the neurilemma, a living cell containing its own nucleus. The terminal portion of the axon characteristically divides into a number of fine branches called telodendria. The telodendria frequently terminate by forming tiny enlargements resembling knobs or buttons (see Figure 2.4). Through these terminal structures neurons make contact with other cells, so that signals can be transmitted from cell to cell. The point at which the end knobs of one axon make contact with another cell is known as the synapse. Axons may terminate either on the soma or the dendrites of other neurons; the synaptic contacts shown on the cell body in Figure 2.4 are axosomatic.

However, the distinction between dendrites and axons is often arbitrary. There are a variety of neurons whose fibers are quite different from those shown in Figure 2.4, and cannot be readily labeled as either dendrites or axons. Rather than using these terms Bodian (1962) suggested that the different parts of neurons be defined in terms of three broad classes of functions. First, each neuron has a receptive portion, which receives an input either from receptors or from other neurons via synaptic contacts. The dendrites and the soma form the receptive portion of the neuron. Also, investigators have described axons synapsing upon the axons of other neurons in some organisms. Another portion of the neuron is involved in the conduction of electrical messages from the input source to other cells. A structure involved in this function is traditionally referred to as an axon. Finally, the telodendritic endings of axons are responsible for the third function—the transmission of signals to other cells.

So far we have discussed those aspects of structure and function which all neurons share. However, as mentioned previously, the nervous system contains a wide variety of neurons which differ from each other structurally. Presumably, these variations in structure reflect differences in function. One way of classifying neurons in a way which reflects their functional properties is in terms of the estimated number of inputs they receive (see Figure 2.5). For example, some afferent neurons (those that conduct sensory information to the CNS) tend to have fairly restricted inputs. They receive their inputs from one or a small group of receptors, and their function is apparently to directly transmit electrical signals from receptors to the CNS. Thus, the restricted inputs of these neurons reflect their transmission functions. On the other hand, the motor neurons of the spinal cord (such as the one shown in Figure

2.4), whose efferent fibers innervate muscle, have large somas and extensive dendrites which receive the endings of many axons. Thus, these neurons have a greater magnitude of input sources than do the afferent neurons described previously. Apparently, then, these neurons are controlled by many afferent and internuncial neurons so that the muscle they innervate is reactive to a variety of signals. Compared to other neurons, the internuncial neurons found throughout the CNS have the greatest number of input sources. Several examples of these neurons are shown in Figure 2.5. It will be noted that three of these cells have very profuse dendrites which receive the terminals of a great many axons of other neurons. The large somas of these cells also provide input sites for many sources. The extensive receptive surfaces of these neurons suggest that they receive signals from a large number of other neurons and are responsible for integrating from many different sources.

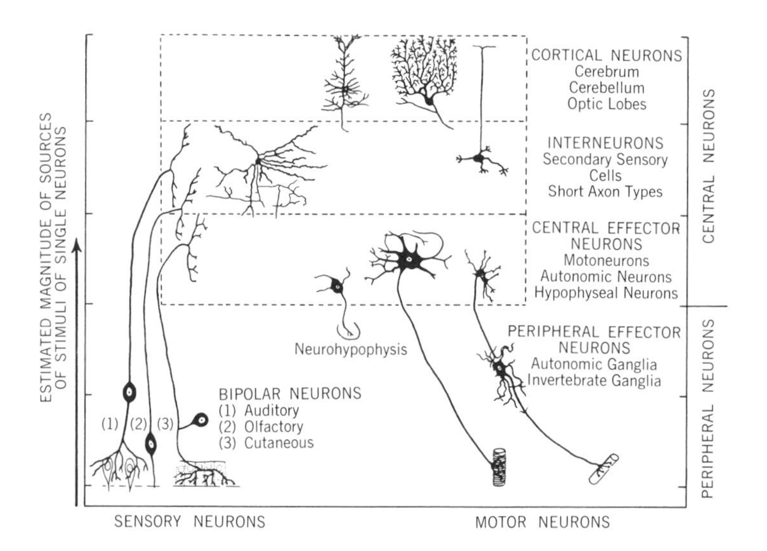

Figure 2.5

Neurons from different parts of the nervous system arranged according to their number of inputs, estimated from the degree of branching and from the spread of their dendrites. Note that neurons in the CNS tend to have greater magnitude of inputs than do peripheral neurons, and neurons in the cortical regions (shown at the top of the figure) tend to have the greatest magnitude of inputs. One exception to this rule is the cell shown in the top right-hand corner of the figure. From Bodian, D., Introductory survey of neurons, Figure 1, page 3. In Cold Spring Harbor Symposium on quantitative Biology, 17, *1952.*

NEUROGLIA

In addition to neurons, the nervous system also contains cells called neuroglia. These cells are found throughout the nervous system, close to the cell bodies and fibers of neurons. Like neurons, neurolgia may be classified into several groups on the basis of their structure. Some have branching fibers that resemble those of neurons. Many are in contact with nearby neurons and may also have fibers attached to blood vessels. It has been suggested that these neuroglia may provide a functional link between neurons and blood vessels, and pass nutritive substances from vessels to neurons. Some neuroglia seem to act as scavengers, devouring dead cells when the nervous system is damaged or diseased. It has been observed that several kinds of neuroglia proliferate and fill in areas of the nervous system that have been damaged. It is not known to what extent neuroglia can directly influence the functions of neurons. However, neuroglia are responsive to electrical stimulation, and, once stimulated, they might, in turn, influence the functional state of nearby neurons.

THE ELECTRICAL ACTIVITY OF NEURONS

In the previous section we described the structure of neurons as it relates to their functions—the generation of electrical signals in response to external events and the conduction of these signals to other neural or effector units. In this section we will describe some of these electrical events as they have been investigated directly by electrical recording and stimulation techniques.

THE NERVE IMPULSE

The electrical message which is conducted along a fiber is referred to as the nerve impulse. The nerve impulse consists of a progressive change or disturbance in the electrical properties of the fiber's membrane. It is measured electrically as an abrupt increase in negativity as it rapidly passes under a recording electrode placed on the membrane (see Figure 2.6). It is important to point out that the energy for transmission of the impulse comes from the neuron itself and not from the stimulus, which acts merely as a trigger. From this fact an important principle follows: If a nerve impulse is strong enough to be conducted, its amplitude (as well as its conduction speed) are independent of the strength of the stimulus. This is known as the All-or-None Principle. According to this law, the amplitude of the nerve impulse is the same as it travels down a fiber membrane, as long as the condition of the membrane is the same throughout its extent. The same is true of the nerve impulse's conduction speed. While the speed and amplitude of the nerve impulse are constant in a single nerve fiber, they vary

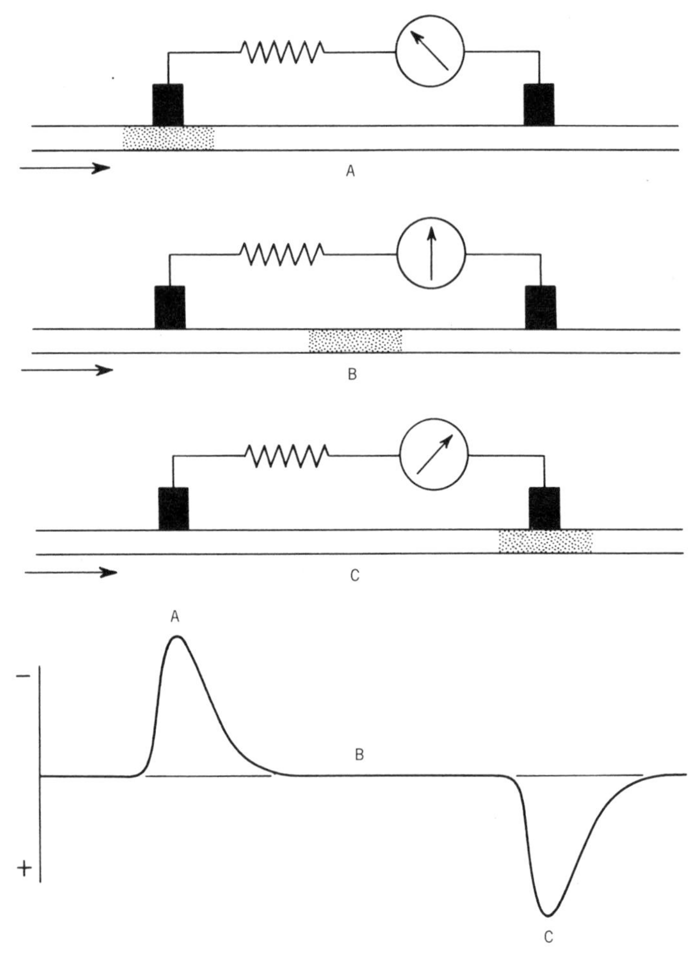

Figure 2.6

Electrical recording of the passage of the nerve impulse along a nerve fiber. The nerve impulse, represented by the stippled region, is under the left recording electrode in **(A)**, *at top of figure. Dial indicates that there is an electrical potential difference between the two electrodes and that the left electrode is recording a negative potential with respect to the right electrode. In* **(B)** *the nerve impulse has reached the region between the two recording electrodes, and thus there is no potential difference between the electrodes. In* **(C)** *the nerve impulse has reached the area under the right recording electrode, which is now negative with respect to the left electrode. Thus, the pointer registers a potential opposite in sign to the one shown in* (A). *At the bottom of the figure, the potential difference* from one neuron to another, depending on the diameter of the fiber; the larger the fiber's diameter, the higher the amplitude of its impulse and the more rapid its transmission.

Furthermore, the nerve impulse is not simply a unitary electrical event, but is made up of several component "waves," or potentials (see Figure 2.7). The first of these is known as the spike potential, which is the largest of the potentials and the shortest in duration. The spike potential represents the nerve impulse's passage along the axon; it is quite stable and is not readily affected by changes in the state of the nerve fiber. The other potentials, which follow the spike potential, are referred to as afterpotentials, also shown in Figure 2.7. The afterpotentials are much less stable than the spike. They do not signify the passage of an impulse, as does the spike potential. Rather, they reflect changes in excitability of the nerve, in other words, its readiness to transmit other spike potentials. Excitability of nerves is measured by the stimulus strength necessary to initiate a nerve impulse. Thus, during the brief interval occupied by the passage of the spike potential, the fiber cannot transmit another impulse, no matter how strong the stimulus. This interval is known as the absolute refractory period. Following the absolute refractory period, the nerve can be excited, but only by a greater than normal stimulus. This interval is referred to as the relative refractory period, which, in turn, is followed by the supernormal period, during which the nerve is more readily excited than it is normally. Finally, before returning to its normal resting state, the nerve fiber goes through a subnormal period, in which its excitability is lower than normal.

ELECTROCHEMICAL EVENTS UNDERLYING THE TRANSMISSION OF NERVE IMPULSES

So far we have described the nerve impulse or action potential as a static event at one point on the nerve fiber, without considering how the impulse is transmitted. In order to understand impulse transmission, we must consider the electrical properties of the neuron's membrane. As indicated before, the neuron membrane forms a boundary between the cell and its environment. This membrane, however, is porous; thus, certain particles can leave and enter the cell. Among these particles are molecules, called ions, which carry electrical charges. In its resting state,

---

recorded between the two electrodes is displayed over time, and the three points in time labeled (A), (B), *and* (C) *correspond to the three positions of the nerve impulse shown in the diagram above. From Brazier, M. A. B.,* The electrical activity of the nervous system, *2nd ed., Figure 8, page 14. New York: Macmillan, 1960.*

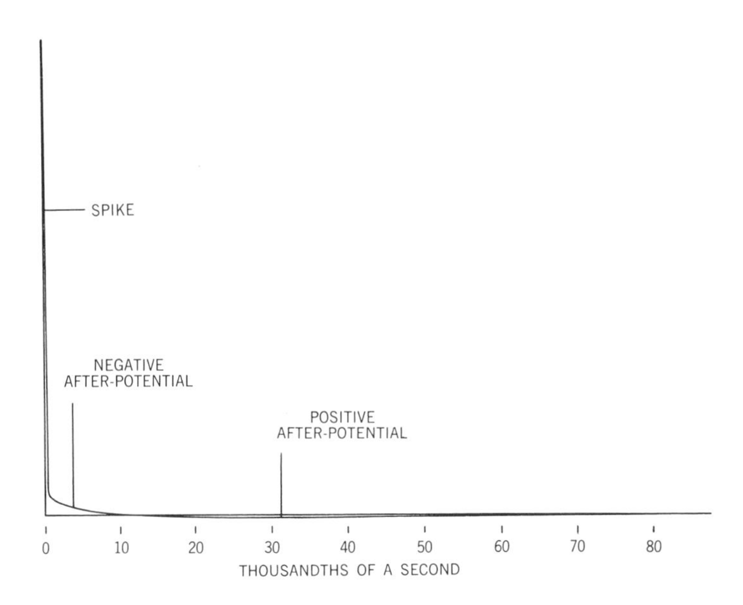

Figure 2.7

The nerve impulse, illustrating the relative sizes of the spike potential and after-potentials and their time relationships. From Gasser, H. S., The control of excitation in the nervous system. *Figure 2, page 175. Harvey Lectures, series 32, 1937.*

the membrane is much more permeable to small ions, such as potassium and chloride, than it is to large ones such as sodium. Thus, sodium tends to remain outside the membrane. In addition, the sodium which does diffuse through the membrane is actively pushed out of the cell by energy derived from cell metabolism. There is also a tendency for potassium to diffuse outside and chloride to diffuse inside the membrane. As a result, ions are distributed in such a way that the membrane is electrically polarized, the outside of the membrane being positive in relation to the inside.

When the nerve impulse passes down a fiber, the permeability of the membrane at that point suddenly increases. Sodium ions then tend to enter the fiber (see Figure 2.8), attracted both by the lower concentration of sodium inside the cell and by ions of the opposite charge. The entrance of sodium ions into the membrane results in an inward flow of current, or "sink," as it is called. As a result of this disturbance in the electrical charge at the active region, currents flow to this region from adjoining electrically inactive portions of the fiber, thus creating a "source." This outward flow of current in an inactive region of the membrane in turn upsets the resting potential in that region, thereby increasing the permeability of that portion of the membrane to sodium ions; that portion, in turn, becomes a sink. In this manner, the nerve impulse continuously and rapidly moves from one region of the nerve membrane to another. After the nerve impulse passes, the resting potential of the nerve membrane is restored. This process seems to involve a decrease in the membrane's permeability to sodium ions as well as an increase in permeability to potassium ions, which consequently move outside the membrane (see Figure 2.8).

It appears that in myelinated nerve fibers, there is a somewhat different mode of impulse conduction, although the basic principles are the same as those described above. The presence of myelin retards the flow of current out the membrane ahead of the spike potential. The current, then, spreads passively down the membrane. When the current reaches a point on the membrane where the myelin is interrupted (at a node of Ranvier) it can readily flow out of the membrane, thus decreasing the membrane permeability at that point so that a spike potential is generated. Thus, the full-blown spike potential jumps from node to node in myelinated fibers. This saltatory (derived from the

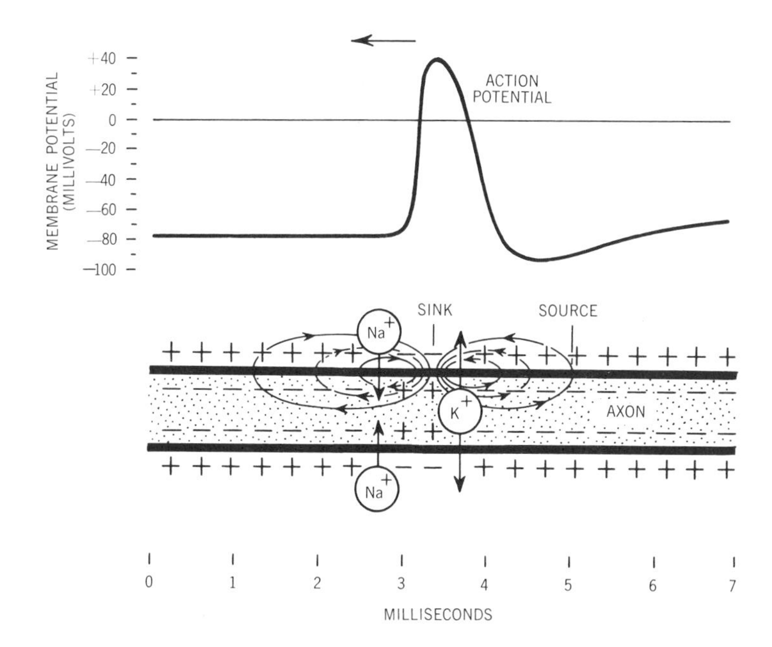

Figure 2.8

Ionic events underlying the propagation of the nerve impulse. The nerve impulse is propagated from right to left. The curved lines going through the axon membrane represent the flow of current. (See text for explanation.) From Katz, B., How cells communicate. Sci. Amer., *September 1961.*

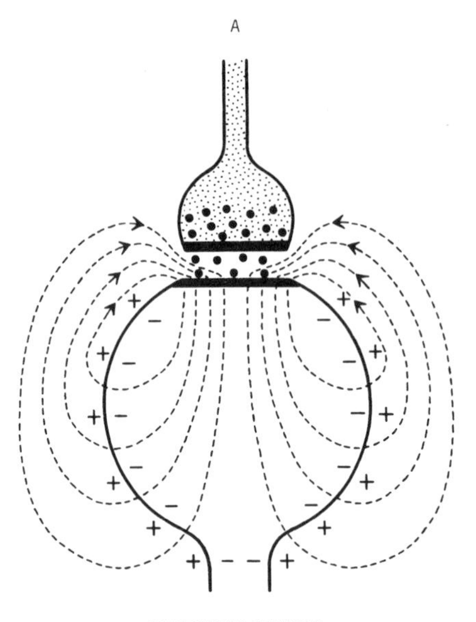

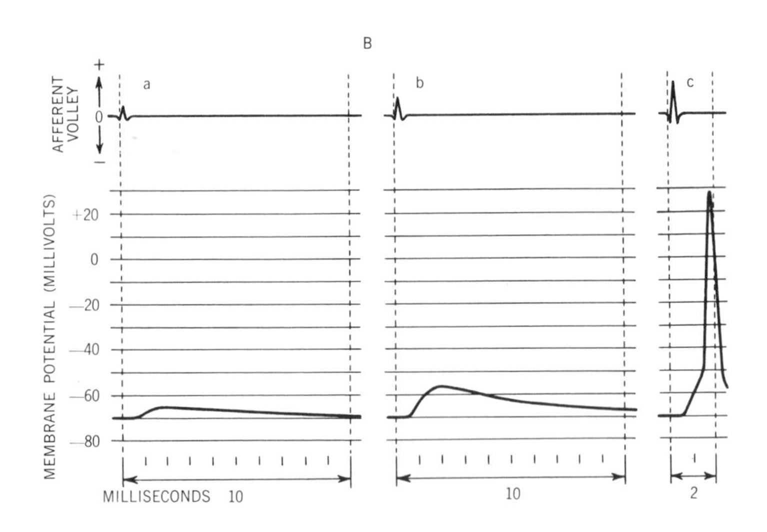

Figure 2.9

The excitatory postsynaptic potential. **(A)** *Diagrammatic representation of an excitatory synapse, showing chemical transmitter substance (filled circles) released from the presynaptic fiber terminal (stippled) and traveling across the synaptic gap to the postsynaptic membrane. As a result, the postsynaptic membrane in the region of the synapse is depolarized so that current flows into the cell at that point. From Eccles, J. C., The behaviour of nerve cells, Figure 3, page 33. In G.E.W. Wolstenholme*

Latin *saltare,* meaning "to jump") mode of conduction in myelinated fibers permits greater impulse velocity and is thus more efficient than is the continuous conduction of impulses in unmyelinated fibers.

SYNAPTIC POTENTIALS

When the nerve impulse reaches the axon terminal which synapses with another neuron, it produces effects which alter the other neuron's electrical state. However, the nerve impulse does not jump across the synapse from the presynaptic membrane to the postsynaptic membrane of the adjoining cell. Rather, when the impulse reaches the axon terminal, it releases a chemical substance from tiny vesicles in the region of the presynaptic membrane. The chemical travels across the synaptic gap and produces a depolarization of the membrane by setting up local electrical currents shown in Figure 2.9. This membrane depolarization is referred to as a postsynaptic potential, and the chemical agents which produce such potentials are called chemical transmitters. If the postsynaptic potential depolarizes the membrane of the receiving neuron sufficiently, a nerve impulse is then triggered in the neuron (see facing page). It is significant that synaptic conduction occurs in one direction only. That is, a potential cannot be initiated in the presynaptic membrane by stimulating the postsynaptic membrane.

Postsynaptic potentials differ in several ways from nerve impulses. Unlike the nerve impulse, postsynaptic potentials are not all-or-none, but graded; the greater the frequency of nerve impulses arriving at the axon terminal, the greater the amplitude of the postsynaptic potential

---

and C. M. O'Connor (Eds.), The neurological basis of behaviour, *CIBA Foundation Symposia. London: Churchill, 1958.* **(B)** *Electrical recordings of excitatory postsynaptic potentials. In the experiment from which recordings like these were obtained, the tip of a very small electrode is placed inside a neuron in the spinal cord of a cat to measure postsynaptic potentials. Afferent fibers which synapse upon this neuron are then electrically stimulated at low intensity* (a), *moderate intensity* (b), *and high intensity* (c). *As the intensity of stimulation increases, more and more afferent fibers fire nerve impulses, and thus the magnitude of the afferent volley of impulses indicated by the amplitude of the waves in upper tracings, is increased. In* (a) *the afferent volley is small, and the excitatory postsynaptic potential, indicated in the lower tracing by depolarization of the membrane, is small. As the magnitude of the afferent volley increases, the size of the excitatory postsynaptic potential increases. From Eccles, J. C., The behaviour of nerve cells, Figure 1, page 30. In G. E. W. Wolstenholme and C. M. O'Connor (Eds.),* The neurological basis of behaviour, *CIBA Foundation Symposia. London: Churchill, 1958.*

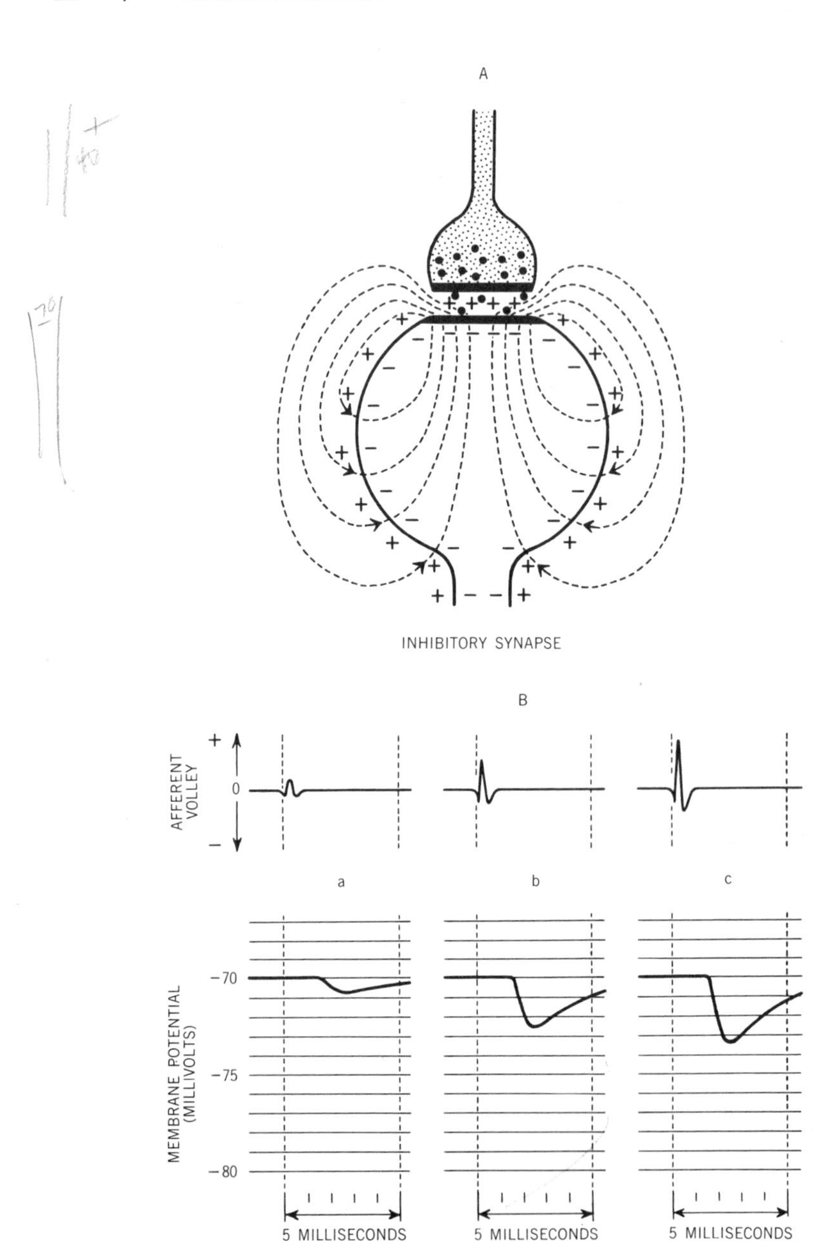

Figure 2.10

The inhibitory postsynaptic potential. **(A)** *Diagrammatic representation of an inhibitory synapse. An inhibitory chemical transmitter substance is released from the presynaptic fiber terminal. This transmitter substance hyperpolarizes the postsynaptic membrane, and the current flow is the reverse of that shown in* (see Figure 2.9). Also, postsynaptic potentials are not propagated, but are local, their intensity falling off with increasing distance from the site of stimulation. Furthermore, postsynaptic potentials have no refractory period, and they can summate with one another, as shown in Figure 2.9. Finally, postsynaptic potentials are mediated only by chemical transmitters, whereas the nerve impulse is thought to be mediated by electrical events, as described previously.

So far we have described the kind of postsynaptic potential which depolarizes the membrane. In addition there is another kind of postsynaptic potential, which affects the membrane in an opposite manner. That is, it hyperpolarizes the membrane and thus decreases its excitability (see Figure 2.10). This potential is called the inhibitory postsynaptic potential, and it is mediated by chemical transmitters which are different from those mediating excitatory postsynaptic potentials.

Inhibition at synaptic junctions plays an important role in the nervous system. If it were not for inhibition, it is likely that excitation would spread in an uncontrolled manner through the complex network of interconnected neurons composing the nervous system. As a result, the organism would be in a continuous state of convulsive activity. Inhibition, then helps to keep excitation channeled in appropriate networks and prevents it from "spilling over" into other networks. In subsequent chapters we shall describe some specific roles that inhibition plays in neural regulation.

It appears that in most nervous systems no synaptic terminals produce both excitatory and inhibitory postsynaptic potentials; a synapse is either of one type or another. However, both excitatory and inhibitory neurons may make synaptic contact with the same neuron. Whether a nerve impulse will be triggered in a neuron depends on the summation of excitatory and inhibitory postsynaptic potentials. It is at the synapse, then, that electrical messages converge and alterations in the electrical activity of neurons take place. The events which occur at the synapse provide a mechanism for integrating neuronal activity by linking

---

Figure 2.9A. From Eccles, J. C., The behaviour of nerve cells, Figure 6, page 39. In G.E.W. Wolstenholme and C. M. O'Connor (Eds.), The neurological basis of behaviour, *CIBA Foundation Symposia. London: Churchill, 1958.* **(B)** *Electrical recordings of inhibitory postsynaptic potentials. The methods of stimulation and recording are similar to those in Figure 2.9B. Here, the afferent volley produces membrane potential changes opposite to those seen in the previous figure. From Eccles, J. C., The behaviour of nerve cells, Figure 5, page 38. In G.E.W Wolstenholme and C. M. O'Connor (Eds.),* The neurological basis of behaviour, *CIBA Foundation Symposia. London: Churchill, 1958.*

together various kinds of neurons—afferent, internuncial, efferent, and reafferent. These integrative functions of the synapse will be discussed in more detail in Chapter 4, Sensory Systems, and Chapter 5, Motor Systems.

SUGGESTED READINGS*

RECEPTORS AND EFFECTORS

Gardner, E. *Fundamentals of neurology*, 4th ed., Chapter 6. Philadelphia: Saunders, 1963.
Huxley, H. E. The contraction of muscle. *Sci. Amer.*, November 1958.
Miller, W. H., Ratliff, F., and Hartline, H. K. How cells receive stimuli. *Sci. Amer.*, September 1961.
Stevens, C. F. *Neurophysiology: A primer*, Chapter 6. New York: Wiley, 1966.

NEURON STRUCTURE

Gardner, E. *Fundamentals of neurology*, 4th ed., Chapter 6. Philadelphia: Saunders, 1963.

THE NERVE IMPULSE

Brazier, M. A. B. *The electrical activity of the nervous system*, 2nd ed., Chapters 2, 3, 4, and 6. New York: MacMillan, 1960.
Katz, B. The nerve impulse. *Sci. Amer.*, November 1952.
________. How cells communicate. *Sci. Amer.*, September 1961.
Stevens, C. F. *Neurophysiology: A primer*, Chapter 2. New York: Wiley, 1966.

SYNAPTIC POTENTIALS

Eccles, J. The synapse. *Sci Amer.*, January 1965.
Stevens, C. F. *Neurophysiology: A primer*, Chapters 3 and 4. New York: Wiley, 1966.

*References that are also suggested readings are marked with asterisks. The references are at the back of the book.

THE STRUCTURE OF THE NERVOUS SYSTEM 3

The nervous system is composed of all the neurons within the body, together with cells which provide support and nutrition. Like other body systems, the nervous system has its own structural organization. Some acquaintance with this structural organization is necessary for an understanding of the nervous system's functions. This chapter will serve to identify and locate the structures to which later chapters will refer.

The nervous system may be divided into a central (CNS) and a peripheral portion. The peripheral nervous system consists mainly of nerves—bundles of nerve fibers which arise from the CNS and travel to various parts of the body. Some of these fibers (the afferent fibers) conduct information from receptors to the CNS, while others (the efferent fibers) send signals from the CNS to effector organs. Nerve cell bodies are also found in the peripheral nervous system, where they collectively form ganglia (singular: ganglion). However, of the two major portions of the nervous system, the CNS, which includes the brain and spinal cord, contains many more nerve cells, numbering over 12 billion in the human. These nerve cells are frequently collected together to form nuclei (singular: nucleus). Nerve fibers in the CNS, as in the peripheral nervous system, frequently run together and form bundles, which are referred to as nerve tracts. Some of these nerve fibers conduct sensory information within the CNS, others control effector organs in the periphery, while still others form communication links between different parts of the CNS.

DEVELOPMENT OF THE NERVOUS SYSTEM

Space does not permit a detailed discussion of the embryonic development of the CNS. However, it is worthwhile to consider some of the more salient features of CNS growth, for the basic structural plan of the CNS is more clearly revealed in its earlier stages of development than it is in its more complex, mature form.

As the embryonic cells which are the precursors of the CNS multiply, they form a closed tube which occupies a midline position in the body. In the course of growth, this neural tube expands more rapidly at the head, or rostral, end than it does at the hind, or caudal, portion. The rostral end forms three enlarged cavities, as shown Figure 3.1A. These three enlargements eventually develop into the three major subdivisions of the brain: forebrain, midbrain and hindbrain. As the brain con-

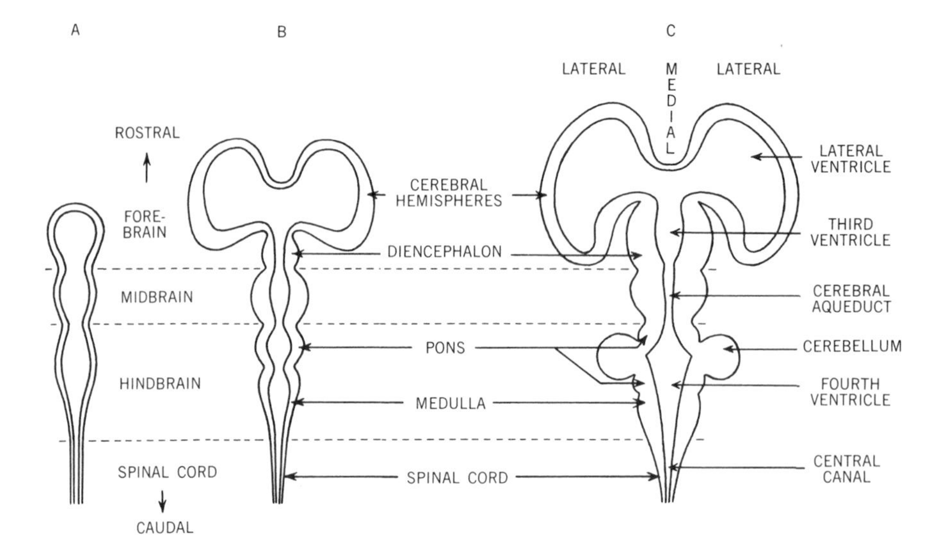

Figure 3.1

The embryonic development of the CNS. Note the two sets of terms which refer to direction in the CNS. These terms refer not to fixed but to relative positions in the CNS. Rostral *refers to structures toward the front of the CNS and* caudal *refers to structures toward the back of the CNS.* Medial *refers to structures near the median plane while* lateral *refers to structures away from the median plane. From Gardner, E.,* Fundamentals of neurology, *4th ed., Figure 36, page 57. Philadelphia: Saunders, 1963.*

tinues to grow, the rostral part of the forebrain becomes evaginated and enlarged, forming the two cerebral hemispheres, while the caudal portion of the forebrain develops into the diencephalon (see Figure 3.1, B and C). The midbrain or mesencephalon also becomes enlarged, but less so than does the forebrain, so that it tends to retain its simpler, primitive form in the adult brain. The hindbrain becomes differentiated into two structures: the pons and the medulla. In addition, the cerebellum develops on the upper or dorsal surface of the pons (see Figure 3.1C). Because the mesencephalon, pons, and medulla together form a central trunk-like structure underlying the expanded forebrain, they are collectively referred to as the brain stem. Furthermore, as the embryo grows, the neural tube becomes flexed in several places so that it bends over on itself. While some of these flexures tend to straighten out in later development, the mature human brain retains a sharp bend, seen most clearly at the junction of the mesencephalon and diencephalon. Consequently, the axis of the medulla forms an angle of approximately 90° with the axis of the cerebral hemispheres. Because of this bending, the rostral part of the cerebral hemispheres is located anteriorly (toward the front), while the caudal part of the cerebral hemispheres is located posteriorly (toward the back) as shown in Figure 3.2. This figure also shows that brain structures in an upper position are referred to as dorsal, while those in a lower position are referred to as ventral. The dorsal-ventral axis is shifted 90° in the brain stem and spinal cord.

As the CNS develops, the central cavity of the neural tube is retained, but its form is markedly altered by the growth of the surrounding walls. As seen in Figure 3.1, the cavity forms a small canal in some places. In other places it becomes enlarged into chambers or ventricles, the names of which are shown in Figure 3.1C. This system of openings, referred to as the ventricular system, is filled with cerebrospinal fluid, a clear fluid similar to blood plasma. The cerebrospinal fluid is probably formed by specialized cells found in the walls of the ventricles. It circulates through the ventricular system and passes through openings in the fourth ventricle to enter a narrow space (the subarachnoid space) surrounding the brain. Little is known about the functions of the cerebrospinal fluid. It may serve to protect the brain against sudden shocks; it may also supply the CNS with nutritive fluids.

Some of the cells in the developing CNS grow fibers which leave the neural tube and are distributed to various parts of the body. These fibers are part of the peripheral nervous system. Those which arise from cells in the spinal cord are referred to as the spinal nerves, while those which arise from the brain are referred to as the cranial nerves. In the next section some of the features of the peripheral nervous system will be briefly described.

PERIPHERAL NERVOUS SYSTEM: SPINAL AND CRANIAL NERVES

The spinal nerves emerge from the spinal cord, passing between the bony vertebrae which surround the cord (see Figure 3.2) and then branch into smaller nerves which distribute fibers to various parts of the body. Each segment of the spinal cord is associated with a pair of spinal nerves, one on the left side and the other on the right side of the spinal cord. Each nerve splits into a dorsal and a ventral root which branch and enter the spinal cord (see Figure 3.3). The dorsal roots contain afferent fibers, the cell bodies of which are located in the dorsal root ganglion, as shown in Figure 3.3. Some of these afferent fibers innervate the skin, while other innervate organs and tissues within the body. The ventral roots contain efferent fibers, whose cell bodies are located in the spinal cord (see Figure 3.3). Many of these efferent fibers directly innervate effector organs within the body. Thus, at the spinal cord, sensory and motor functions are anatomically distinguished by the fibers of the dorsal and the ventral roots.

The cranial nerves conduct information from receptors located in the head, as well as from receptors in visceral organs within the body (see Figure 3.4). Many of these nerves also contain efferent fibers innervating various effector organs, as shown in Figure 3.4. As seen in this figure, some of these cranial nerves, unlike the spinal roots, contain both afferent and efferent fibers.

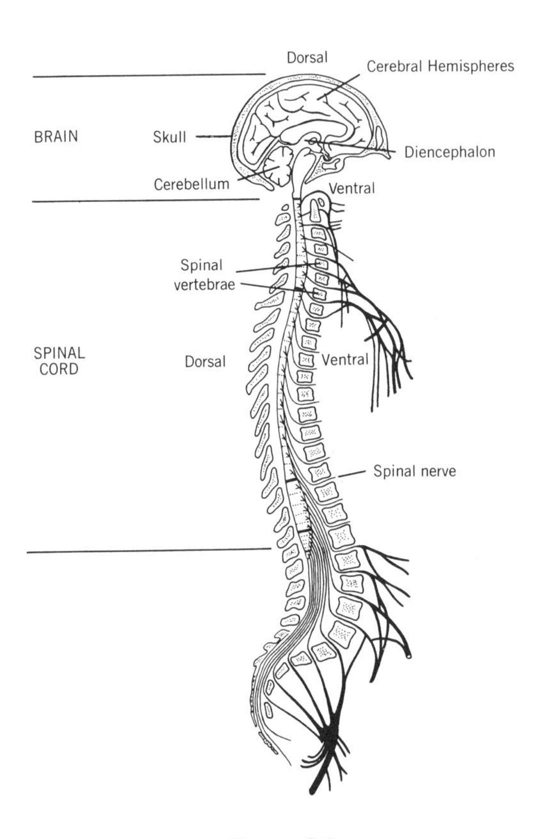

Figure 3.2

The human brain and spinal cord shown in their bony enclosures, the skull and spinal vertebrae. The spinal nerves shown emerging from the bony vertebrae are distributed to various organs and tissues of the body. The brain is viewed from the midline, or median plane. From Gardner, E., Fundamentals of neurology, *4th ed., Figure 23, page 35. Philadelphia: Saunders, 1963.*

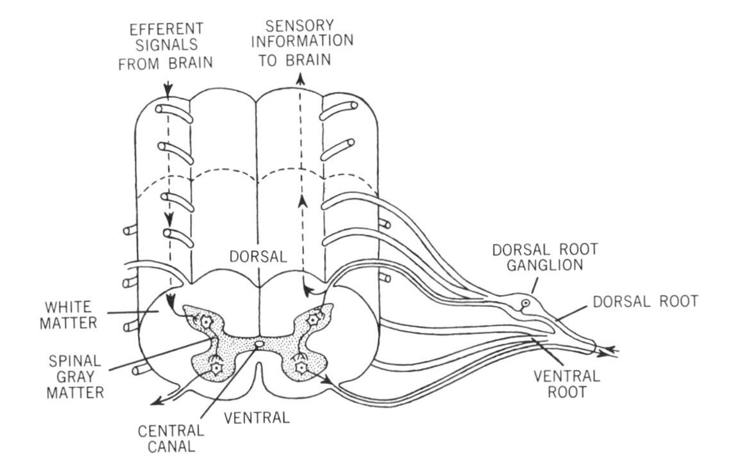

Figure 3.3

A portion of the spinal cord showing dorsal and ventral roots splitting off from a spinal nerve, and some of the pathways taken by afferent and efferent fibers. The spinal white matter is composed of fibers while the spinal gray matter (the stippled area) contains cell bodies. From Smith, C. G., Basic neuroanatomy, *Figure 11, page 14. Toronto: University of Toronto Press, 1964.*

In addition to the distinction between sensory and motor functions, there is another important distinction to be made—the difference between somatic and visceral fibers. Somatic nerve fibers are distributed to sense organs in the skin, deep-lying tissue, joints, and to striped muscles. Visceral nerve fibers, on the other hand, are distributed to glands and to the smooth muscles (in visceral organs and in blood vessels), described in Chapter 2—those effectors which are controlled mainly through reflex action. Visceral efferent fibers, like somatic efferent fibers, originate from cells located in the spinal cord and brain stem. Unlike somatic nerve fibers, however, visceral efferent fibers do not go directly to effector organs, but form synaptic connections in peripheral ganglia with other neurons which send their fibers to effector organs. The visceral efferent fibers collectively form a portion of the nervous system called the autonomic nervous system, which is illustrated diagrammatically in Figure 7.1 (see page 141). The role of the autonomic nervous system in the regulation of internal states of the body will be discussed in Chapter 7.

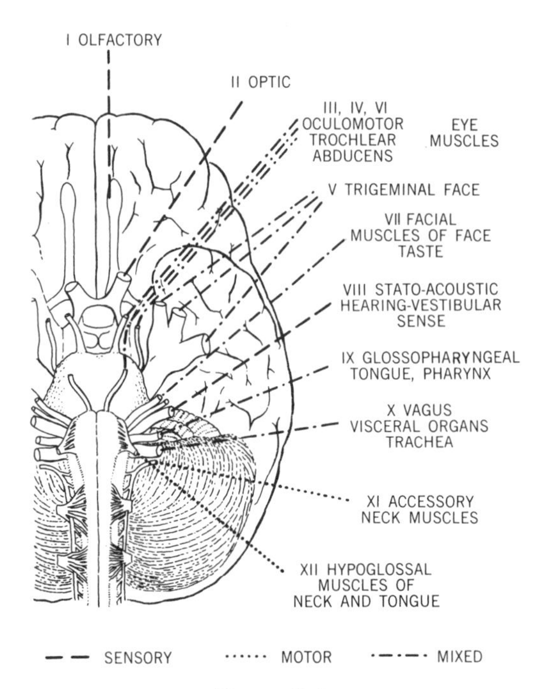

Figure 3.4

The twelve pairs of cranial nerves shown emerging from the ventral surface of the brain. Copyright The CIBA collection of medical illustrations *by Frank H. Netter, M.D. Vol. I.* Nervous system, *plate 20, page 42. CIBA Pharmaceutical Co., 1962.*

CENTRAL NERVOUS SYSTEM

SPINAL CORD

The spinal cord transmits sensory and motor impulses to and from the brain. It also links together sensory information and motor reactions, an integrative function which will be described in Chapter 5. The spinal cord receives various sensory messages from the dorsal root fibers, which ascend to higher levels of the CNS in fiber tracts (see Figure 3.5). Branches of these dorsal root fibers terminate in the gray matter of the spinal cord (which consists primarily of cell bodies), either upon internuncial neurons or directly upon motor neurons. Efferent fibers from higher levels of the CNS also terminate on these cells. The motor neurons of the spinal cord give rise to ventral root fibers which innervate effector organs, such as muscles. Through the synaptic connections illustrated in Figure 3.5, the spinal cord provides associations between incoming sensory information and outgoing motor impulses.

MEDULLA

We recall that the medulla originates from the caudal portion of the developing hindbrain. Like the spinal cord, the medulla contains afferent and efferent tracts, as well as collections of cells, as seen in Figure 3.5B. Many of these cells form nuclei from which cranial nerves emerge; some of these cellular groups are involved in the regulation of internal processes, such as blood pressure and respiration. Many of the nuclei are embedded in a large, diffuse mass of cells and interlacing fibers called the reticular formation. This structure receives its name from the many short fibers which form a dense network or reticulum. The reticular formation, which extends throughout the brain stem, is involved in the regulation of movements, as described in Chapter 5, and in the control of states of wakefulness and sleep, as described in Chapter 6. Since the medulla is concerned with the control of such fundamental body processes, it is not surprising that its structure is quite similar in various vertebrate species.

PONS AND CEREBELLUM

As shown in Figure 3.5C, the pons includes many of the same afferent and efferent tracts which course through the medulla. Like the medulla, it also includes cranial nerve nuclei and the reticular formation. Thus, structurally, the pons is similar to the medulla. However, as seen in Figure 3.5C, the pons also contains a unique structure—a thick band of transverse fibers (i.e., fibers crossing from one side of the brain to the other) from which the term pons, meaning bridge, is derived. These fibers originate in the cerebral hemispheres and terminate in cells of the pontile nuclei, which in turn project fibers to the cerebellum.

Cerebellum means "little brain," and in many ways this structure resembles a miniature forebrain (see Figure 3.5A). Like the cerebral hemispheres, described on pages 34-37, the cerebellum is separated into a number of lobes, within which the overlying cortex (the outermost layers of cells) folds in to form fissures. The underlying white matter of the cerebellum consists of fibers going to and from the cerebellum and contains a number of nuclei. The cerebellum receives sensory information from various parts of the body, via fibers from the spinal cord and brain stem, as well as a projection from the cerebral hemispheres via the pontile nuclei, described above. Efferent fibers leaving the cerebellum travel to brain structures, such as the reticular formation, involved in the regulation of movement. The role of the cerebellum in the control of movement will be discussed in Chapter 5.

MESENCEPHALON

The mesencephalon is sometimes referred to as the midbrain, because it is derived from the intermediate portion of the neural tube.

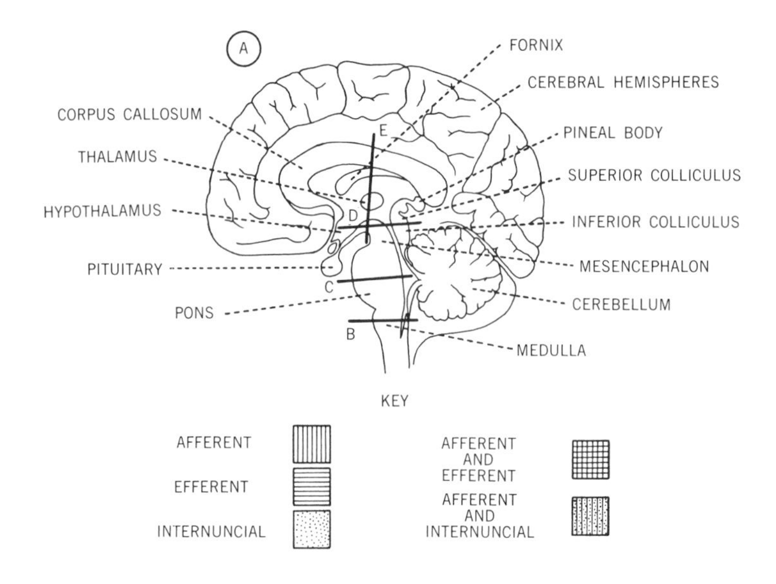
A
FORNIX
CEREBRAL HEMISPHERES
CORPUS CALLOSUM
PINEAL BODY
THALAMUS
SUPERIOR COLLICULUS
HYPOTHALAMUS
INFERIOR COLLICULUS
PITUITARY
MESENCEPHALON
CEREBELLUM
PONS
MEDULLA
E
D
C
B
KEY
AFFERENT
EFFERENT
INTERNUNCIAL
AFFERENT AND EFFERENT
AFFERENT AND INTERNUNCIAL

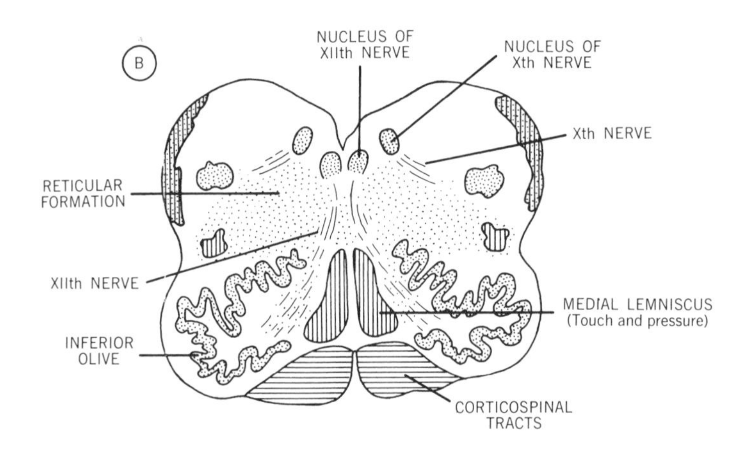
B
NUCLEUS OF XIIth NERVE
NUCLEUS OF Xth NERVE
Xth NERVE
RETICULAR FORMATION
XIIth NERVE
MEDIAL LEMNISCUS
(Touch and pressure)
INFERIOR OLIVE
CORTICOSPINAL TRACTS

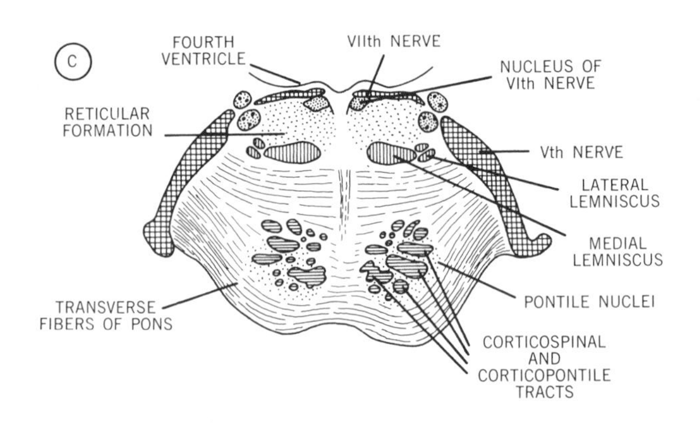
C
FOURTH VENTRICLE
VIIth NERVE
NUCLEUS OF VIth NERVE
RETICULAR FORMATION
Vth NERVE
LATERAL LEMNISCUS
MEDIAL LEMNISCUS
PONTILE NUCLEI
TRANSVERSE FIBERS OF PONS
CORTICOSPINAL AND CORTICOPONTILE TRACTS

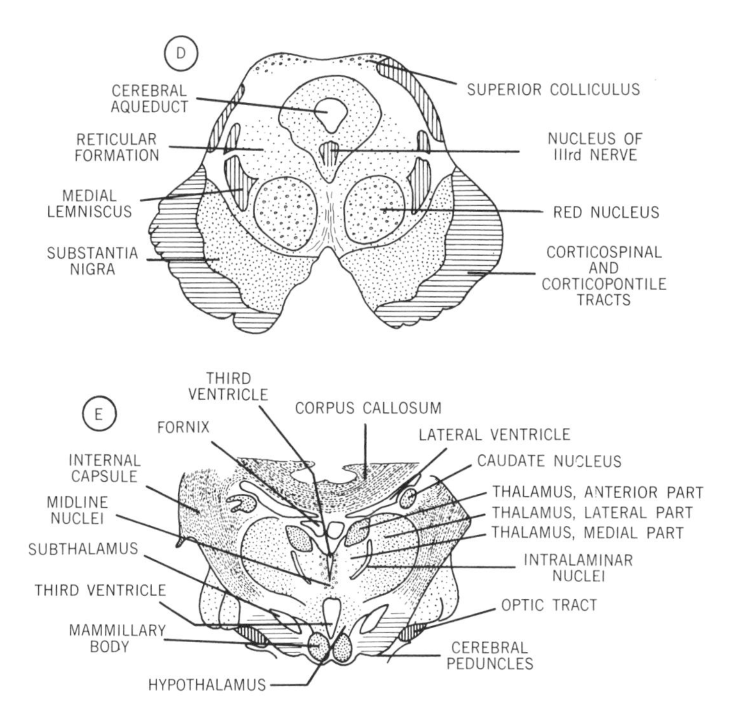

Figure 3.5

(A) *Midline view of the brain. The heavy lines labeled* B-E *indicate the planes of the cross sections shown in the remainder of the figure. Copyright* The CIBA collection of medical illustrations *by Frank H. Netter, M.D. Vol. I.* Nervous system, *plate 18, page 40. CIBA Pharmaceutical Co., 1962.* **(B)** *Cross section through the medulla. In this and in the following portions of the figure, some major brain structures and fiber pathways are identified with reference to their afferent, efferent or internuncial functions, according to the key shown at the bottom of* (A). *From Ranson, S. W., and Clark, S. L.,* The anatomy of the nervous system, *10th ed., Figure 322, page 474. Philadelphia: Saunders, 1959.* **(C)** *Cross section through the pons. From Ranson, S. W., and Clark, S. L.,* The anatomy of the nervous system, *10th ed., Figure 345, page 486. Philadelphia: Saunders, 1959.* **(D)** *Cross section through the mesencephalon. From Ranson, S. W., and Clark, S. L.,* The anatomy of the nervous system, *10th ed., Figure 365, page 498. Philadelphia: Saunders, 1959.* **(E)** *Cross section through the diencephalon. From Ranson, S. W., and Clark, S. L.,* The anatomy of the nervous system, *10th ed., Figure 206, page 300. Philadelphia: Saunders, 1959.*

This structure may be divided into two portions—a dorsal part called the tectum (which means roof) and a ventral part called the tegmentum (see Figure 3.5D). On the surface of the tectum two pairs of elevations may be seen. These are the superior and inferior colliculi (singular: colliculus), which receive afferent fibers from the visual and auditory systems, respectively. The roles of these structures in sensory functions will be discussed in Chapter 4. As seen in Figure 3.5D, efferent fibers travelling from the cerebral hemispheres to the brain stem and spinal cord form two large, pedestal-like structures in the most ventral part of the mesencephalon. Lying above these fiber tracts are two large nuclei called the substantia nigra (meaning black substance) and the red nucleus. These nuclei are closely related to motor systems of the brain, as described in Chapter 5. The remainder of the tegmentum, like the corresponding part of the pons, contains cranial nerve nuclei, reticular formation and afferent tracts.

DIENCEPHALON

The diencephalon, which develops from the lower portion of the embryonic forebrain, consists of a variety of structures surrounding the third ventricle (see Figure 3.5E). The diencephalon may be divided into an epithalamus (most dorsal), thalamus, subthalamus and hypothalamus (most ventral). The epithalamus includes the pineal body (see Figure 3.5A). The thalamus consists of a number of different nuclei, many of which have afferent and efferent connections with the cortex of the cerebral hemispheres. All the afferent systems which conduct information to the brain, with the exception of the olfactory (smell) sense, send fibers to particular thalamic nuclei, those located in the lateral part of the thalamus (see Figure 3.5E). The role of these structures in information processing will be described in Chapter 4. The medial portion of the thalamus, on the other hand, is closely related to the reticular formation of the brain stem, and it is involved in sleep and waking. The subthalamus is also related to the reticular formation, and, as shall be seen in Chapter 5, it seems to be involved in motor functions. The hypothalamus, shown in Figure 3.5, A and E, consists of structures around the walls of the third ventricle in the ventral diencephalon. This region, which consists of both nuclei and fiber tracts, is closely related to structures in the brain stem, as well as to the pituitary body, to which it is attached by a slender stalk (see Figure 3.5A). The hypothalamus is involved in the regulation of internal states of the body and motivational states, and its functions will be discussed in Chapter 7.

TELENCEPHALON

The telencephalon, which is an outgrowth of the anterior embryonic forebrain, consists of the two cerebral hemispheres and structures within the hemispheres (see Figures 3.6 and 3.7). Unlike the lower brain stem and hypothalamus, these forebrain structures grow quite large in higher mammals (such as monkey and man), so large that in man the cerebral hemispheres cover large portions of the cerebellum and part of the brain stem. The cerebral hemispheres contain a large variety of structures interconnected in a complex manner with each other by fiber systems, and they involve a variety of different functions. In the medial portion of the cerebral hemispheres are found several structures which collectively are referred to as the limbic system (see Figures 3.7 and 3.8). Some of these structures consist of nuclei, while others consist of cortex, in which the cells are arranged in orderly layers. These limbic structures are interconnected with other portions of the cerebral hemispheres and with the thalamus and hypothalamus. Their functions are not well understood, but they seem to be involved in emotional behavior and perhaps in learning, as described in Chapters 7 and 8.

Within the interior of the cerebral hemispheres are found a group of nuclei which are collectively referred to as the basal ganglia (see Figure 3.7). These nuclei are interconnected with the overlying cerebral cortex, as well as with the brain stem and thalamus. They seem to participate in the control of movement and posture, and their functions will be discussed in Chapter 5.

The cortex of the cerebral hemispheres, like that of the cerebellum, is folded in to form deep fissures which divide the hemispheres into lobes (see Figures 3.6 and 3.7). Within these lobes, smaller infoldings of the cortex form sulci (singular: sulcus) which are separated from each other by "hills" of cortex. The cerebral cortex may also be divided

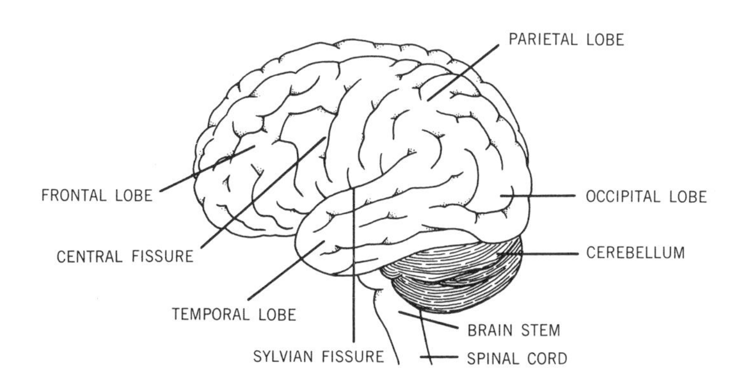

Figure 3.6

Lateral view of the left cerebral hemisphere. Copyright The CIBA collection of medical illustrations *by Frank H. Netter, M.D. Vol. I.* Nervous system, *plate 23, page 46. CIBA Pharmaceutical Co., 1962.*

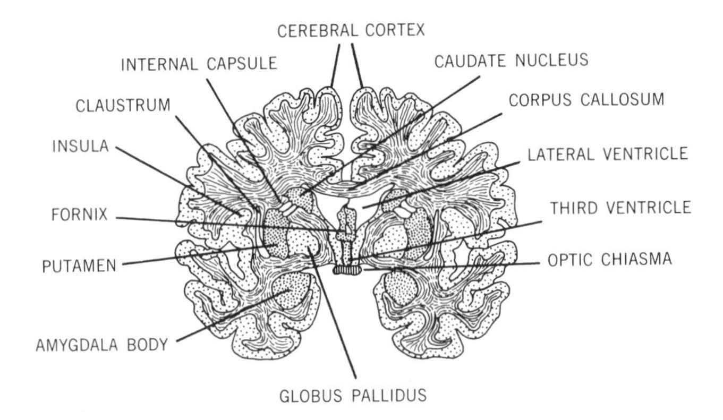

Figure 3.7

Cross section through the cerebral hemisphere in a plane anterior to (E) *in Figure 3.5. The caudate nucleus, putamen, and globus pallidus constitute the basal ganglia. From Ranson, S. W., and Clark, S. L.,* The anatomy of the nervous system, *10th ed., Figure 394, page 520. Philadelphia: Saunders, 1959.*

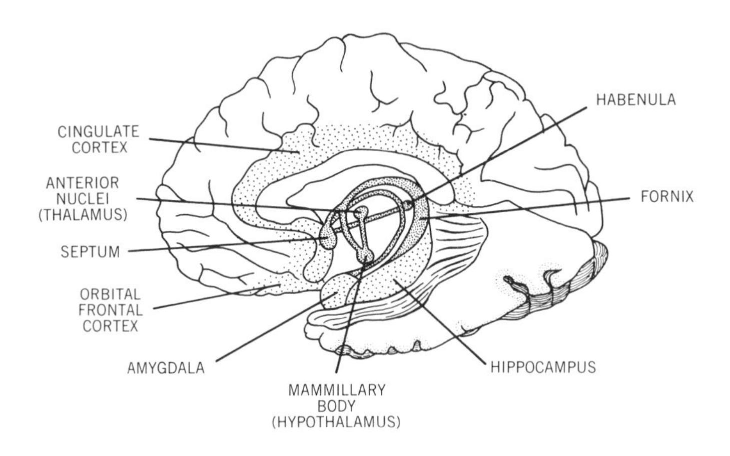

Figure 3.8

Limbic structures of the cerebral hemispheres shown in stippling. The temporal lobe has been cut away to show the amygdala and hippocampus. From Crosby, E. C., Humphrey, T., and Lauer, E. W., Correlative anatomy of the nervous system, *Figure 234, page 346, and Figure 247, page 358, New York: Macmillan, 1962.*

on the basis of its afferent and efferent connections with subcortical structures. Many thalamic nuclei are connected with particular areas of cerebral cortex. Through these connections, sensory information is conveyed to the cerebral cortex. Other cortical regions seem to be more closely involved in motor processes. On the other hand, large areas of the human cerebral cortex do not seem to be directly involved in sensory or motor functions, but rather appear to participate in cognitive or intellectual functions as described in Chapter 8. Note in Figure 3.7 that a broad band of fibers, called the corpus callosum, interconnects the two hemispheres and thus provides a pathway for the transmission of information between them.

This brief survey of the nervous system is intended to provide some initial acquaintance with various neural structures which will be referred to in subsequent chapters. In this chapter, the CNS has been described in terms of subdivisions at different levels, starting with the spinal cord and ending with the cerebral hemispheres. In other words, we have shown the "horizontal" organization of the CNS. On the other hand, the CNS also has a "vertical" organization, as is evident from the afferent and efferent tracts coursing up and down the brain and spinal cord. The functional neural systems described in the following chapters are all vertically organized. That is, they involve structures and pathways at several levels of the CNS. The reader may find it helpful to turn back to some of the illustrations in this chapter when reading about these neural systems.

SUGGESTED READING

Gardner, E. *Fundamentals of neurology*, 4th ed., Chapters 1, 2, 3, 4, and 5. Philadelphia: Saunders, 1963.

SENSORY SYSTEMS

4

All responses may be considered adjustments of the organism to environmental situations or events. The rabbit scurrying for cover at the sound of rustling leaves, the hungry fish attracted by the flash of a minnow, the kitten snuggling against its mother's fur—all are examples of behavioral adaptation to environmental stimuli. Our own daily activities are likewise guided by environmental events. This basic fact is taken so much for granted that it becomes apparent only under unusual circumstances, as when one is suddenly deprived of the use of a sense.

If behavior is to be effectively directed toward events in the environment, then the organism must be equipped with neural apparatus (1) for sensing these events, (2) for coding them in the form of electrical impulses, and (3) for transmitting these impulses along nerve pathways to the receptive areas of the brain. The neural mechanisms which mediate these functions are referred to as the sensory systems. Within these systems a complex chain of events takes place after a stimulus impinges on a sense organ: The receptors first respond to a particular form of energy (such as light for visual receptors, or mechanical force for tactile receptors); this electrical response is referred to as a receptor potential.[1] The receptor potential, in turn, gives rise to nerve impulses which are conducted by afferent fibers to the CNS. Each of the senses has its own set of afferent fibers which terminate upon cells in neural substations or sensory nuclei. Because of the complex synaptic connections between cells in these nuclei, the neural messages from the periphery are altered or recoded in the process of transmission through these nuclei. Further recoding of information takes place in the sensory areas of the cortex, to which the sensory nuclei send their messages. Thus, the coding or processing of sensory information takes place not only in the peripheral sense organ but at all levels of the sensory systems at which synapses are found.

In addition, the sensory systems also give rise to efferent neurons, which, through their connections with motor mechanisms, control responses contributing to the reception of sensory information. For example, the visual areas of the brain control eye movements which alter the pattern of light on the visual receptors; and the olfactory areas of the brain control sniffing movements. These movements have an adjustive or investigatory function, for they serve to direct the sense organs

[1] The term "generator potential" is sometimes used to refer to the same event.

toward environmental stimuli (or, in the case of sniffing, direct the stimulus toward the sense organ) and so increase the sensory information sent to the brain. These sensory feedback mechanisms are a part of the perceptual process and play an important role in the adjustment of the organism to its surroundings. Through adjustive responses the CNS can also select its own input so that the brain does not continuously register all the events occurring in the environment, but only a small number of them. Thus, out of all the environmental events which are potential stimuli, only a portion become effective stimuli in determining behavior.

The selection of stimuli is achieved not only by means of adjustive responses which reorient sense organs, but also by means of filtering processes within the sensory pathways themselves. This filtering, or gating, of sensory information is accomplished by efferent fibers which arise from higher levels of the sensory systems and terminate in lower levels, extending as far as the peripheral sense organs in some cases. Through these feedback, or centrifugal, pathways within the sensory systems, certain messages can be selected for further processing or rejected. Such mechanisms may play an important role in the process of selective attention. The focussing of attention is a pervasive phenomenon and a fundamental aspect of perception. Without it we would be continuously responding to all features of the environment which strike our sense organs, and behavior would be disorganized.

The activities of the sensory systems, then, encompass several processes, including information processing at various levels and the centrifugal control of information transmission, as well as the coding of information by peripheral sense organs. The particular ways in which these processes contribute to the functioning of the sensory systems and their roles in perception will be dealt with in the following sections.

VISION

Of all the senses, vision provides the greatest number and variety of sensory experiences; and it is one of our main avenues of information about the external world. The physical stimulus for vision consists of a band of frequencies in the electromagnetic spectrum of radiant energy from approximately 380 to 780 mμ in wavelength. The physical aspects of visible light include wavelength, luminance (a measure of intensity), and wavelength purity, the degree to which different wavelengths are mixed together. Each of these physical aspects has a corresponding psychological term: hue, brightness, and saturation. See Chapter 2 in *Sensory Processes* (Alpern, Lawrence, and Wolsk, 1967, in this series) for a more complete discussion of the psychophysical measurements of light. The visual sense picks up a wealth of information about our surroundings because at the least some of the wavelengths in the visible portion of the spectrum are reflected from the surfaces of objects to the visual receptors. These receptors, together with their associated neural pathways, can thereby code a variety of object features.

These object features, in contrast to the simple features mentioned above, forms the useful dimensions of visual stimulation (Gibson, 1963)—that is, those aspects of light which specify invariant properties of the environment and therefore have adaptive value. Unlike the simple physical aspects of light, the useful dimensions of light are complex and relational. For example, what we refer to as the brightness of an object's surface is determined not only by the intensity of light reflected from it, but by the level of illumination. While the amount of light reflected from an object's surface varies enormously from twilight to broad daylight, the ratio of reflected light to level of background illumination remains invariant under the same conditions. Thus, when we say that the brightness of a piece of coal remains invariant, or constant, we mean that it reflects an equal percentage of the light falling on it under all conditions. The phenomenon of brightness constancy and other kinds of perceptual constancies are described in detail in Chapters 5 and 7 of *Perception* (Weintraub and Walker, 1965, in this series). The problem of how the visual system codes the relational features of visual stimulation is one which is currently being attacked through a number of experimental investigations, although it is very far from settled.

Another outstanding feature of visual perception is the stability of our visual world. Whenever we move our eyes or head, the pattern of light striking the visual receptors changes, as it does when objects move while we are stationary. Nevertheless, we can readily differentiate between the movement of objects and the change in visual stimulation produced by our own movements; we can identify "up" and "down" despite changes in our own orientation. How visual information is integrated with information about movements so that vision remains stable is one of the most intriguing problems in perception, and one we shall consider at the end of this section.

PHYSIOLOGICAL OPTICS

Before light can strike the retina—the receptive surface at the back of the eye—it must first pass through several structures which modify its direction and intensity. In order to understand how patterned light is focussed on the retina, it is convenient to consider an object viewed visually as consisting of a number of points, from each of which divergent rays are reflected. Those rays which are intercepted by the eye are refracted or bent, in passing from one ocular structure to another, so that the rays converge at another point, called the image point, at the back of the eye (see Figure 4.1A). When the rays from all object points converge to image points on the retina, then the image is in focus.

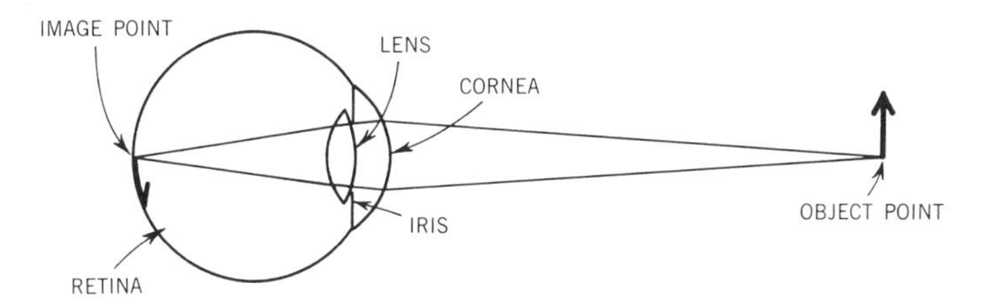

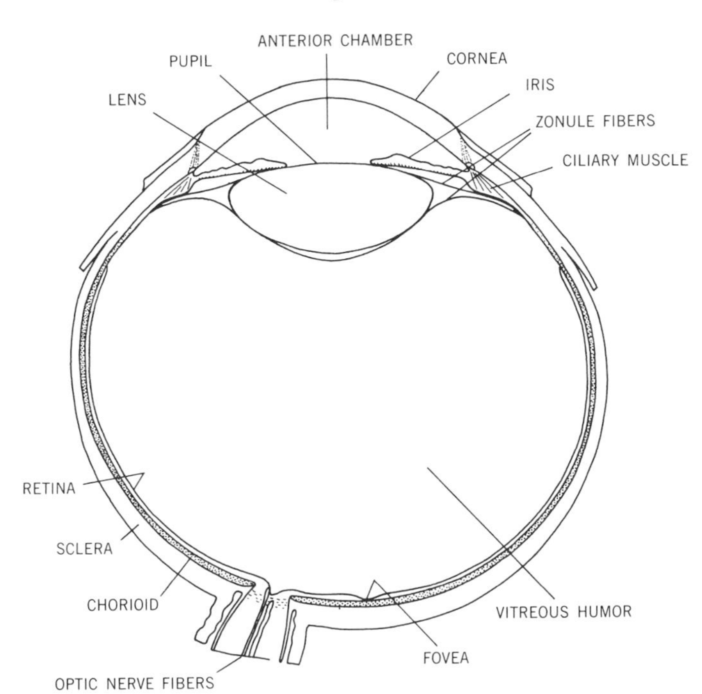

Figure 4.1

(A) *Diagrammatic view of the eye, showing how light rays emanating from an object point are refracted at the cornea and lens, so that they are focussed on the retina as an image point. Note that the image on the retina is upside down as a result of refraction through the lens. From Ruch, T. C., Patton, H. D., Woodbury, J. W., and Towe, A. L.,* Neurophysiology, *2nd ed., Figure 4, page 403. Philadelphia: Saunders, 1965.* **(B)** *The internal structure of the eye. From Walls, G. L.* The vertebrate eye and its adaptive radiation, *Figure 3, page 7. Bloomfield Hills, Michigan: Cranbrook Institute of Science, 1942.*

The greatest amount of refraction takes place at the surfaces of the cornea. However, the change in refraction necessary to bring objects into focus on the retina is achieved by a change in the form of the lens, referred to as accommodation. If the image from a near object is out of focus and falls behind the retina, then a bulging and forward movement of the lens will increase its refractive power and thus bring the image into focus. This change in the shape of the lens is brought about by a contraction of the ciliary muscle, which cancels the tension exerted by the zonule fibers on the lens (see Figure 4.1B). The tension of these fibers keeps the lense flattened. When the lens is released from their tension by action of the ciliary muscles, the anterior part of the lens becomes more curved because of the elastic properties of its capsule. When the eye focusses on far objects, the ciliary muscle relaxes so that under the increased tension of the zonule fibers, the lens flattens, thus decreasing its refractive power so that the image is brought into focus.

While the lens changes the direction of light rays entering the eye, the pupil alters the amount of light which enters the eye. Through its constriction and dilation, the pupil decreases or increases the amount of light striking the retina. An increase in light evokes reflex contraction of the sphincter muscle of the iris (light reflex) which constricts the pupil and thus decreases the amount of light striking the retina. In dim light, the sphincter muscle relaxes and the pupil dilates. Thus, the width of the pupil is regulated so that the retina receives the maximum available light under dim illumination and is protected from excessive stimulation of bright light.

THE EXTRAOCULAR MUSCLES

The light striking the retina is altered not only by the intrinsic eye muscles controlling lens shape and pupillary size, but also by the extrinsic muscles of the eye, which control eye movements. There are six pairs of these muscles which attach to the orbit and control movements of the eyes in all planes. The extrinsic eye muscles play a major role in directing the eyes toward an object, so that its image is directed onto the fovea (the center of the retina) which is used for seeing detail. Normally the two eyes move together in what is called conjugate movement, achieved by the coordinated activity of several eye muscles. Also, through convergent movements of the two eyes, images of objects at varying distances are projected onto homologous or corresponding points of the two retinas—a condition which is necessary for perceiving an object as single.

THE RETINA: RECEPTORS

We now turn to the problem of how the retinal receptors detect and code the features of visual stimuli. The retina is a complex structure containing a variety of neural elements, but basically it is three-layered. The first of these layers contains the visual receptors, tightly packed together in a dense mosaic and oriented toward the back of the eye next to the pigmented epithelium. This structure strongly absorbs light and so helps to prevent light scattering and thus blurring the retinal image. The visual receptors consist of the rods and the cones (see Figure 4.2). When light strikes the outer segment of the rods adjacent to the pigmented epithelium, it is absorbed by a photochemical substance called rhodopsin, which is bleached or broken down into retinene, a derivative of Vitamin A, and opsin, a protein. The breakdown of rhodopsin is a reversible process, so that it is synthesized from its constituents. (Further details of the photochemical process may be found in Chapter 2 in *Sensory Processes.*) Somehow, the breakdown of rhodopsin triggers off electrical activity in the rods. Presumably, the energy released by absorption of light produces a depolarization of the rod membrane which, in turn, produces action potentials in neurons with which the rods synapse. There is no evidence that visual receptors themselves generate action potentials.

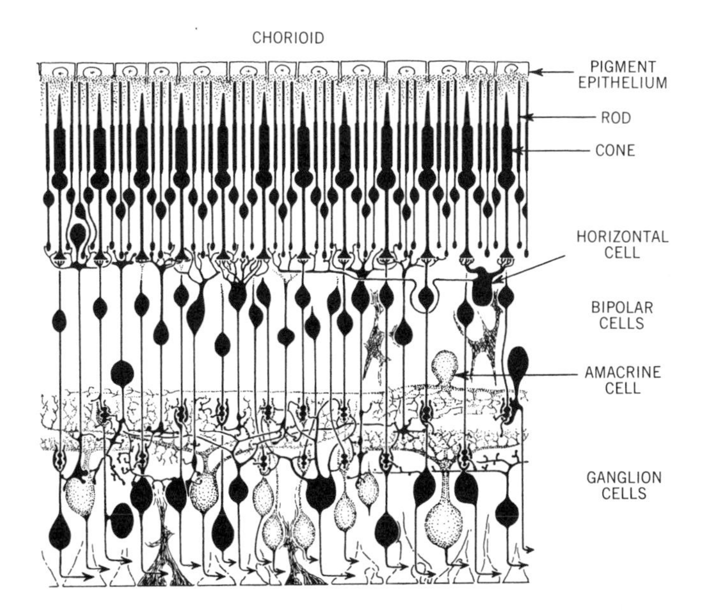

Figure 4.2

Structure of the primate retina showing the receptors and neurons together with their synaptic connections. From Polyak, S. L., The retina, Figure 96. By permission of the University of Chicago Press, 1941.

It is clear, however, that the rods are responsible for certain visual functions by virtue of the properties of rhodopsin. There is a striking similarity between the selective manner in which rhodopsin absorbs different wavelengths and the sensitivity of observers to these wavelengths under dim illumination (scotopic vision). Rhodopsin maximally absorbs light in the blue–green region of the spectrum, around 500 mμ, the same region of the spectrum in which observers are most sensitive in detecting dim light (see Figure 4.3). This close correlation strongly suggests that the rods are the mediators of vision under dim illumination, and rhodopsin is responsible for coding luminance under these conditions. Further evidence for the role of rods in scotopic vision is presented in Chapter 2 in *Sensory Processes.* Scotopic vision is also characterized by poor visual acuity (i.e., the ability to resolve details) and the absence of color vision.

Unlike the rods, the cones are found in the fovea, where they are densely packed; their density decreases toward the periphery, where the rods are located. Compared to rhodopsin, less is known about the photochemical properties of the cone pigment. Photosensitive pigments have been extracted from chickens' retinas, which contain all cones. Recently, however, two groups of investigators have succeeded in measuring the absorption spectra of individual cones from monkey and human retinas. Three kinds of cones, each with its own absorption spectrum have been found (Brown and Wald, 1963; Marks, Dobelle, and MacNichol, 1964). One kind shows peak absorption of light in the red region, another kind a peak in the green region, and a third kind has its peak in the blue region of the spectrum. It is assumed that a specific pigment is associated with each of these types of cones. These findings are of great significance, for over one hundred years ago Helmholtz postulated the same three kinds of wavelength coders as the basis of the trichromatic theory of color vision. Since various combinations of the three primary hues (red, green, and blue) will yield all spectral hues, it is quite likely that the three different kinds of cones recently discovered form the basis of the primate color coding mechanism. A more complete description of the trichromatic theory of color vision may be found in *Sensory Processes.*

The functions of the cones also include perception of luminance under high illumination, and acuity. Together with color vision, these functions constitute photopic vision. The detection of luminance under high illumination is described by the photopic sensitivity function which has its peak around 550 mμ; in other words, under high illumination observers are most sensitive to wavelengths in this region (see Figure 4.3). Since the cone system seems to involve three different pigments, each with its own absorption spectrum, it is assumed that brightness under photopic conditions is mediated by the pooled activity of

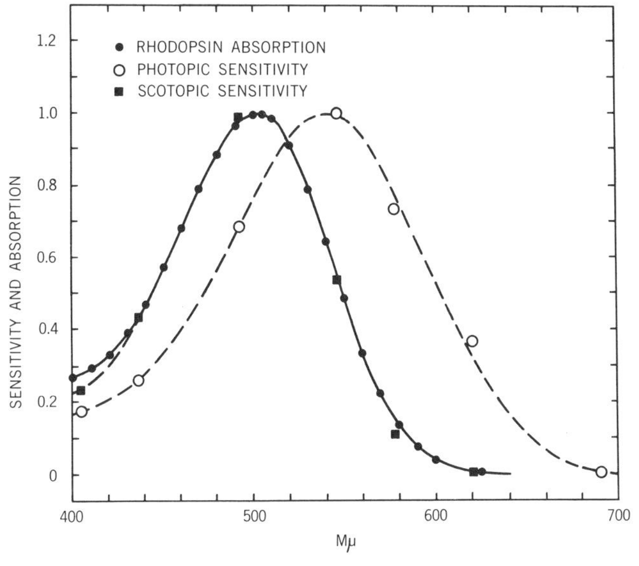

Figure 4.3

Amount of light absorbed by rhodopsin, plotted as a function of wavelength in mμ. *The sensitivity of human observers to different wavelengths under conditions of dim illumination (i.e., scotopic sensitivity) is virtually identical to the absorption spectrum of rhodopsin. Note that the spectral sensitivity of observers under high illumination (i.e., photopic sensitivity) is greater at longer wavelengths compared to scotopic sensitivity. From Wald, G., The photoreceptor process in vision, Figure 15, page 684. In J. Field (Ed.),* Handbook of physiology. *Vol. I. Chapter 28. Washington: American Physiological Society, 1959.*

red, green, and blue cones. The neural events which are thought to underlie this integration will be described later in this section.

THE RETINA: ANATOMICAL ORANIZATION

Before describing how the retina further codes hue as well as brightness and spatial features, it is necessary to describe the neural organization of the retina. The second layer of the retina, below the level of the receptors, contains the bipolar cells. These cells receive information from the rods and cones and pass it along to the ganglion cells in the third layer. The axons of the ganglion cells leave the retina and form the fibers of the optic nerve which terminate in the brain (see Figure 4.2). Some bipolar cells form overlapping synaptic connections with groups of receptors and project in an overlapping manner to large ganglion cells; other bipolars synapse with single cones in the fovea and, in turn, synapse upon single, midget ganglion cells. In addition, as seen in Figure 4.2, the horizontal and amacrine cells form lateral connections in the retina, and thus provide even more diverging pathways. The overlapping distribution of receptor and bipolar cells plus the connections made by horizontal and amacrine cells suggest that the activity of the receptors is recoded so that the visual information sent back to the brain is already highly organized. The nature of these coding operations is brought to light by electrophysiological investigations of retinal neurons.

THE RETINA: BRIGHTNESS AND COLOR CODING

First, with regard to brightness and color, the studies of Granit (1947) suggest that these features are coded by different kinds of ganglion cells. Granit found that one kind of ganglion cell shows spectral-sensitivity curves very much like the sensitivity functions shown in Figure 4.3; these ganglion cells are called dominators (see Figure 4.4A). Since some of these ganglion cells show both photopic-like and scotopic-like curves, depending on light intensity, they apparently receive convergent input from both rods and cones, and so can code luminosity information, in the form of the frequency code, for both the photopic and scotopic systems. The second kind of ganglion cell Granit describes is called a modulator; these cells have narrow spectral-sensitivity curves, and seem to be involved in color coding (see Figure 4.4B).

The behavior of these modulators, together with the evidence for three different pigments in cones cited earlier, suggests that color is

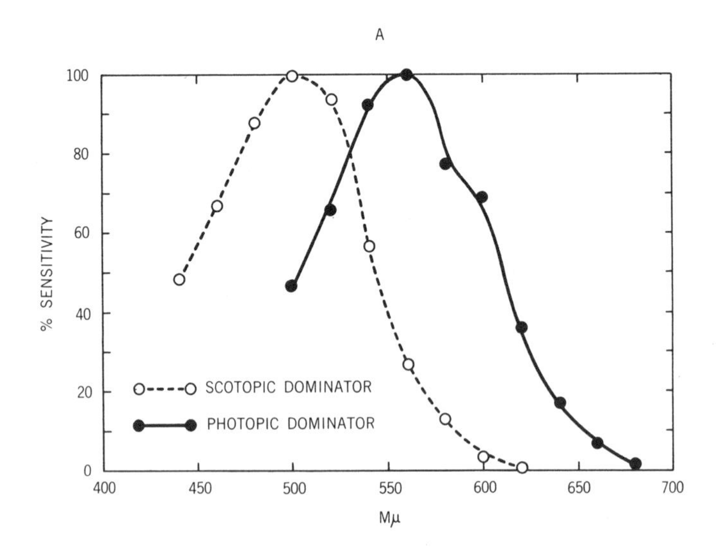

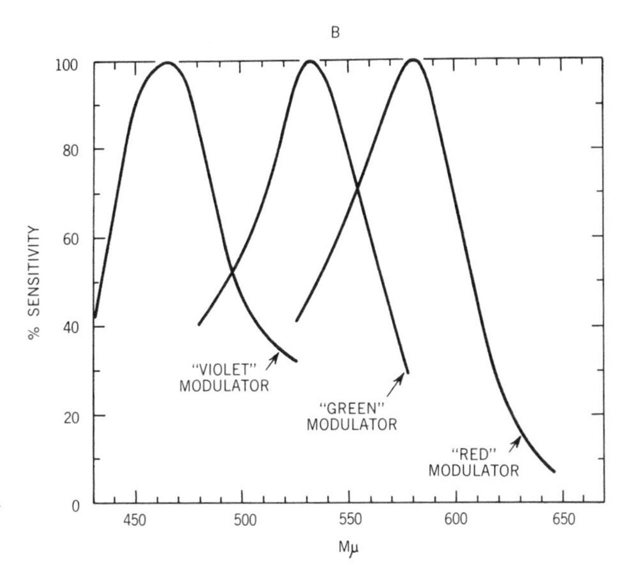

Figure 4.4

(A) *Photopic and scotopic dominator curves from ganglion cells of cat. These spectral sensitivity curves were obtained by first determining how much energy is required in different wavelengths to produce a constant number of action potentials from a ganglion cell and then taking the reciprocal of these energy values as a measure of the cell's sensitivity to these wavelengths. From Donner, K. O., and Granit, R., Scotopic dominators and the state of visual purple in the retina, Figure 4, page 164.* Acta Physiol. Scand., *1949,* 17, *161–169; and from Granit, R., The spectral properties of the visual receptors of the cat, Figure 3, page 223.* Acta Physiol. Scand., *1943,* 5, *219–229.* **(B)** *Modulator curves from three different ganglion cells in the retina of frogs. Note that these curves are narrower than those shown in* (A) *and show peaks in different portions of the spectrum, suggesting that each cell may selectively code a particular wavelength or narrow wavelength band. These curves were obtained in a manner similar to those shown in* (A). *From Granit, R., A physiological theory of colour perception, Figure 3, page 13.* Nature, *1943,* 151, *11–14. New York: Macmillan, 1943.*

coded by a component system, like the one proposed by Helmholtz. On the other hand, the results of other studies suggest a rather different kind of color coding mechanism. Recording electrical activity with microelectrodes within the retinas of fish and frogs, MacNichol and

Svaetichin (1958) and Tomita (1963) described a "chromaticity response," consisting of graded potentials, positive to some wavelengths and negative to others. One of these chromaticity responses, for example, consists of positive potentials to blue light and negative potentials to yellow light. Responses of opposite potential to red and green lights have also been shown. The sources of these potentials have not yet been determined. However, their characteristics suggest that they integrate information concerning color in a manner consistent with a theory of opponent processes, originally proposed by Hering. According to this theory, red and green, and blue and yellow form paired opposing color systems, each member of which is antagonistic to the other. This kind of theory can explain color contrast phenomena, in which exposure to a particular hue enhances the perceived hue of its opponent (see Chapter 8 in *Perception* for a further description of color contrast phenomena). The biphasic chromaticity response behaves in just the way this theory would predict. For, not only does it consist of opposite responses to opposing hues, but the responses are antagonistic; when the retina is simultaneously exposed to red and green lights, there is no response (i.e., no potential change) in a "red-green coder." And, if the retina is first exposed to red light, its response to a flash of red light is now depressed, while the opposite response to green is enhanced. In addition, there is evidence that ganglion cells in the goldfish retina respond in an antagonistic fashion to different spectral hues. That is, their rate of impulse discharge is enhanced or inhibited, depending on the wavelength of the light stimulating the retina (Wagner, MacNichol, and Wolbarsht, 1960). Similar findings have been obtained from cells in the lateral geniculate nucleus, which is a major receiving station for the optic nerve fibers (Wiesel and Hubel, 1966). Thus, recent investigations of color mechanisms have offered evidence that both component and opponent processes occur in the visual system. Apparently, the coding of color is more complex than has been envisaged by either of these theories.

THE RETINA: CODING OF SPATIAL FEATURES

The coding of spatial features by the retina, like the coding of color and luminosity, is made possible by the synaptic connections between neural elements. As noted previously, each ganglion cell may receive its input from many bipolar cells, each of which has synaptic connections with a large number of receptors. In other words, a ganglion cell is indirectly connected with many receptors extending over a small area of the retina. On the basis of this anatomical arrangement, one might expect that a particular ganglion cell would be responsive to light anywhere within an area including many receptors. In fact, this is what electrophysiological investigations have shown.

A ganglion cell's rate of discharge is altered by a small spot of light anywhere within a retinal area of a few millimeters (which contains several hundred receptors). This region is called the receptive field of the ganglion cell. However, as seen in Figure 4.5, light stimulation alters the ganglion cell's discharge rate in different ways, depending on the part of the receptive field which is stimulated. One kind of ganglion cell may discharge impulses at the onset of a spot of light in the center of its receptive field. This is called the "on-response." On the other hand, in a peripheral region surrounding this central area, light stimulation suppresses the ganglion cell's discharge rate, and when the light is removed, the cell gives a burst of impulses. This is called the "off-response." Another kind of ganglion cell gives off-responses when light stimulates the center of its receptive field and on-responses when light stimulates the periphery of its receptive field. Furthermore, there is evidence that the on- and the off-response are mutually antagonistic. For, simultaneous illumination of an "on-center" and "off-periphery" suppresses the strength of both the on- and off-response. These facts suggest that each ganglion cell receives an input from two kinds of bipolar cells, an excitatory bipolar cell responsible for the on-response, and an inhibitory bipolar cell responsible for the off-response (see Figure 4.5B). The opposing processes vie, so to speak, for control of the ganglion cell. This mutual antagonism between excitatory and inhibitory processes may provide the physiological basis for brightness contrast, in which the perceived brightness of a surface decreases as the intensity of the background surface is raised (see Chapter 2 in *Sensory Processes* for a description of another inhibitory mechanism in the eye of *Limulus*). Another consequence of this receptive field organization is that as the intensity of light striking the "off-periphery" is raised, the intensity of light striking the "on-center" must also be raised in order to maintain the same rate of discharge of the ganglion cell. These cells, then, respond at a constant rate to equal ratios of light intensities falling in the two portions of their receptive field; thus, they may provide a primitive mechanism for coding the brightness, or reflectance, of object surfaces, which is determined by background illumination and light reflected from object surfaces.

Even more complex and selective coding operations are performed by ganglion cells in a frog's retina (Maturana, Lettvin, McCulloch, and Pitts, 1960). These investigators have described five different kinds of units in the optic nerve of the frog. Each kind detects a different set of properties of visual stimuli within its receptive field. For example, one kind of ganglion cell responds selectively to small moving objects which are darker than the background. In addition, these units only fire if the edge of the object is convex and moving into the unit's receptive field. Another kind of unit responds not to edges or movement but only

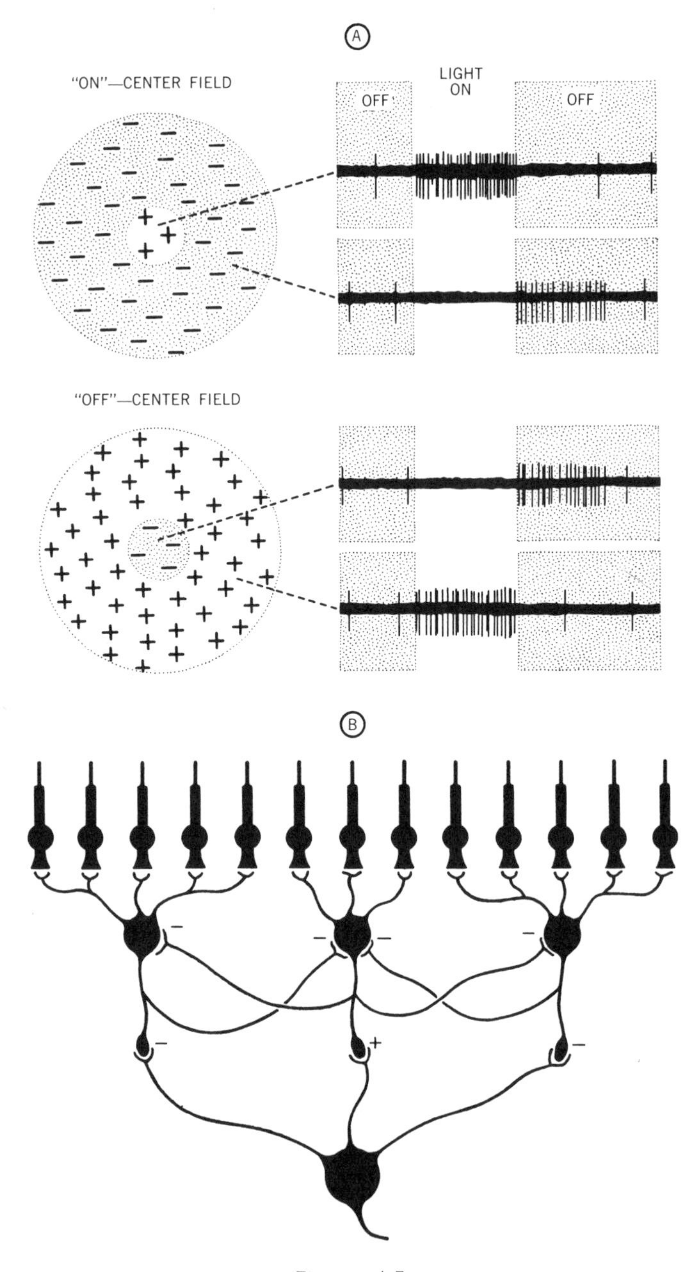

Figure 4.5

(A) *Receptive fields of ganglion cells in the cat's retina. In the top half is shown the receptive field of one kind of ganglion cell, which discharges nerve impulses when light is turned on in the center of its receptive field ("on" response), as shown by the spike* to the lowering, or offset, of light. Moreover, the magnitude of its response is determined by the relative degree of dimming, independent of the absolute level of illumination.

It will be noted that the stimulus features coded by these units are relational rather than absolute, a characteristic, we previously noted, of the useful dimensions of visual stimulation. Moreover, the information coded by these units has adaptive value for the frog. Thus, activity in units which respond to small, convex, moving objects might be interpreted by the brain as a moving bug or other small insect on which frogs feed. On the other hand, activity in units which respond to a sudden lowering of background illumination might be interpreted by the brain as a shadow cast by a large animal that preys on frogs. Thus, out of the shifting patterns of light and dark which strike the receptors, the frog's retina is capable of abstracting particular features which are of biological significance. The neural circuitry mediating these coding processes in the frog's retina is just beginning to be understood; however, it cannot be described in detail here (see Lettvin, Maturana, Pitts, and McCulloch, 1961).

THE CENTRAL VISUAL PATHWAYS

In order to understand how the brain utilizes the information coded by the retina, we must first examine the neural pathways over which visual information is conducted from the retina (see Figure 4.6). Coursing back toward the brain, the optic-nerve fibers converge at the

---

discharges in the upper right. When light illuminates the periphery of its receptive field, spontaneous discharges are suppressed, and when the light in the periphery is turned off, the cell discharges impulses ("off" response), as shown on the right side of the figure. The receptive field of another kind of ganglion cell, shown in the lower half, is organized in the opposite manner to the one shown in the top half. From Hubel, D. H., The visual cortex of the brain. Sci. Amer., *November 1963. Copyright © 1963 by Scientific American, Inc. All rights reserved.* **(B)** *Representation of the kinds of synaptic connections between receptors (top), bipolar cells (middle), and ganglion cells (bottom), that might account for the receptive field characteristics of a cell with an "on" center and an "off" periphery. The excitatory synapse is labeled (+), and the inhibitory synapses are labeled (−). It is assumed that the synaptic connections between receptor and bipolar cells are excitatory. Note that the excitatory (center) and inhibitory (periphery) bipolar cells mutually inhibit each other through inhibitory synapses.*

optic chiasm. Here, fibers from the nasal halves of each retina cross, and, together with the uncrossed fibers from the temporal halves of each retina, form the optic tract. Some of these fibers terminate in the midbrain, and serve as inputs for circuits which control pupillary constriction. Other optic-tract fibers terminate in the superior colliculus of the tectum, which also receives fibers from the visual areas of the cerebral hemispheres. The superior colliculus sends fibers to brain stem and spinal cord motor centers which control head and eye movements. Thus, this structure is probably involved in the integration of orienting movements of the eyes and head. It is likely that the superior colliculus is also involved in more complex integrative processes in vision, for its removal impairs visual-discrimination learning and attention in cats. (Blake, 1959; Sprague and Meikle, 1965).

In addition, many optic-tract fibers terminate upon the cells of the lateral geniculate nucleus of the thalamus. The termination is an orderly one; fibers from adjacent parts of the retina project to adjacent parts

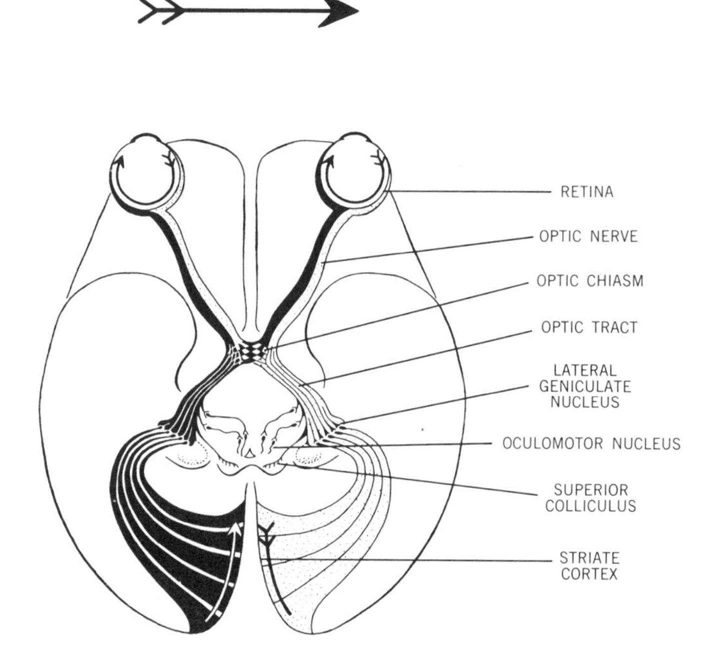

Figure 4.6

Diagram of the ascending visual pathways, including the representation of an object in space (arrow) *as it is projected on the retina and on striate cortex. From Polyak, S.,* The vertebrate visual system, *Figure 180, page 289. By permission of the University of Chicago Press, 1957.*

of the lateral geniculate. Furthermore, the crossed and uncrossed fibers terminate in different cell layers of this nucleus. Thus, messages from the two eyes probably do not interact at this level of the visual system. With regard to coding operations, the responses of lateral geniculate cells to the spatial features of visual stimuli are very similar to those of ganglion cells (Hubel and Wiesel, 1961), a finding which is not surprising in view of the small degree of convergence and divergence of optic-tract fibers onto lateral geniculate cells.

The fibers of lateral geniculate cells project to the cortex of the occipital lobes of the cerebral hemispheres (see Figure 4.6). This region is referred to as striate cortex because microscopically it shows prominent striations formed by layers of cells and fibers. The fibers of the lateral geniculate project in an orderly manner upon striate cortex, just as the optic-tract fibers themselves project in an orderly manner upon the lateral geniculate. Consequently, the retina is "mapped out" on striate cortex in the manner shown in Figure 4.6.

The role of striate cortex in coding spatial features of visual stimuli is brought to light by the studies of Hubel and Wiesel (1962). These investigators have studied the receptive fields of single cells in striate cortex by means of microelectrode techniques like those used to study retinal ganglion cells. They found that many neurons in striate cortex, unlike neurons in the lateral geniculate, discharge impulses when light strikes corresponding points in either retina. In other words, these neurons in striate cortex receive dual projections from the two retinas. Apparently, it is this dual projection which underlies binocular fusion—the perception of a stimulus striking the two retinas as one. Hubel and Wiesel also have described two kinds of cells in striate cortex. Cells with simple receptive fields discharge nerve impulses at the onset or offset of light anywhere within a narrow, elongated region surrounded on either side by regions in which stimulation produces the opposite response (see Figure 4.7A). Because of this receptive-field organization, these cells respond best to illuminated bars or edges (or dark bars if the central region responds to offset of light) in a particular orientation. In addition, these cells respond strongly to bars moving through their receptive fields. The second group of cells, those with complex receptive fields, also responds to bars at a particular orientation, but over a much larger receptive field than do cells with simple receptive fields (see Figure 4.7B). These "complex cells," then, seem to combine the properties of several "simple cells." Each simple cell seems to receive its input from several lateral geniculate cells (see Figure 4.7D). It appears, then, that striate cortex is involved in the perception of the spatial aspects of light, more specifically, in detecting borders and edges. Complete removal of striate cortex abolishes the ability to perceive spatial features of light, and animals with complete striate cortex removal apparently react only to variations in the physical intensity of light.

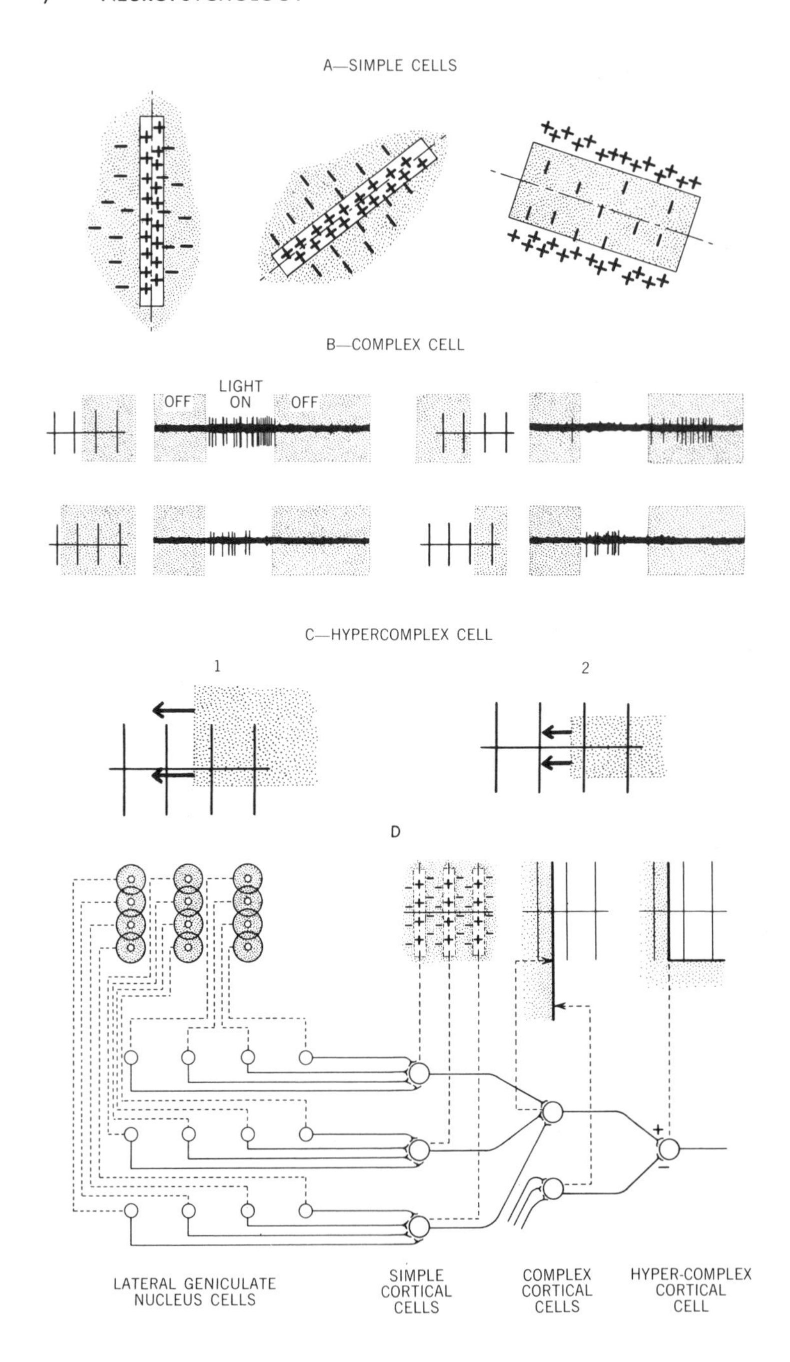

Figure 4.7

Receptive fields of cortical cells. **(A)** *Example of simple receptive fields. (+) and (−) refer to "on" and "off" response regions as in Figure 4.5.* **(B)** *Ex-*

In order to understand how visual information is further processed by the brain, we turn to those regions of the cortex to which the striate area projects. One of these regions is called prestriate cortex, located in front of striate cortex. Hubel and Wiesel (1965) have also investigated the receptive fields of neurons in this portion of the visual system. Here they have found cells with complex receptive fields like those in striate cortex. In addition, they found other cells that respond even more selectively to visual stimuli; these they termed hypercomplex cells. Some hypercomplex cells respond best to edges or bars at a particular orientation but only if they are cut off or "stopped" at one end or at both ends (see Figure 4.7C). These hypercomplex cells seem to combine the properties of complex cells; they behave as though they receive excitatory and inhibitory inputs from two or more complex cells, as shown in Figure 4.7D. These findings suggest that some of the complex relational features of visual patterns are coded hierarchically, by putting together in a stepwise manner information about simpler events coded by neurons at lower levels (see Figure 4.7D). Moreover, Hubel and Wiesel's finding that cells in prestriate cortex code spatial features is consistent with the finding that monkeys in which the prestriate cortex is ablated are impaired in learning visual discriminations, especially those involving objects and patterns (Riopelle and Ades, 1953). In addition, the region of the temporal lobes which receives input from prestriate cortex is also involved in visual processes. Removal of this temporal cortical region in monkeys (see Figure 8.2, page 160) produces a selective impairment in visual discrimination learning, especially discriminations involving patterns (Mishkin and Pribram, 1954). The area of the temporal lobe which is involved in visual learning receives its input from prestriate cortex (Mishkin, 1966). Thus, it is possible that

---

ample of a complex receptive field. The cell gives an "on" response when a vertical edge of light is to the left, and gives an "off" response when the light is to the right. **(C)** *Example of a hypercomplex receptive field. Unlike a complex cell, this hypercomplex cell does not respond to a long bar entering its receptive field (left), but does if the bar is "stopped" or cut off at the top (right). From Hubel, D. H., The visual cortex of the brain.* Sci. Amer., *November 1963.* **(D)** *Diagram indicating the kinds of neuronal connections that would account for receptive field characteristics of cortical cells. The receptive field of each cell is indicated at the top by the dashed line leading from the cell body, represented as a circle. All synaptic connections, except the one from the lower complex cortical cell to the hypercomplex cell, are assumed to be excitatory.*

temporal cortex is another part of the mechanism which Hubel and Wiesel have shown is involved in the coding of visual patterns.

EFFERENT CONTROL OF VISUAL INFORMATION PROCESSING

Through efferent pathways, many structures in the visual system can control the transmission of visual information in other parts of the system. Temporal cortex sends fibers to prestriate cortex, which, in turn, sends fibers to striate cortex. Thus, through these anatomical pathways, higher regions of the visual system can control their own input. Through its projections back to the lateral geniculate, striate cortex can modulate its own input; this modulating influence is seen in the inhibition of lateral geniculate neurons by electrical stimulation of striate cortex (Widen and Ajmone-Marsan, 1961). Furthermore, the visual areas of the cortex all send projections to the superior colliculus, thus allowing higher visual processes to control this integrating center for eye movements. Thus, visual areas of the cortex can alter the information projected on the retina. It also appears that the reticular formation of the brain stem exerts control over information transmission at the lateral geniculate and at the retina. For, stimulation of this structure can enhance or depress the activity of neurons in the lateral geniculate (Arden and Soderberg, 1961) and the excitability of retinal ganglion cells to light (Granit, 1955). Presumably, this reticular-retinal control is mediated by efferent fibers which travel out the optic nerve.

In the introduction to this section we raised the problem of how the visual world remains stable despite alterations in the pattern of light on the retina due to movements of the head and eyes. Somehow it appears that the nervous system takes account of these movements so that the world appears to remain stable during self-produced movements. One way in which this might be accomplished is by feedback from proprioceptors in the extrinsic eye muscles. However, Brindley and Merton (1960) have shown that subjects whose extrinsic eye muscles are temporarily paralyzed are not aware of their eyes' being passively moved (achieved by pulling on an eye muscle tendon), and they conclude that proprioceptors in eye muscles do not carry information about the position of the eyeball. An experiment by von Holst and Mittelstaedt (1950) helps to clarify the particular role played by efferent processes in stabilizing the visual world. First, these investigators showed that when a subject whose eye muscles are temporarily paralyzed is told to move his eyes to the right, objects in the visual field appear to jump to the right (even though the eyes do not move) (see Figure 4.8A). Next, they showed that passive movement of the paralyzed eye to the right produces a perceived movement of the visual field to the left (see Figure 4.8B). Finally, when passive movement of the paralyzed eye to the right is accompanied by an attempt to move the eyes to the right, the visual field does not move but remains stationary (see Figure 4.8C). Von Holst and Mittelstaedt concluded that the following events occur in the nervous system during the three stages of their experiment (see Figure 4.8): (1) In the first stage, when the subject is told to move his eyes to the right, the efferent discharge from centers controlling eye movements contains the information "objects moved to the right." (2) Secondly, the change in afferent stimulation, or reafference, produced by passively moving the eye to the right contains the information "objects moved to the left." (3) When the conditions of the first two stages are combined in the third, the efferent and reafferent messages cancel each other and, as a result, the visual field appears stationary. Presumably, these messages would also cancel each other under normal conditions in which the efferent discharge produces a change in the position of the eyes and a change

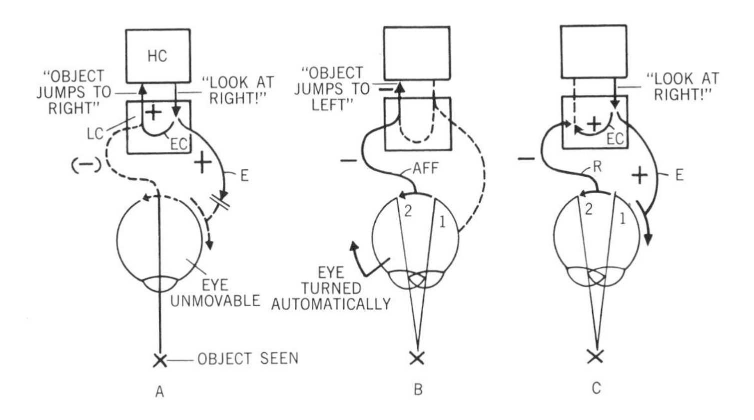

Figure 4.8

The three stages of the experiment by von Holst and Mittelstaedt referred to in the text. In the first stage, **(A)**, *a higher center* (HC) *issues a command to a lower center* (LC) *which is not carried out, since the eye muscles are paralyzed. A copy of this command, or "efferent copy"* (EC) *contains the information "object jumps to right." In* **(B)** *the eye is passively rotated, and the change in the afferent message* (A) *from the retina contains the information "object jumps to left." In* **(C)** *the procedures of* (A) *and* (B) *are combined, and the efferent copy and reafferent message* (R) *cancel each other, so that objects appear stationary. From von Holst, E., Relations between the central nervous system and the peripheral organs, Figure 5, page 92.* Brit. J. Anim. Behav., *1954, 2, 89–94.*

in afferent stimulation. Thus it appears that stability of vision is achieved by some neural correlation between efferent and reafferent information.

AUDITORY SYSTEM

Many species of animals utilize sounds as sources of information about events occurring in their surroundings. Animal sounds serve as signals of danger for prey and as signals of food for predators. Sounds emitted in the air by bats and underwater by porpoises are reflected back to their ears and are used by these animals to localize objects in space. Many of the sounds produced by animals, such as the songs of birds and the cries of young, serve as signals for communicating with other members of their species. Social communication in its most complex form is achieved in human language, not so much by the multiplication of different sounds but by the combination of a limited number of basic sounds in an enormously large number of ways.

Physically, sounds consist of pressure waves which are transmitted through the air or water. The characteristics of these pressure waves are described in detail in Chapter 3 in *Sensory Processes.* Briefly, they are described in terms of their frequency, in cycles per second (cps), and their amplitude. Changes in frequency are primarily responsible for variations in the perceived pitch of a sound, while changes in amplitude are primarily responsible for variations in loudness. Pressure waves of a single frequency (pure tones) are frequently used to study sensory processes in audition. These sounds, however, are rarely if ever encountered outside the laboratory. The sounds which characteristically convey information to organisms consist of complex waves, which contain a number of different frequencies of varying intensity. A visual display on film of the complex sound waves of a bird song and of a human voice is shown in Figure 4.9. It appears that sounds such as these are identified not by any particular frequency or intensity, but by the relationship between frequencies at any moment and their pattern over time. Thus, in order to understand how the brain recognizes the kinds of auditory signals which carry useful information, we must know how the auditory system—the organs of hearing and their associated central neural pathways—codes these complex patterns. Unfortunately, we know very little at present about the neural coding of tonal patterns. Most research on the auditory system, as in audition in general, has been concerned with discrimination of frequency and intensity, which may be considered the elements composing tonal patterns. However, as we shall see, the results of recent experiments provide some clues concerning the neural structures involved in coding the more complex patterns of auditory stimuli. But first, we shall describe the events which take place prior to pattern analysis—the reception of sound waves and the coding of frequency and intensity.

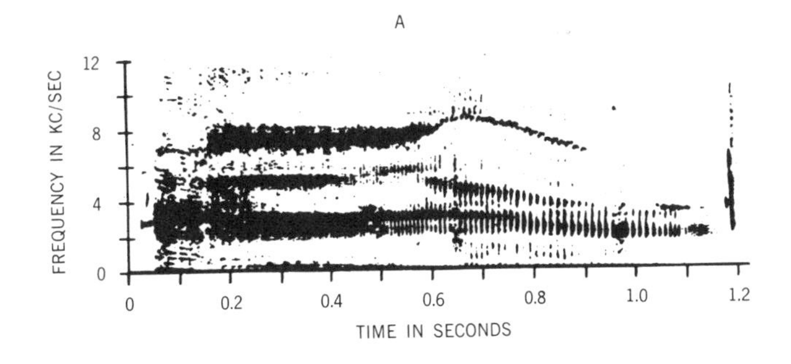

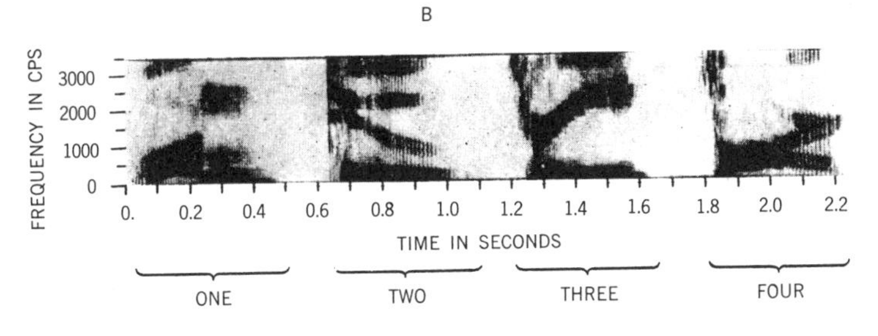

Figure 4.9

Visual displays, or spectrograms, of sounds involved in communication. The dark bands represent those frequencies which are most intense. **(A)** *Spectogram of song of male African village weaverbird* (textor cucullatus). *From Collias, N. E., A spectographic analysis of the vocal repertoire of the African village weaverbird, Figure 2b, page 522.* Condor, *1963,* 65, *517–527.* **(B)** *Spectrogram of the words "one, two, three, four," spoken by a person. From Steinberg, J. C., and French, N. R., The portrayal of visible speech, Figure 1, page 5.* J. Acoust. Soc. Amer., *1946,* 18, *4–18.*

AUDITORY RECEPTION: THE CONDUCTION OF VIBRATIONS

The reception of sound waves may be divided into two stages: (1) the conduction of vibrations to the auditory receptors located in the spiral cochlea, and (2) the transduction of these vibrations into nerve impulses. The conduction of vibrations to the receptors is described in detail in Chapter 3 of *Sensory Processes*; hence it will only be briefly described here. Sound waves are transmitted from the air to the auditory receptors through the series of structures shown in Figure 4.10A. After passing through the external meatus, sound waves produce vibrations of the tympanic membrane. These movements of the tympanic membrane are then transmitted through the ossicles of the middle ear to the oval window of the spiral cochlea, located in the inner ear. The lever action of the ossicles is concentrated on the small oval window so that sound waves are transmitted from the external ear to the inner ear with little loss of pressure.

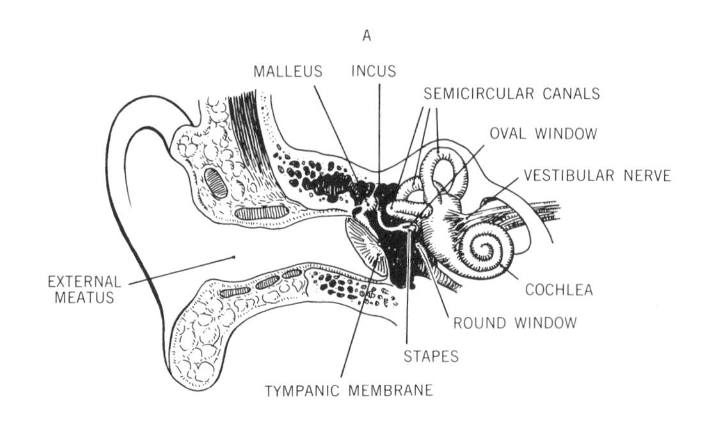

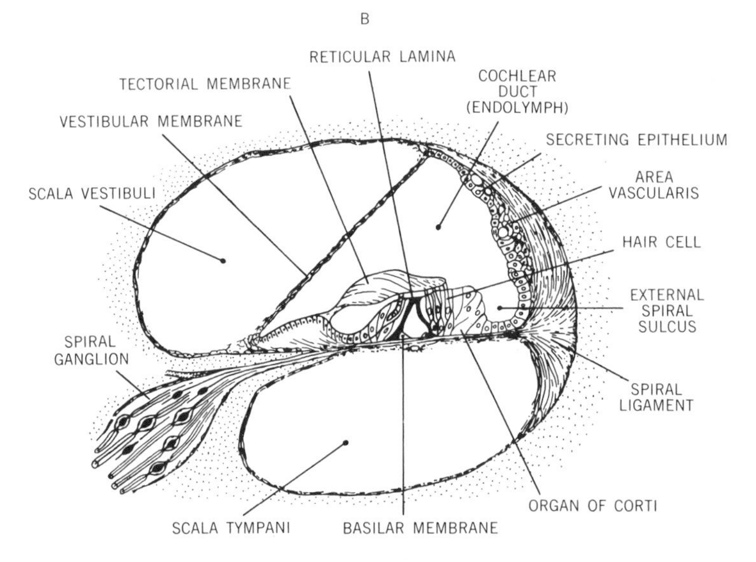

Figure 4.10

(A) *The external, middle, and inner ear, illustrating the structures through which sound waves are transmitted. From Davis, H., Excitation of auditory receptors, Figure 1, page 566. In J. Field (Ed.),* Handbook of physiology, *Vol. I. Chapter 23. Washington: American Physiological Society, 1959.* **(B)** *The internal structure of the cochlea. From Gardner, E.,* Fundamentals of neurology, *5th ed., Figure 119. Philadelphia: Saunders, 1968.*

The cochlea is a complex structure which consists of three compartments (see Figure 4.10B). One of these, the cochlear duct, is filled with endolymphatic fluid and is separated from the scala tympani by the basilar membrane. On this membrane is located the organ of Corti, consisting of the hair cells, which are the auditory receptors, together with supporting cells. The hair cells are innervated by afferent fibers of the eighth (auditory) nerve, whose cell bodies are located in the spiral ganglion. The hair cells are also innervated by efferent fibers. Vibrations of the oval window set the endolymph in motion, and the movements of this fluid, in turn, cause the basilar membrane to bulge. As the basilar membrane moves up and down in response to pressure waves, the overlying tectorial membrane swings back and forth. Thus, a bending or shearing action is produced on the hairs of the receptors, which protrude through the reticular lamina and are embedded in the tectorial membrane. This bending of the hairs is the mechanical response of the receptor to pressure waves, and it initiates the second stage of auditory reception—the transduction of sound waves into nerve impulses. What we know about this transduction process is based upon the following evidence.

THE AUDITORY TRANSDUCTION PROCESS

When recording electrodes are placed on the cochlea, an electrical response to sound stimulation is recorded. This electrical response is called the cochlear potential. The cochlear potential, unlike the all-or-none impulses in the eighth nerve fibers, is a graded response which reproduces the waveform of sounds presented to the ear. By probing different parts of the cochlea with microelectrodes, it has been determined that the cochlear potential originates in the hair cells. Thus, it is quite likely that this electrical response represents a summation of receptor potentials of the hair cells. Furthermore, it has been suggested that this electrical response is triggered by the bending of the hairs which, in turn, produces a depolarization of the receptor membrane. This membrane depolarization might then excite the terminals of the auditory nerve fibers so that nerve impulses are triggered.

FREQUENCY CODING IN THE PERIPHERAL AUDITORY MECHANISM

The basilar membrane is not displaced equally throughout its length in response to sound waves of a particular frequency. Rather, as described in Chapter 3 in *Sensory Processes*, the properties of the membrane are such that low frequency tones cause maximal displacement of the upper end, or apex, of the basilar membrane, while high frequency tones cause maximal displacement of the lower end or base of the membrane (see Figure 4.11). Thus, hair cells along the length of the basilar membrane are differentially stimulated by tones of different frequencies. While the basilar membrane provides a mechanism for coding frequency, its response to single frequencies is quite broad, as seen in Figure 4.11, and it becomes even broader as the intensity of the tone is increased. Obviously the basilar membrane is not sufficiently attuned to particular frequencies to explain how we are able to distinguish between frequency differences as small as three cps. We shall describe later how the central auditory pathways contribute to frequency analysis.

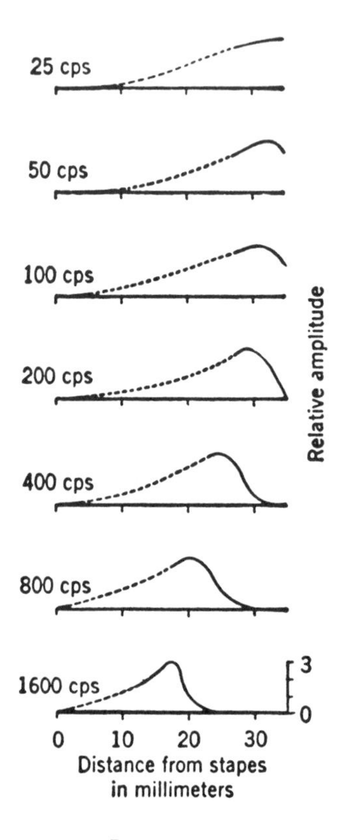

Figure 4.11

Displacement patterns of the basilar membrane to different frequencies of stimulation. The lower end of the basilar membrane is closest to the stapes, while the upper end of the basilar membrane is farthest from the stapes. Note that the maximum displacement amplitude shifts toward the lower end of the basilar membrane as the frequency is increased. From Békésy, G. von, On the resonance curve and decay period at various points on the cochlear partition. Figure 1, page 246. J. Acoust. Soc. Amer., *1949,* 21, *245–254.*

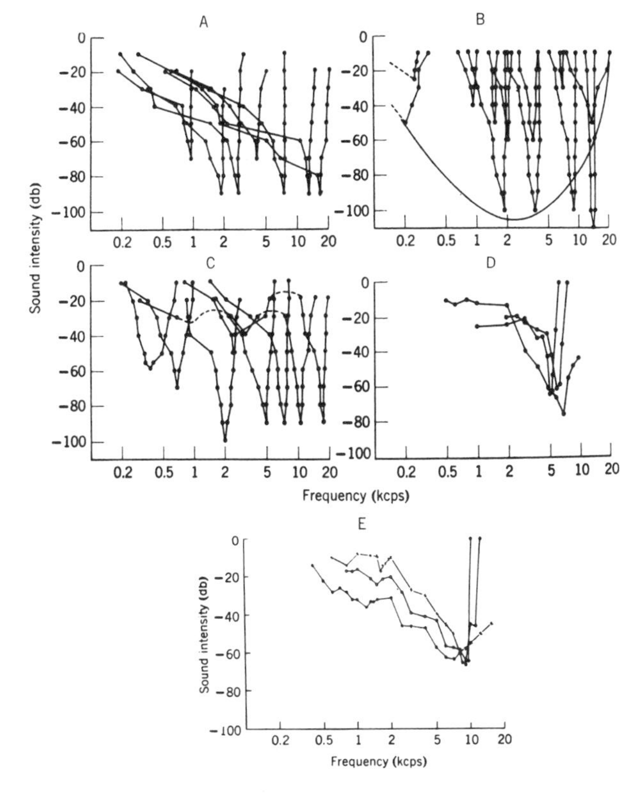

Figure 4.12

*Response areas of neurons in different portions of the auditory system of the cat. Each set of points connected by a line encloses an area which includes all the combinations of frequencies and intensities to which a particular neuron responds. (***A***: auditory nerve fibers,* **B***: inferior colliculus,* **C***: trapezoid body,* **D***: mediate geniculate nucleus,* **E***: auditory cortex.) From Katsuki, Y., Neural mechanism of auditory sensation in cats, Figure 2, page 566. In W. A. Rosenblith (Ed.),* Sensory communication. *New York-Wiley, 1961.*

Since frequency is coded by the part of the basilar membrane which is most displaced, one might expect that individual auditory nerve fibers, which innervate hair cells on different parts of the membrane, would respond selectively to different frequencies. To some extent this is the case. Figure 4.12A shows the combinations of frequency and intensity which produce action potentials in single auditory nerve fibers. The areas enclosed by the lines include all the combinations of frequency and intensity to which a particular neuron is responsive; hence it is referred to as the response area of that fiber. At high intensities of stimulation each fiber responds to a rather broad range of frequencies, apparently because a large extent of the basilar membrane is displaced in response to high-intensity tones. As the intensity is decreased, the fiber responds to a narrower frequency band. At the lowest intensities to which it is reactive, the neuron responds only to a particular frequency, called the characteristic frequency of the neuron. Each neuron, then, is attuned to a particular frequency, at least at low levels of intensity.

It has also been observed that impulses in auditory nerve fibers respond to each individual pressure wave of tones with frequencies below 1,000 cps, a limit which is set by the refractory period of nerve fibers. There is also evidence that individual nerve fibers may "take turns" responding to alternate or every third or fourth pressure wave so that "frequency following" may extend up to 4,000 cps. While these observations suggest that frequency may be coded in terms of frequency of nerve firing (at the lower frequency range), as well as by place on the basilar membrane, it is not likely that the former mechanism is utilized by the CNS. For, temporal dispersion is produced in nerve impulses at the synapse so that neurons at higher levels would not follow the frequency of firing of input neurons.

INTENSITY CODING IN THE PERIPHERAL AUDITORY MECHANISM

As the intensity of a tone is increased, the basilar membrane is displaced to a greater extent. Thus a larger number of receptors are stimulated, and, consequently, more nerve fibers discharge. In addition, as the intensity of stimulation is increased, the frequency of impulses in individual neurons increases (Galambos and Davis, 1943), as it does in neurons of other sensory systems when stimulus intensity is increased. It is also possible that particular neurons in the auditory nerve specialize in coding intensity, while others specialize in coding frequency. For, there is evidence for two types of neurons in the auditory nerve of monkey: One kind is quite sensitive to intensity changes, but shows poor frequency tuning (i.e., they have broad response areas), while the other kind is relatively insensitive to frequency changes but shows sharp frequency tuning, that is, the neurons have narrow response areas (Katsuki, Suga, and Kanno, 1962).

ANATOMY OF THE CENTRAL AUDITORY PATHWAYS

In order to understand how the brain makes use of auditory information we must first describe the central pathways over which this information is conducted. Anatomically, the auditory system consists of a large number of nuclei and connecting pathways, shown diagrammatically in Figure 4.13. In the ascending pathways, five subcortical nuclei may be interposed between the eighth nerve and the cortical reception area for audition. It is probably an oversimplification to assume that only one synapse intervenes between an incoming and outgoing fiber from these nuclei (as shown in Figure 4.13), for these nuclei all have complex internal neural connections. Furthermore, there is a large increase in the number of nerve cells in successively higher nuclei, and apparently a comparable increase in the number and complexity of synaptic connections within these nuclei (Chow, 1951). Thus it appears that there are many opportunities for neural messages to be recoded as they ascend to higher areas of the brain. It will also be noted that there are both crossed and uncrossed pathways in the auditory system. Thus, information originating from each ear is bilaterally represented in the brain.

The auditory system also contains a number of efferent pathways, some of which reciprocate the ascending connections (see Figure 4.13). It will be noted that one of these efferent pathways, the olivocochlear bundle, travels out to the basilar membrane, and its fibers probably terminate upon hair cells. These efferent pathways are most likely involved in the control and selection of auditory information, a topic we will discuss later.

INFORMATION PROCESSING IN THE CENTRAL AUDITORY PATHWAYS: FREQUENCY CODING

How is auditory information processed by the central auditory system? Just as in the visual system, some clues to information processing are provided by electrophysiological and lesion techniques. We previously mentioned that single fibers in the auditory nerve are to some extent attuned to specific frequencies. Coding frequency through activity in specific fibers would be effective only if the fibers terminated on different neural elements in the cochlear nucleus. Otherwise, structures at higher levels of the brain could not distinguish between information concerning different frequencies. The fibers of the auditory nerve do in fact terminate in an orderly manner in different portions of the cochlear nucleus so that neurons in one portion of this structure respond to high frequencies, while those in other portions respond to low frequencies. In other words, this structure has a "tonotopic" organization, as do other structures in the auditory pathways, including the auditory cortex. Thus, frequency coding in the central auditory system follows the same kind of "place principle" that frequency coding follows on the basilar membrane.

Furthermore, it appears that the central auditory system continues and further refines the frequency analysis which is begun on the basilar membrane. Figure 4.12 shows the response areas of single neural elements in different portions of the auditory pathways. It is apparent that the response areas of neurons tend to become narrower at higher levels of the system, up to the medial geniculate. Thus, neurons at higher levels of the auditory system become more selectively attuned to specific frequencies. It will be noted in Figure 4.12 that the frequency tuning of neurons in auditory cortex is poor compared to the frequency tuning of units in the medial geniculate or inferior colliculus. Moreover, these neurons respond with only few impulses to pure tones, even to their characteristic frequencies. Thus, although auditory cortex has a tonotopic organization, it does not seem to be involved in frequency analysis. This conclusion is supported by the finding that removal of auditory cortex does not impair the capacity of cats to detect frequency changes (Butler, Diamond, and Neff, 1957).

INFORMATION PROCESSING IN THE CENTRAL AUDITORY PATHWAYS: INTENSITY CODING

While the coding of frequency seems to involve a sharpening process in the central auditory pathways, intensity coding seems to take place primarily at the lowest level of the system. For, it has been shown that neurons in the lower levels of the system, especially those in the cochlear nucleus, are highly responsive to small changes in intensity, showing large increases in rate of firing as intensity of stimulation is increased. On the other hand, neurons at higher levels show much smaller increases in rate of firing to increments in intensity, and cortical neurons do not follow intensity changes at all (Katsuki, 1961). It appears then, that auditory cortex is not involved in coding intensity, a conclusion which is supported by the finding that cats with auditory cortex removed are not impaired in detecting intensity changes (Neff, 1961).

SOUND LOCALIZATION

One aspect of auditory function not mentioned so far is the ability to localize sounds in space. This ability is dependent upon differential stimulation of the two ears by sounds coming from one side of the head, as described in Chapter 3 in *Sensory Processes.* Sounds coming from one side arrive at the near ear before the far ear. While this binaural difference in arrival time of sounds is quite small—in the order of microseconds—it is an effective cue for localizing the direction of sounds in space. In addition, high-frequency sounds coming from one side of the head are more intense to the ear on that side than they are to the opposite ear, since the head acts as a sound shadow for sounds above 1,000 cps. Since neurons in the auditory system show decreased latency of response as intensity of a stimulating sound is increased, it is likely that differential latency of neural discharge from stimulation of the two ears is the cue used by the auditory system for localizing sounds in space.

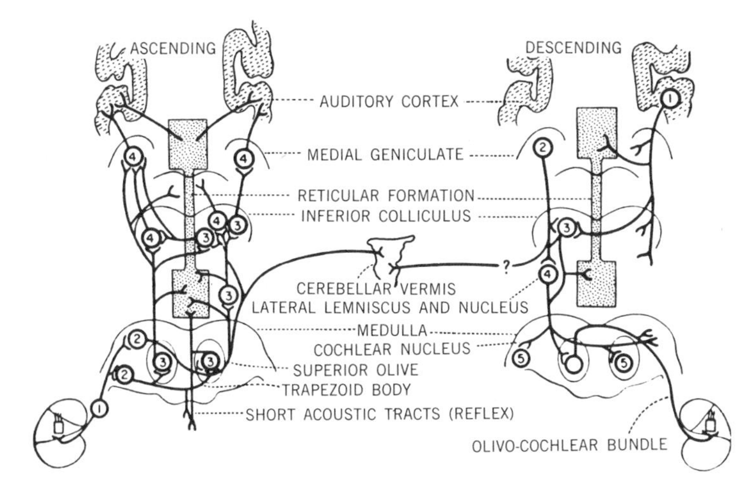

Figure 4.13

The ascending and descending auditory pathways. The cochlea is represented in the lower part of each diagram, along with the auditory nerve fibers leading from hair cells in the cochlea shown in the diagram on the left side. From Galambos, R., Some recent experiments on the neurophysiology of hearing, Figure 2, page 1059. Ann. Otol., Rhinol., Laryngol., *1956,* 65, *1053–1059.*

In order for binaural time differences to become an effective cue for localization, neural signals coming from each of the ears must converge somewhere in the central auditory system. As seen in Figure 4.13, information from one ear can cross to the opposite side of the brain and interact with information from the opposite ear at the superior olive in the brain stem, as well as at higher levels of the brain. There is physiological evidence that the superior olive is involved in the detection of binaural differences in the arrival time of sounds. Neurons in this structure respond selectively to clicks, delivered to the two ears, depending on the difference in arrival time of clicks at the two ears (see Figure 4.14). Moreover, the critical time difference for these neural responses to binaural stimulation is approximately the same as the time differences which are effective cues for localizing sounds in space. When the afferent pathways to this structure are destroyed, cats can no longer detect small disparities in the arrival time of clicks delivered to the two ears (Masterson, Jane, and Diamond, 1967). There is also evidence that the auditory cortex is involved in sound localization, for cats with damage to auditory cortex show a loss in the ability to localize sounds in space (Neff, 1961). It has been suggested that auditory cortex integrates the temporal disparity cue with other cues for sound localiza-

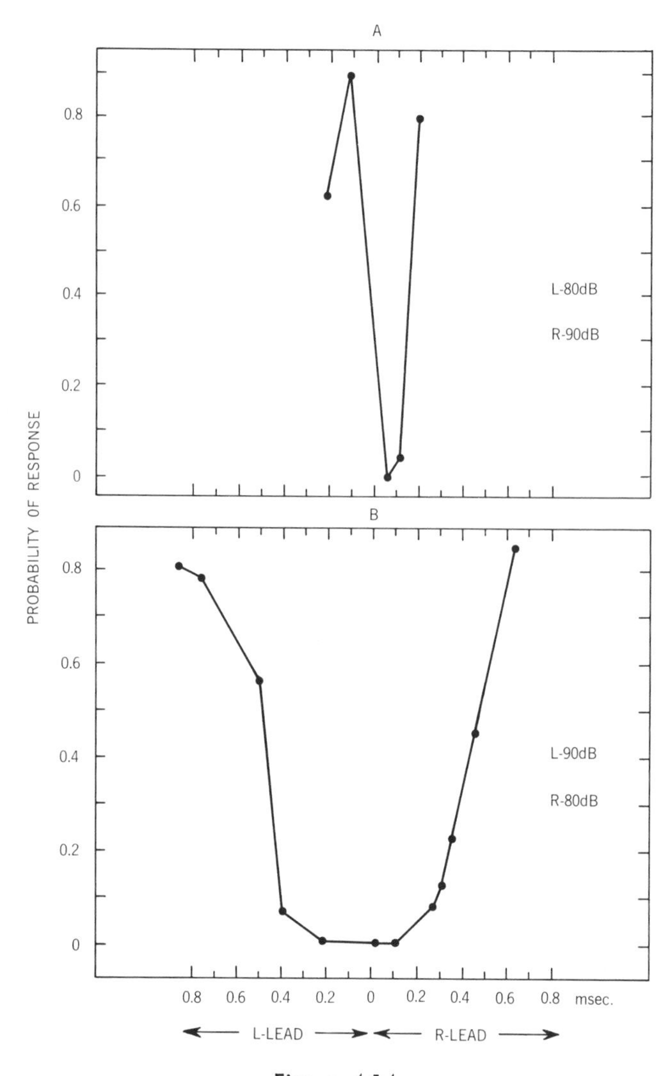

Figure 4.14

Inhibitory interactions of two neurons in the superior olive to stimulation of the two ears. The horizontal axis represents the time differences of arrival of clicks at the two ears. The vertical axis represents a measure of nerve impulse frequency. In **(A)** *the neuron responds best when stimulation of either ear leads the other by a small fraction of a msec. The neuron whose discharges are plotted in* **(B)** *reacts in a similar manner, but at longer time intervals. From Moushegian, G., Rupert, A. L., and Langford, T. L., Stimulus coding by medial superior olivary neurons, Figure 14, page, 1253.* J. Neurophysiol, *1967, 30, 1239–1261.*

tion so that the perception of auditory space is made possible (Masterson, Jane, and Diamond, 1967).

TONAL PATTERN ANALYSIS

As mentioned previously, auditory cortex does not seem to be involved in intensity or frequency discrimination. However, there is evidence that auditory cortical areas participate in the coding of tonal patterns. While neurons in auditory cortex respond only weakly to single tones, they show sustained bursts of discharges to beating tones, produced by two pure tones whose frequencies are closely related. They also give strong responses as well to complex tones whose component frequencies are harmonically related (Katsuki, 1961). Further research by Oonishi and Katsuki (1965) indicates that the capacity of cortical neurons to respond to tonal patterns seems to depend on their reception of convergent inputs from frequency-specific thalamic neurons. Thus, it appears that the coding of tonal patterns in auditory cortex involves the same kind of hierarchical mechanism that the visual system uses to code visual patterns (see pages 53-55). There is also behavioral evidence that auditory cortex is involved in tonal pattern perception. Removal of auditory cortex in cats abolishes the ability to discriminate between temporal patterns of tones (Diamond and Neff, 1957). Similarly, patients in whom large areas of the right temporal lobe have been surgically removed discriminate poorly between tonal sequences and also between chords differing in timbre. However, their ability to discriminate between tones varying in frequency is not significantly impaired (Milner, 1962). On the other hand, patients with surgical removal of the left temporal lobe do not show these deficiencies. Rather, unlike those with right temporal lobe removal, they are impaired in understanding spoken language (Luria, 1966). This impairment in understanding spoken language appears to be due to a failure to discriminate and identify the complex tonal patterns, called phonemes, of which spoken words are composed (Luria, 1966).

EFFERENT CONTROL AND SELECTION OF AUDITORY INFORMATION

The transmission of auditory information from the ear to the brain is altered by several kinds of efferent processes. First of all, there are negative feedback mechanisms which produce their effect at the periphery. One of these involves the middle ear muscles, which contract in response to intense sounds, thus dampening the movements of the middle ear ossicles and reducing the amplitude of pressure waves stimulating the cochlea. Through this feedback circuit, the possibility of damage to the receptors is reduced. Another mechanism for reducing auditory input is provided by the olivocochlear bundle, consisting of efferent fibers which arise from the cochlear nucleus, travel out the opposite auditory nerve and terminate upon hair cells (see Figure 4.13). These nerve fibers discharge in response to stimulation of afferent auditory nerve fibers. When they are electrically stimulated, discharges of afferent fibers to auditory stimuli are suppressed (Galambos, 1956). It is likely, then, that these fibers, together with afferent fibers, form a closed feedback circuit which acts to reduce afferent activity, possibly by inhibiting the receptors directly.

Other efferent mechanisms can produce an increase in auditory input. Sounds, especially meaningful or novel sounds, evoke head movements directed toward their source and, in animals, pricking up of the ears—responses which increase the amount of auditory information available to the receptors. In addition, movements of the head play an important role in localizing sounds in space. These orienting movements are controlled by efferent pathways which arise from auditory centers in the brain stem. These auditory centers can be activated not only by auditory signals ascending from the periphery, but also by fibers directed downward from the cortex. By means of these latter pathways, the cortex, which provides mechanisms for processing meaningful patterns of stimulation, can control orienting movements toward the source of these signals. Furthermore, we can select auditory inputs not only by the appropriate orienting movements, but also by means of some central process whereby attention is focussed on some auditory messages and not others. For example, it is a well known fact that one can listen to one conversation and ignore others in a crowded room where many people are talking. Furthermore, the brain waves of a sleeping person show larger reactions to his spoken name than to other names (Oswald, Taylor, and Treisman, 1961). Such instances of selective listening may involve corticofugal pathways by means of which particular auditory messages at lower-order stations are selected for further transmission, while others are rejected. The influence of such corticofugal pathways on auditory information transmission is shown by the finding that stimulation of auditory cortical areas in the cat blocks electrical responses to sounds at the cochlear nucleus (Desmedt, 1960) or, under other conditions, can increase the rate at which auditory information is processed (Dewson, Nobel, and Pribram, unpublished experiments).

SOMATIC SENSORY SYSTEMS

The somatic senses comprise those sensory channels which provide information about stimulation of the body surface and of deep-lying tissue and structures within the body. Like the other sensory systems, the somatic sensory systems convey information which is important and in many instances vital for the well-being of the organism. This is readily apparent in the case of pain, which serves as a signal of bodily harm which may threaten the existence of the organism. It is perhaps less apparent that the signalling of limb position and limb movement (of which we are usually unaware) by receptors in joints plays a crucial role in the control of movement.

The kinds of sensory events mediated by the somatic sensory systems are many and varied. The smooth texture of satin held in the hand, the burning pain of inflammation, and the hollow feeling accompanying an empty stomach are just a few instances of the diverse experiences aroused by somatic stimuli. One example will suffice to show the complexity of the neural events which the brain receives from somatic receptors and integrates. When we move our fingers over the surface of an object, trying to identify it by touch, a complex and continuously varying pattern of discharges is produced in receptors by displacement of the skin and the movements of joints. This spatial and temporal pattern of neural discharges is conveyed to the brain and somehow integrated so that we are able to identify a variety of object qualities such as shape, texture, and even composition. The manner in which receptors transduce somatic stimuli into neural messages and the manner in which the brain interprets these messages is to a large extent unknown. Nevertheless, through the efforts of a number of researchers, a clearer conception of these processes is gradually emerging.

It is customary to divide the somatic senses into two groups—those which provide information about external events impinging upon the skin, referred to as exteroceptive, and those which signal events taking place within the body itself, referred to as proprioceptive. Within this latter class one may differentiate between interoceptive sensory events, which may arise from physical tension or chemical conditions in deep tissues and organs, and kinesthesis, the sense of limb position and movement arising from tissue surrounding the joints. It is more useful, however, to classify the somatic senses in terms of the distinctive sensory experiences which they mediate, although, as we shall see, a separate and independent neural mechanism does not necessarily correspond to each of these categories. Pain, which can be produced by a number of events within and at the surface of the body, qualifies as one kind of sensory experience, as does perception of warmth and perception of cold. Touch and pressure, which arise from displacement of skin or hairs or of underlying tissues, forms another category of sensory experience; kinesthetic sensibility forms still another. In addition, a variety of complex object qualities, such as texture, size, and shape, can be appreciated by active touch, when the hand is used as an exploring organ (Gibson, 1962). Thus, the perception of object qualities through active touch may qualify as a distinct class of sensory experiences, one which depends on the integration of touch and kinesthesis. Finally, there are a number of complex somatic sensory experiences, such as tickle, visceral, and sexual sensations, which are difficult to describe and classify; some of them are described in Chapter 5 in *Sensory Processes.* In this section we will describe first the sensitivity of the skin (which has been more extensively investigated than has the sensitivity of deep tissue), then the functions of somatic receptors and their afferent pathways, and, finally, the central mechanisms mediating the integration of somatosensory information.

CUTANEOUS SENSITIVITY

Before techniques had been devised for measuring the electrical activity of somatic receptors, the sensitivity of the skin to various stimuli was extensively investigated through the verbal reports of human subjects. These investigations indicate that sensitivity to various cutaneous stimuli is not uniformly distributed over an area of skin. Rather, in any one area, there are tiny spots, stimulation of which gives rise to different experiences, either touch, pain, warmth, cold, or no experience at all. In order to determine the extension and density of the four qualities, the punctiform character of cutaneous sensitivity has been explored experimentally with devices called esthesiometers. These devices are constructed to control the relevant variables such as the size of the area stimulated, the physical force and rate of application of the force, or the temperature of the point of contact. More specialized devices have been used for the study of special problems. Thus, some have two points of contact for the determination of two-point thresholds (i.e., the minimal distance between two points applied on the skin that are perceived as two and not as one), which provides an index of tactile sensitivity. Temperature has been explored with radiant energy; touch, with controlled puffs of air; vibratory thresholds, with sets of very small mechanical vibrators.

Studies of cutaneous sensitivity have also demonstrated that each kind of modality-specific spot is not uniformly distributed over the body surface. For example, the density of pressure spots is much greater in regions such as the fingers and face than it is in regions such as the leg. The density of cold spots also varies considerably, from a maximum of 19/sq. cm. on the upper lip to a minimum of 1 to 5/sq. cm. on the palm of the hand.

Furthermore, the number and size of warm and cold spots depends on the difference in temperature between the stimulus and the skin. The greater this temperature difference, the greater the number and size of spots found. The sensation of pain can be evoked from appropriate stimulation of every part of the body surface and of various tissues within the body. However, three regions have been asserted to be pain-free. One is a spot in the inner lining of the cheek (which has been exploited by the so-called "human pincushion" in sideshow exhibits). The back of the tongue and the uvula are also said to be lacking in pain sensibility.

CUTANEOUS RECEPTORS

Given these variations in the distribution of sensory spots, it might appear simple and straightforward to determine whether there is any correlation between particular sensory spots and the kinds of cutaneous receptors that are seen in microscopic examination of the skin. The findings obtained in such studies, however, have been inconsistent and inconclusive, and it appears that the relation between cutaneous receptors and sensory qualities is far from simple. Microscopic examination of the skin discloses a variety of morphologically different receptor structures as well as free nerve endings, which form the majority of cutaneous nerve terminals (see Figure 4.15). These fibers, some of which are unmyelinated, travel to the dermis or epidermis, often branching profusely over a wide area; the branches sometimes interweave to form

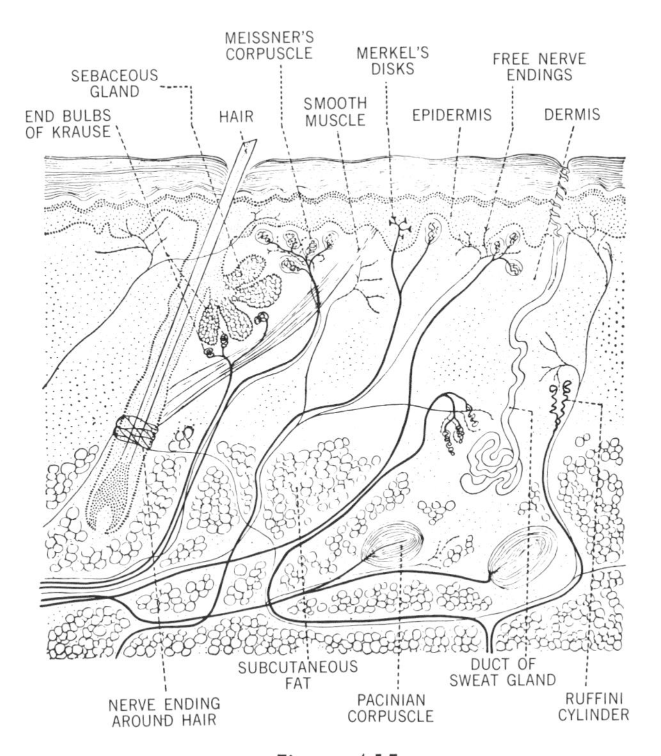

Figure 4.15

A schematic cross section through the skin, showing free nerve endings and specialized nerve endings that have been described in various areas of skin. From Wollard, H. H., Weddell, G., and Harpman, J. A., Observations on the neurohistological basis of cutaneous pain, Figure 13, page 427. J. Anat. Lond., *1940, 74, 413–420.*

a dense network. The myelinated branches loose their myelin sheaths and terminate freely. Different parent fibers overlap considerably in their distribution, so that each sensory spot receives multiple innervation. Free nerve endings also terminate around hair follicles in the skin, as shown in Figure 4.15. In addition, a variety of specialized endings are also found in some areas of the skin (see Figure 4.15). Some of these form terminal disks or protuberances (Merkl's disks), while others (Krause end bulbs, Meissner's corpuscles, Ruffini cylinders) consist of more elaborate terminal filaments which coil or spiral, sometimes forming varicose branches enclosed by capsules. The Pacinian corpuscle, which is the largest of the encapsulated endings (.6 mm. in thickness) forms a large oval capsule within which a single fiber terminates. These structures are found in subcutaneous tissue of the palms of the hand and the soles of the feet, as well as in many other body tissues.

According to the traditional theory of cutaneous sensitivity, each particular kind of nerve ending mediates a particular kind of sensory quality. However, the correlation between sensory spots and end organs is far from perfect. Traditional theory assumes that only the Meissner's corpuscles and Pacinian corpuscles are the mediators of touch, while free nerve endings (which are found in almost all cutaneous tissue) are responsible only for pain. As will be described later, electrophysiological findings have shown that the Pacinian corpuscle is selectively sensitive to displacement. Despite this fact, there is no simple one-to-one correlation between the presence of either of these structures and tactile sensitivity. In some hairy regions in which tactile sensitivity is high, neither Meissner's corpuscles nor Pacinian corpuscles have been found. In these regions the sense of touch may be mediated by free nerve endings, most likely those which are associated with hair follicles. Since gentle displacement of hairs gives rise to a sensation of touch, this event would seem to be an adequate stimulus for the net of free nerve endings surrounding the base of the hair follicle. However, the presence of free nerve endings does not guarantee tactile sensitivity, for the conjunctiva of the eye, which contains many free nerve endings, is reported to be insensitive to touch. Thus it seems likely that while touch sensitivity can arise from deformation of the skin in the presence of free nerve endings, the presence of these endings is not always associated with tactile sensitivity.

Traditional theory also asserts that the Krause end bulbs are the mediators of cold, while the Ruffini cylinders mediate warmth. In some tissue a rough correspondence between the relative number of warm and cold spots and the frequency of Krause end bulbs and Ruffini cylinders has been found. In fact, this correlation is almost exact in the prepuce (Bazett, McGlone, Williams, and Lufkin, 1932). However, there are many skin areas sensitive to warmth or cold which do not appear to contain these structures. Furthermore, biopsy studies have shown that some cold and warm spots marked on the skin contain only free nerve endings. Thus, it appears that thermal sensations may arise from stimulation of specific endings or from stimulation of some free nerve endings. But since stimulation of some free nerve endings may give rise only to tactile sensations, the presence of free nerve endings is apparently not sufficient for thermal sensitivity.

As mentioned previously, it has been argued that pain is mediated by free nerve endings, since nearly every area of the skin is sensitive to pain, and nearly every area of the skin contains free nerve endings. On closer examination, however, this correlation appears no better than the correlations between other modes of cutaneous sensitivity and the presence of particular encapsulated endings. The fact that sensation of only touch, warmth, or cold can arise in the presence of free nerve endings indicates that the correspondence between the experience of pain and stimulation of free nerve endings is not exact.

Given all these puzzling facts, it is not surprising that there is a good deal of controversy concerning the correspondence between the structure and function of cutaneous receptors. In fact, some investigators have gone so far as to maintain that there are no modality-specific cutaneous endings. Weddell, Palmer, and Pallie (1955) state that only free nerve endings are found in hairy regions of human skin. They also claim that the specialized end organs found in certain other regions show a diversity of structure which defies classification into the few "basic" types shown in Figure 4.15. Furthermore, Lele and Weddell (1956) found thermal and tactile sensitivity as well as pain sensitivity in the human cornea, which contains only free nerve endings. This finding, like those mentioned above suggests that free nerve endings may mediate several kinds of cutaneous sensations. On the basis of his histological and psychological studies, Weddell has concluded that there are no modality-specific cutaneous receptors, but that different sense qualities arise from different patterns of excitation of many endings.

PHYSIOLOGICAL RESPONSES OF SOMATIC RECEPTORS

While it is possible that some free nerve endings may mediate all cutaneous modalities, not all cutaneous receptors are nonspecific in their responses to somatic stimuli. For, electrophysiological findings indicate that one receptor—the Pacinian corpuscle—responds selectively to mechanical stimulation. In fact, this receptor is markedly sensitive to this mode of stimulation; its fiber discharges action potentials to displacements as small as $.5\mu$ (one two-thousandths of a millimeter). Furthermore, the Pacinian corpuscle is selectively sensitive to transient displacements; its fiber fires action potentials only at the onset and offset of displacement and not during maintained displacement (Gray and Sato, 1953). This rapid adaptation of the Pacinian corpuscle to maintained displacement is what one might expect, since it is probably a mediator of the sense of light touch, which is well known to be rapidly adapting. In addition, electrical recordings from Pacinian corpuscles disclose not only action potentials, but also graded responses which have the characteristics of receptor potentials (see Figure 4.16). It appears that this rapid adaptation of the receptor potential is determined by the structure of the capsule itself; when the capsule is removed, the receptor potential no longer shows rapid adaptation (Mendelson and Loewenstein, 1964). It thus appears that the capsule acts as a mechanical filter allowing only transient pressures produced at the onset and offset of displacement to excite the terminal axon.

PHYSIOLOGICAL RESPONSES OF AFFERENT NERVE FIBERS

The technical feat of recording electrical responses from individual Pacinian corpuscles has been possible because these receptors are quite large and can be isolated from surrounding tissue. Yet other cutaneous end organs are much smaller, and consequently it has not been possible to isolate them so that their electrical responses to somatic stimuli can be recorded. However, electrical recordings from somatic

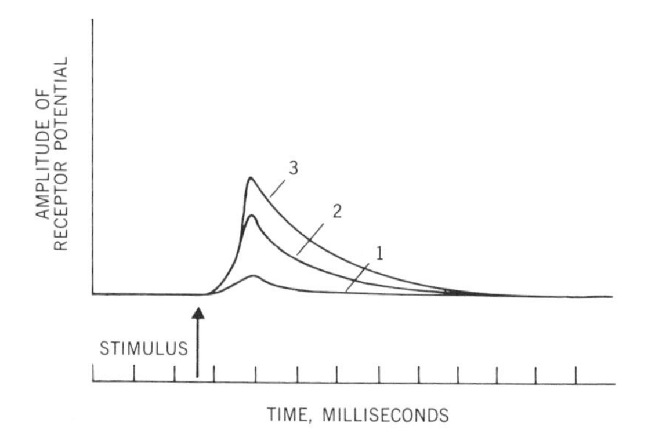

Figure 4.16

Receptor potentials recorded from a Pacinian corpuscle in a cat. The potentials labeled (1), (2), and (3) represent receptor potentials to successively greater displacement of the corpuscle. Note that as the displacement of the corpuscle increases, the peak amplitude of the receptor potential increases, and the time to reach peak amplitude decreases. From Gray, J. A. B., and Sato, M., Properties of the receptor potential in Pacinian corpuscles, Figure 6, page 620. J. Physiol., *1953,* 122, *610–636.*

nerve fibers have provided findings bearing on the issue of modality specificity of cutaneous receptors. It is known that some large-diameter myelinated fibers which rapidly conduct action potentials are selectively activated by light touch applied to a region of skin (Maruhashi, Mizuguchi, and Tasaki, 1952). This finding implies that some cutaneous tactile receptors which are supplied with such large-diameter axons may be selectively activated by light touch. In fact, fibers terminating in one kind of encapsulated ending in the skin of cats and monkeys do respond selectively to light pressure over the end organs (Iggo, 1963). Maruhashi, Mizuguchi, and Tasaki (1952) also found that unmyelinated, slowly conducting fibers which supply free nerve endings to the skin are activated by light touch and pressure. In addition, noxious stimulation (such as burning or pricking the skin) can activate these fibers (Adrian and Zotterman, 1926). Thus, free nerve endings in the skin can apparently respond to either pain or touch, although any particular fiber may not respond to both.

Werner and Mountcastle (1965) have revealed an interesting correlation between physiological activity in mechanoreceptive fibers and sensory psychological findings. These investigators found that the frequency of nerve impulses in mechanoreceptive fibers is proportional to the intensity of tactile stimulation raised to a power: $f = I^n$ where f is the frequency of nerve impulses, I is the intensity of the tactile stimulus, and n is constant for a particular fiber. This same kind of power function best describes the relationship between the perceived magnitude of a stimulus judged by human subjects and the intensity of the stimulus (Stevens, 1957). In fact, for pressure on the skin, the exponent, n, is very similar to the exponents obtained in the physiological study of Werner and Mountcastle.

With regard to thermal sensitivity, there is clear evidence that specific fibers (and presumably specific end organs) are involved. Zotterman (1936) first demonstrated that individual nerve fibers originating in the cat's tongue respond to either warming or cooling of the tongue. Since this initial discovery, Zotterman and his colleagues have determined many of the functional properties of these fibers. Figure 4.17 shows the responses of a "warm fiber" and a "cold fiber" to temperature changes. Each kind of fiber initially discharges a burst of impulses to the appropriate temperature change and then responds at a lower, irregular rate as long as a constant temperature is maintained. It will also be noted in Figure 4.17 that the warm fiber's discharge frequency at first increases as temperature rises above 20° C and then, above 40° C, it rapidly decreases. Since none of these warm fibers respond above 47° C, the sensation of heat evoked by higher temperatures is apparently mediated by other kinds of fibers. The cold fibers show peak frequencies of discharge between 20° and 34° C and then a secondary rise reaching a peak around 55° C. This "paradoxical discharge" of cold fibers parallels the paradoxical sensation of cold experienced when the human skin is heated to these same temperatures. According to Zotterman (1959), the paradoxical discharge of cold fibers might also be involved in the sensation of heat, which, as noted previously, occurs beyond the range of the warm fibers' discharge. As the temperature of the skin rises between 30° and 45°, warm fibers will discharge. As the temperature rises further, cold fibers will begin to fire; in addition, fibers which respond to painful stimuli will begin to discharge in this temperature range. Thus, it is likely that the perception of heat is mediated by a combined discharge of cold fibers and fibers which respond to painful stimulation.

The electrical discharges of warm and cold fibers from the cat's tongue also show some of the features of thermal adaptation characteristic of the human skin. It is well known that sensations of warmth and cold are subject to adaptation and may cease altogether when a stimulus of constant temperature is maintained for a period of time on the skin. Furthermore, the threshold for detecting warmth or cold shifts following such adaptation: If one hand is immersed in cold water and the other in warm water, water of normal skin temperature now feels warm to the first hand and cold to the second hand. Cold and warm fibers also show adaptation in their rate of firing to a constant temperature and a subsequent shift in threshold. Thus, after a cold fiber is adapted to a temperature of 44° C on the cat's tongue, a decrease in temperature to 42° C produces a discharge, even though this temperature is above the upper limit of the fiber's steady discharge when the tongue is unadapted (Hensel and Zotterman, 1951).

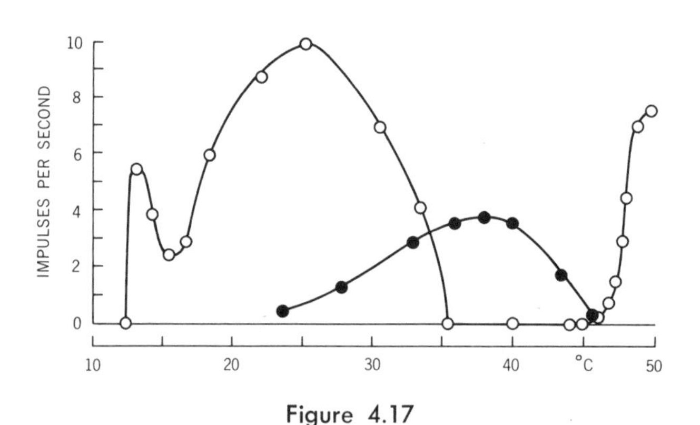

Figure 4.17

Impulse frequency of a single cold fiber (open circles), and a single warm fiber (filled circles) as a function of the temperature of the tongue in degrees centigrade. From Zotterman, Y., Special senses: Thermal receptors, Figure 1, page 363. Ann. Rev. Physiol., *1953,* 15, *357–372.*

In summary, then, electrophysiological findings, like the psychological findings mentioned previously, are not consistent either with the traditional view that there is a specific receptor for each cutaneous sense quality, nor with the view that there are no modality-specific nerve endings. Rather, it appears that some fibers (warm and cold fibers, "tactile" fibers) are modality specific, and it seems reasonable to assume that the receptors with which these fibers are associated are also modality specific. On the other hand, it appears that the unmyelinated fibers which supply the skin with free nerve endings may respond to either noxious stimuli or to touch, although it has not been determined whether an individual free nerve ending can respond to more than one kind of stimulus. Furthermore, since thinly myelinated fibers as well as unmyelinated fibers can respond to painful stimulation, it would appear that there is no particular set of "pain fibers."

CENTRAL SOMATIC SENSORY PATHWAYS: THE LEMNISCAL SYSTEM

We turn now to the central somatic sensory pathways and studies which deal with the problem of how somatosensory information is utilized by the CNS. The afferent fibers from somatic receptors in the trunk and limbs enter the spinal cord through the dorsal roots, just outside of which their cell bodies are located (see Figure 4.18). The cutaneous fibers in each dorsal root supply an area of skin called a dermatome, and fibers originating from dermatomes at successively higher levels of the body enter the spinal cord through successively higher dorsal roots. Many of the large fibers in the dorsal root, including those originating from tactile and joint receptors, send branches into the dorsal columns and form the first link in a major pathway called the lemniscal system (see Figure 4.18). This system seems to be concerned primarily, if not exclusively, with the mediation of touch and kinesthesis. Each neural element in this system conveys precise information about either light touch on a particular region of the skin or the movement of a particular joint. This information tends to be preserved as it is conducted upward through successive synapses in the lemniscal system, despite convergence and divergence in the pathways. Furthermore, these neurons code the kinds of information which are useful in identifying the features of stimuli impinging on the body surface. Thus, neurons in the central pathways, like those in the periphery described previously, code the intensity of cutaneous stimulation in accordance with the power-function relationship found in psychophysical experiments (Poggio and Mountcastle, 1963). In addition, some lemniscal neurons code the frequency of repetitive peripheral stimuli with a high degree of precision; that is, they discharge nerve impulses in synchrony with stimulation frequencies up to approximately 80/sec. (Mountcastle, 1961). This "frequency following" of lemniscal

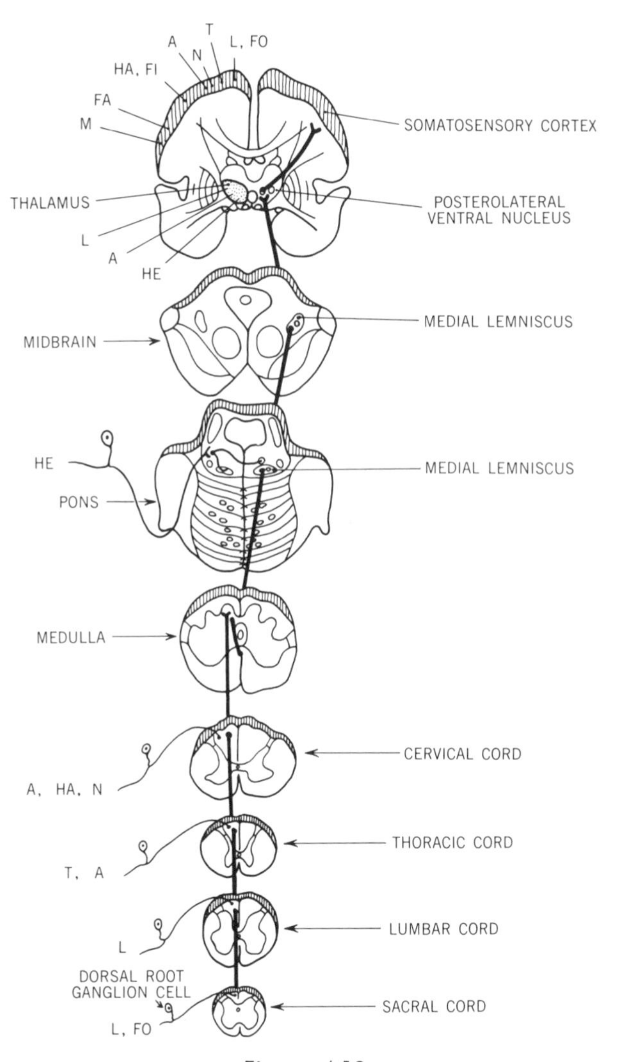

Figure 4.18

Diagrammatic view of the lemniscal system, showing nerve fibers arising from different parts of the body, the central pathways and projection of the body surface on somatosensory cortex. A: *arm;* FA: *face;* FI: *finger;* FO: *foot;* HA: *hand;* HE: *head;* L: *leg;* M: *mouth;* N: *neck;* T: *trunk. From Everett, N. B.,* Functional neuroanatory, *5th ed., Philadelphia: Lea and Febiger, 1965.*

neurons may provide a neural basis for discriminating between different surface textures, for the ability to discriminate between different surfaces depends on precise information concerning the frequency of repetitive tactile stimulation as the finger moves across a textured surface, such as sandpaper.

The ability to localize stimulation on the body surface depends on a system of spatial representation of the body parts which is present at all levels of the lemniscal system (see Figure 4.18). This pattern of spatial representation provides another example of the "spatial code," which, as mentioned previously, is utilized by the visual and auditory systems as a means of coding various features of stimulation. Moreover, as seen in Figure 4.18, the different body parts are not represented equally in this system. Rather, those portions of the body (such as the fingers) which are densely innervated by fibers and which are highly sensitive to tactile stimulation have greater representation in the lemniscal system than do less densely innervated and less sensitive regions of the body. Presumably, the greater the area of representation of a part of the body, the more discriminable are the neural messages arriving there as a consequence of stimulating different portions of that part of the body.

The region of cerebral cortex to which somatosensory stimulation projects has the functional characteristics of other areas of the lemniscal system. It is somatotopically organized, and individual neurons are modality specific, responding either to light touch on the skin or to the rotation of a joint. On the other hand, because of convergence at synapses in the lemniscal pathways, the receptive fields of neurons in somatosensory cortex are much larger than the receptive fields of neurons at lower levels in the lemniscal system. Moreover, the receptive fields of neurons in somatosensory cortex overlap to a large extent, as seen in Figure 4.19A. Thus, touching a point on the skin elicits impulses in a number of these neurons. How, then, is it possible that one can make fine discriminations between nearby points on the skin when there is so much convergence and overlap in the system? The research of Mountcastle indicates that there are two mechanisms which might enhance discriminability in somatosensory cortex. First of all, each neuron is not equally sensitive to stimulation in all portions of its receptive field; its sensitivity is greatest near the center and least at the edge of its receptive field. Secondly, neurons in somatosensory cortex have inhibitory surrounds. Figure 4.19B shows the discharges of a neuron which responds to touch within an extensive receptive field on the arm of a monkey, but is inhibited by stimulation in an area surrounding this region. This arrangement, it will be noted, is similar to that of neurons in the visual system. Another nearby neuron may have its excitatory and inhibitory fields arranged in a converse manner. Mountcastle (1961) has suggested that this inhibitory phenomenon may be mediated by inhibitory synaptic connections between cortical cells. Inhibition may play a role in increasing the capacity of the lemniscal system for localizing the site of peripheral stimulation by limiting the number of cortical neurons activated by tactile stimulation.

Additional evidence that somatosensory cortex is involved in tactile and kinesthetic functions derives from observations of animals and humans with lesions of this cortical area. Characteristically, damage to

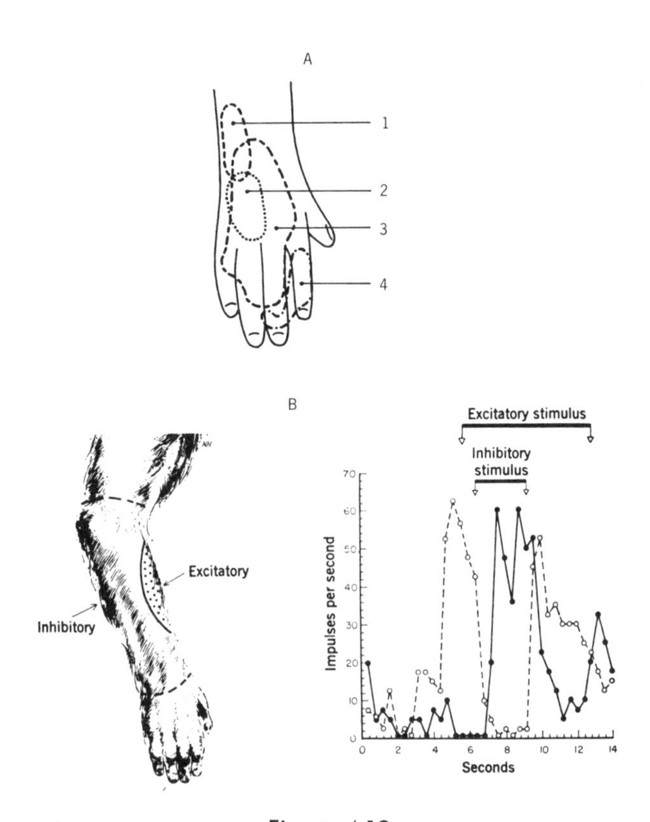

Figure 4.19

Receptive field characteristics of neurons in the lemniscal system. **(A)** *Some examples of cutaneous receptive fields of neurons in somatosensory cortex of the monkey.* **(B)** *Example of a neuron in somatosensory cortex with an excitatory center and an inhibitory surround (left). The impulse frequency of this neuron is plotted in the graph with open circles and dashed lines. Note that the impulse rate drops almost to zero when tactile stimulation is applied to the inhibitory regions of skin. A second neuron, the discharge rate of which is plotted with closed circles and solid lines, reacts in a reciprocal manner to tactile stimulation. From Mountcastle, V.B., Some functional properties of the somatic afferent system, Figure 10, page 420. In W. Rosenblith (Ed.),* Sensory communication. *New York: Wiley, 1961.*

somatosensory cortex results in raised thresholds for detecting tactile stimulation on the side of the body opposite the lesion, increased two-point thresholds and a reduction in sensory spots in these regions. In addition, appreciation of limb and finger position (i.e., kinesthesis) is also impaired. Since touch thresholds and kinesthesis are both impaired following damage to somatosensory cortex, it is not surprising that the ability to identify objects by touch is severely impaired as well. Further, damage to this area is often associated with various forms of apraxia, an inability to perform skilled movements or to draw or make a construction from a model (Critchley, 1953). Parietal lobe injury may also result in a disturbance in spatial orientation, so that the patient easily gets lost in a building or cannot follow a route.

Thus, many of the functions disrupted by parietal lesions involve movement and its integration with sensory information. In this regard, it is significant that the functions of the somatic sensory and motor systems seem to be closely related. Located just in front of the somatosensory cortex is an area which is intimately involved in the control of movement. Electrical stimulation of this region produces contraction of particular muscles. Furthermore, a "map" of the body's muscles, similar in organization to the somatosensory map, has been found by systematic stimulation of this area, as described in Chapter 5. So closely are the functions of the somatosensory and motor areas intermingled that together they may be considered a single mechanism. Thus, stimulation of motor cortex in patients undergoing neurosurgery not only produces movement but also somatic sensations in the corresponding part of the body, even after the somatosensory area has been removed. Conversely, electrical stimulation of somatosensory cortex produces movements, as well as reports of somatic sensations, even after removal of motor cortex (Penfield and Jasper, 1954). Furthermore, motor cortex appears to be a reception area for somatic nerve fibers (Malis, Pribram, and Kruger, 1953), and somatosensory cortex contributes fibers to the efferent pathways which terminate in the spinal cord and mediate the cortical control of movement (Terzuolo and Adey, 1960).

It has also been found that the motor cortex, as well as other cortical areas, project to the subcortical somatosensory nuclei, and motor cortex stimulation can alter electrical activity in these structures. Moreover, electrical stimulation of efferent tracts arising in motor cortex increases the size of receptive fields of neurons in somatosensory cortex. This finding suggests that these efferent tracts are capable of facilitating the transmission of tactile information through subcortical somatosensory nuclei (Adkins, Morse, and Towe, 1966). Thus, cerebral motor mechanisms are capable of altering somatosensory input into higher levels of the brain. Furthermore, through direct feedback, movement alters tactual input, as when the hand moves over the surface of an object. Thus, in active touch, sensory input serves as a stimulus for movement, which, in turn alters sensory input and provides new sources of stimulation. In Chapter 5 we will consider how certain motoneurons of the spinal cord control afferent messages from muscles.

CENTRAL SOMATIC SENSORY PATHWAYS: THE SPINOTHALAMIC SYSTEM

Unlike the lemniscal system, the spinothalamic system is thought to be involved primarily in the mediation of thermal sensibility, pain and tactile sensibility of a crude and relatively unlocalized kind. It receives input from fine afferent fibers which terminate in the spinal gray substance upon cells whose axons cross to the opposite side of the spinal cord and form the spinothalamic tracts (see Figure 4.20). The spinothalamic tracts ascend in the brain and are probably joined in the brain stem by fibers carrying pain and thermal messages from the head and face region (see Figure 4.20). Along its course in the brain stem, the spinothalamic tracts contribute fibers to the reticular formation, a large mass of cells which lies in the central core of the brain stem and extends from the medulla up to the midbrain. Some portions of the reticular formation appear to be concerned with pain perception, for electrical stimulation within this structure produces behavioral signs of pain in monkeys (Delgado, 1955). It is likely that the reticular formation's role in pain is dependent on inputs from the spinothalamic system. Furthermore, the brain-stem reticular formation is initimately involved in arousal, as described in Chapter 6. Thus, through its connections with this system, the spinothalamic system provides control over arousal processes.

The spinothalamic tract terminates in the same region of the thalamus which receives an input from the lemniscal system. In addition, in the cat the spinothalamic tract also distributes fibers to another thalamic region which is not part of the lemniscal system. Hence, by recording discharges of cells in this region it has been possible to study the electrophysiological properties of spinothalamic neurons in the thalamus (Mountcastle, 1961). The receptive fields of these spinothalamic neurons are much larger than those of lemniscal neurons, and they include broad areas on either or both sides of the body. In addition, some of these cells discharge both to tactile and noxious stimulation, and, unlike lemniscal neurons, they may continue to discharge after stimulation has ceased. Apparently, then, these neurons are much more diffuse and general in their coding properties than are lemniscal neurons.

Little is known about the cortical projections of the spinothalamic system. However, there is evidence that the spinothalamic system projects to a region called the second somatosensory area (See Figure 4.20), located below the primary somatosensory area, described previously. This region, like the primary somatosensory area, contains a map of

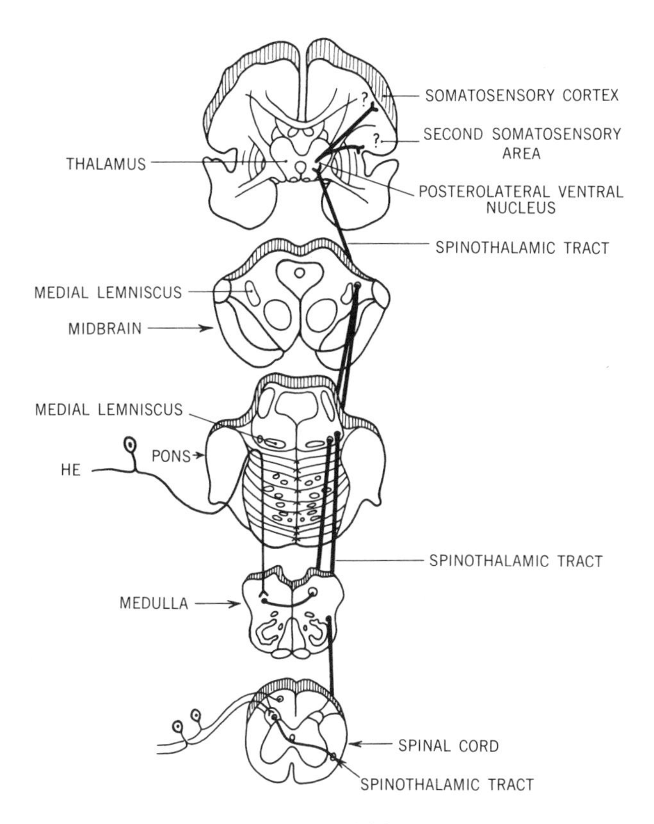

Figure 4.20

Diagrammatic view of the spinothalamic system showing the projection pathways of peripheral nerve fibers from the trunk and one from the head (HE). *From Everett, N. B.* Functional neuroanatomy, *5th ed. Philadelphia: Lea and Febiger, 1965.*

the body surface, but one in which the body is bilaterally represented. In the cat this region contains neurons with receptive fields like those of spinothalamic units in the thalamus. However, other cells have small, modality-specific receptive fields. Thus, the second somatosensory area has features of both the lemniscal and spinothalamic systems.

Compared to the tactile and kinesthetic senses, little is known concerning the neural mechanisms involved in pain perception. There have occasionally been reports of pain being produced by electrical stimulation of somatosensory cortex in man (Sweet, 1961). There are also reports of losses in pain perception following lesions of the parietal lobe (Critchley, 1953). However, there is no evidence for a particular pain pathway or cerebral pain center, since electrical stimulation of large portions of the diencephalon, as well as of the brain stem produces behavioral signs of pain in animals. Furthermore, painful cutaneous stimulation increases the discharge rate of neurons in widespread regions of the thalamus and midbrain. Interestingly, these same neurons also discharge to non-painful stimuli (Casey, 1966). In addition, the frontal lobes of the cerebral hemispheres, a structure which is not directly concerned with sensory functions, have also been implicated in pain mechanisms. Damage to the frontal lobes often reduces the aversive quality of noxious stimulation. In fact, prefrontal lobotomy (cutting the fiber connections between frontal cortex and subcortical structures) has often been performed in order to reduce the distress and suffering which is caused by intractable pain or which accompanies psychotic states.

SMELL AND TASTE

Although smell and taste are separate senses, they have several features in common. Both are chemical senses, responsive to molecules of substances in a dissolved state. Furthermore, both smell and taste are closely related to feeding; they play important roles in guiding the approach to food and in controlling food intake. The olfactory sense is also involved in a variety of other motivational processes, and it is often a key factor in the arousal of sexual, maternal, and other social behaviors, as well as providing cues for the presence of prey and predators. Thus, compared to the other senses, smell and taste are unique in that they provide for the detection of the reinforcing and affective value of stimuli. Moreover, since these sensory channels provide information relevant to the basic biological drives, they have an obvious adaptive role in behavior. For many animals, especially those with a keen olfactory sense, smells coming downwind are the first warning of approaching predators, before sights and sounds are available. The motivational significance of olfactory and taste stimuli is also reflected in the importance we attach to their value, when describing such stimuli. Whereas many sights and sounds are motivationally neutral, our first and often primary reaction to tastes and smells are evaluative. They are typically judged as either "good," "bad," or "indifferent." These behavioral observations are consistent with the anatomical connections of the olfactory and taste systems. As we shall see, the afferent pathways of both these senses project to a part of the forebrain involved in motivational processes and arousal.

OLFACTION: AN INTERSPECIES COMPARISON

The olfactory sense is not equally developed in all species. While some, such as carnivores and rodents, have a keen sense of smell, others, such as whales and porpoises, are anosmic; that is, they have no olfactory sense. Some animals, such as the primates (including man), are said to be microsmic, that is, possessing a poorly developed sense of smell. However, the notion that man has only a rudimentary sense of smell is simply not true. Perfume testers and brandy sniffers make extremely subtle olfactory discriminations. An example of keen olfactory detection is provided by the findings of DeVries and Stuiver, described on page 88. The false idea that man is a microsmic animal is probably due to modern man's tendency to ignore this channel of information.

OLFACTORY RECEPTORS AND STIMULI

While olfactory sensitivity varies enormously between species, there are certain features that all substances which can stimulate the olfactory receptors possess. In order to reach the olfactory epithelium, which is hidden in the nasal cavity, molecules of odorous substances must be airborne. Furthermore, odorous particles do not come into close contact with the olfactory receptors during normal breathing since the olfactory cells are found only in the upper and posterior portions of the nasal cavity. When inspiration is increased, as by sniffing, eddy currents will bring odorous particles into closer contact with the receptors. Secondly, in order that odorous particles come in contact with and be absorbed by the receptors, they must be dissolvable in the solutions in which the olfactory epithelium is bathed.

As seen in Figure 4.21, each sensory cell consists of a bipolar neuron whose peripheral fiber, which is thin and unmyelinated, terminates as a sensory protuberance in the olfactory epithelium. From this terminal ending arise a large number of extremely thin and delicate strands called cilia. Lying near the surface of the aqueous covering

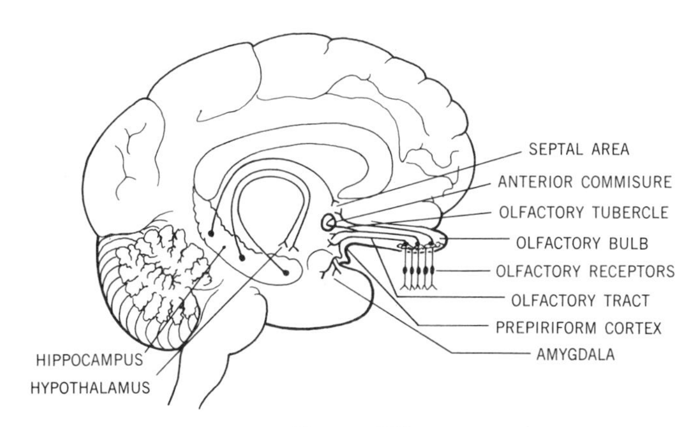

Figure 4.21

Diagrammatic view of the olfactory system. The fibers which enter the anterior commissure terminate in the opposite olfactory bulb. From Rubenstein, H. S., The study of the brain, *Figure 54, page 120. New York: Grune and Stratton, 1953. By permission.*

of the epithelium, these cilia provide a large receptive surface for adsorption of odorous particles. While it is evident that substances must be volatile and soluble in water or fat in order to be sensed by the olfactory receptors, at present little is known about the processes whereby molecules are transduced into electrical responses of the receptor cells. Futhermore, it is not clear what particular physical characteristics substances must possess to be smelled. Consequently, it is not known why some substances, such as musk, are more readily sensed than others. DeVries and Stuiver (1961) have estimated that as few as eight and perhaps only one molecule of mercaptan is sufficient to excite a single olfactory receptor, and as little as 40 molecules of this substance are required for minimal odor detection in man.

The receptor mechanisms which accomplish such feats are for the most part unknown, although a number of theories have been offered to explain the stimulating effectiveness of various substances. These include the nature and kind of atomic bonds of odorous particles, their vibration characteristics, their infrared absorption, and their effect on (possible) enzyme systems in the olfactory cells. However, none of these theories can explain all the known stimulating characteristics of odorous substances, or the perceived similarities between various odors. A number of investigations have been performed to determine the perceived characteristics of odors and how human subjects classify them. One of the most well known of these is a study by Henning (1924), who found that on the basis of subjects' judgments of over one hundred odors, substances could be divided into six groups: flowery, fruity, spicy, resinous, burnt, and foul. There are also a large number of psychophysical studies in which absolute and differential thresholds have been determined for various odorants.

The inaccessibility of the olfactory structures has been a source of difficulty not only for behavioral studies of olfaction, but also for electrophysiological investigations of the receptor cells. Consequently, few of these studies have been reported. Recording from the olfactory epithelium of the frog, Ottoson (1956) has described a slow, long-lasting potential in response to odors introduced into the nasal cavity. This electrical response is referred to as the electro-olfactogram, or EOG. The EOG is graded, becoming larger as the intensity of the stimulating odorant is increased. Since the EOG is obtained only from the olfactory epithelium and is still present when the olfactory nerve fibers are inactivated, it is presumed to reflect the summated effect of olfactory receptor potentials. However, the functional role of the EOG response is not all that clear. For example, the EOG can be completely eliminated without significantly influencing impulse discharges from olfactory nerve fibers (Shibuya, 1964). If the EOG response represented receptor potentials, its elimination would entail elimination of nerve impulses.

For a long time the problem of receptor sensitivity—the substances to which a particular olfactory receptor is responsive—has remained unsolved because of technical difficulties of recording from individual olfactory nerve fibers. But recently Gesteland (1963) has succeeded in recording from frogs the electrical responses of individual olfactory fibers, each of which presumably terminates in a single receptor. He found that single fibers discharge action potentials not to a single odorant, but to several odorants which are different for each fiber. However, each fiber does not respond equally to all odorants to which it is sensitive, but is selectively sensitive, responding more to one substance than to others. Thus, it appears that each receptor is responsive to several substances; different substances are coded in the olfactory nerve by different patterns of discharge involving a large number of fibers. In addition, Lettvin and Gesteland (1965) found that while some odors increase the firing rate of an olfactory fiber, other odors suppress its firing rate. Since there are no synapses between olfactory receptors and their fibers, this finding implies that some substances may directly inhibit olfactory receptors.

CENTRAL OLFACTORY STRUCTURES

As shown in Figure 4.21, the olfactory nerve fibers terminate in the olfactory bulb, where they synapse upon nerve cells. The synaptic pattern of terminating olfactory nerve fibers involves a high degree of convergence: It is estimated that, on the average, approximately 250 receptor cells terminate upon a single cell. The axons of these cells leave the olfactory bulb and terminate in the olfactory receptive areas of the forebrain. Many of the fibers of other cells cross the anterior commissure (a bridge of fibers interconnecting structures on the two sides of the anterior forebrain) and then travel forward to terminate in the opposite olfactory bulb. Thus, by this pathway, activity in one olfactory bulb can influence the activity of the other.

The electrical activity of the olfactory bulb exhibits waves of high frequency in the absence of stimulation. These oscillations arise from the bulb itself, since they persist after the bulb is isolated from the receptors or from the forebrain. These intrinic waves disappear when the olfactory epithelium is stimulated with strong airblown substances, and they are replaced by evoked potentials consisting of large rhythmic oscillations (see Figure 4.22). Electrical recordings from the olfactory bulb have also disclosed discharges of single neurons in response to olfactory stimulation. Like olfactory nerve fibers, these neurons each respond to several odorants, and, as a rule, each neuron responds best to one particular substance. It is not clear from these studies how particular odorants are coded by olfactory nerve circuits. Spatial coding may be used by this system, since olfactory nerve fibers show a topo-

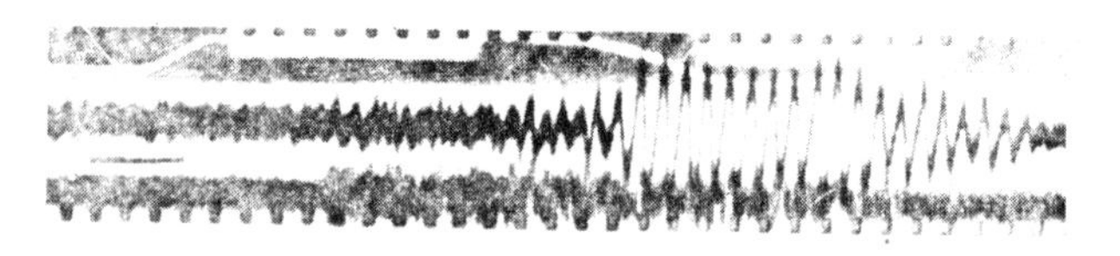

Figure 4.22

Electrical response of the olfactory bulb of the rabbit to amylacetate blown into the nasal cavity. The electrical response consists of the large oscillating waves starting near the center, soon after the odorous stimulus was introduced. The black horizontal line at the left is a time marker which indicates .1 sec. From Adrian, E. D., The electrical activity of the mammalian olfactory bulb, Figure 3, page 378. Electroencephal. and clin. Neurophysiol., *1950,* 2, *377–388.*

graphical projection pattern onto the bulb, and evoked discharges to various substances vary in amplitude with the position of recording electrodes in the bulb. It is possible that the pattern of electrical discharges recorded from the olfactory structures would appear quite different and more orderly if natural odorants (such as those from glandular substances which attract or repel animals) were used as stimuli rather than the "unnatural" substances (such as acetone) most frequently used.

The efferent fibers from the olfactory bulb form the olfactory tracts, which are distributed to a number of structures in the anterior part of the forebrain, such as the olfactory tubercle, the amygdala, and the prepiriform cortex (see Figure 4.21). These structures form the rhinencephalon, which literally means "smell brain," a phylogenetically older portion of the forebrain. These olfactory reception areas, formerly thought to be quite widespread, are limited to the regions shown in Figure 4.21. Ablation of these structures produces deficits in olfactory discriminations (Allen, 1941; Brown and Mishkin, 1963). Furthermore electrical stimulation of many of them, especially the amygdala, evokes responses that usually accompany food-seeking behavior and food intake, responses such as sniffing, salivation, licking, and chewing (Kaada, 1960).

Furthermore, stimulation of many of these structures is rewarding: Animals will learn to perform responses which lead to electrical stimulation of these areas (Olds, 1962). Other evidence that these olfactory structures may participate in motivational processes is provided by the finding that electrical stimulation produces signs of arousal, such as increased heart rate, pupillary dilation, and alerting behavior (Kaada, 1960). There is thus neurophysiological evidence supporting the behavioral observations that olfaction is closely related to motivational processes and arousal.

TASTE: ITS AFFECTIVE VALUE

As mentioned previously, the sense of taste is unique in that it provides sensory stimulation which controls appetitive behavior. Rats learn to perform responses to obtain a sweet-tasting saccharine solution and persist in this behavior despite the liquid's lack of nutritional value (Sheffield and Roby, 1950). Aversion also appears to be directly controlled by taste; guinea pigs raised from birth on a bitter-tasting substance will as adults reject this substance, even though it was formerly associated with the reduction of hunger (Warren and Pfaffmann, 1963). Thus particular substances may be accepted or rejected on the basis of their sensory qualities, irrespective of their associated nutritive value; although, to be sure, taste preferences are altered by bodily needs and by learning. In discussing the neural mechanisms of taste, then, we will consider not only how the taste receptors and afferent pathways code taste qualities, but also the neural associations between taste and preference-aversion mechanisms.

TASTE RECEPTORS AND STIMULI

The sense of taste is mediated by specialized chemoreceptors found in the taste buds on the surface of the tongue and other nearby tissues in the oral cavity and throat. The taste buds are found in structures referred to as papillae—ridges of tissue which are visible on the edges and upper surface of the tongue. Within each taste bud a number of elongated cells are found (see Figure 4.23, below). It has been thought

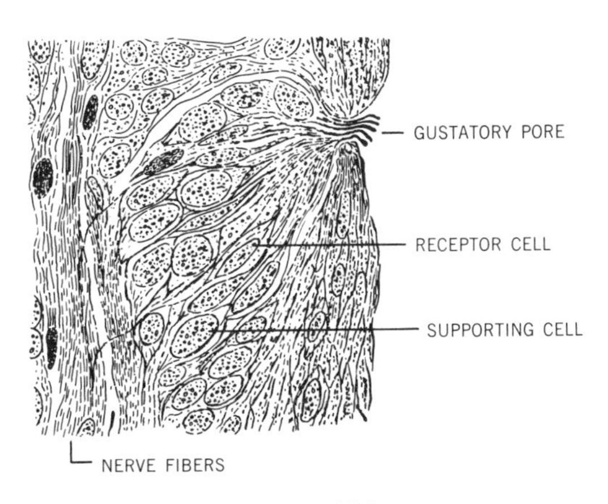

Figure 4.23

Cross section of a taste bud on the surface of the tongue, showing the endings of receptor cells projecting into the gustatory pore. From Ruch, T. C., Patton, H. D., Woodbury, J. W., and Towe, A. L., Neurophysiology, *Figure 217, page 370. Philadelphia: Saunders, 1962.*

that some of these cells are supporting cells and others sensory cells. However, recent evidence suggests that there are no supporting cells in the taste buds of mammals. What have been thought to be supporting cells are most likely to be developing sensory cells, which appear to be continuously in the process of degeneration and replacement by new ones. Fine projections, refered to as microvilli, arise from the top of these cells and project into the gustatory pore which opens on the surface of the tongue. These microvilli are probably involved in taste reception and may serve to enlarge the area of receptive contact with stimulating substances. A number of afferent fibers terminate in each taste bud; each terminates upon one or more cells, and each cell may receive several fibers.

Although the taste receptors are sensitive to a variety of substances in solution, the basic qualities of taste are traditionally limited to four —sourness, sweetness, bitterness, and saltiness. The chemical characteristics which determine each of these sensory qualities are not completely known, although for two qualities, sourness and saltiness, they can be specified to some extent. Thus, there is a close relationship between sourness and acidity; the concentration of hydrogen ions which become dissociated when acids enter solution seems to determine the degree of sourness. However, this relationship is not perfect, for certain organic acids, such as citric acid, taste more sour than other acids which dissociate more hydrogen ions. Furthermore, some acids do not taste sour at all; for example, the amino acids taste sweet. Saltiness is also related to certain chemical structures—those of the salt compounds such as sodium chloride (common table salt), which, in solution, yields sodium and chloride ions. It appears that both of these ions influence the taste of substances. On the other hand, sweetness is associated with a variety of compounds that are chemically unrelated. Certain organic compounds, such as sucrose and glucose, taste quite sweet, but many inorganic compounds, such as beryllium salts and saccharine, are also sweet. Like sweetness, bitterness is produced by a number of chemically different substances. The most well known of these are the alkaloids, such as quinine. Interestingly, a small change in chemical structure will frequently alter the taste of a substance from sweet to bitter. The close relationship between these two taste qualities is also shown by the fact that some substances which are sweet, such as saccharine, leave a bitter aftertaste.

Taste, like other senses, is subject to adaptation, and continuous stimulation of the tongue with a taste solution produces a gradual decrease in its perceived intensity. Adaptation to one substance may also alter the perceived intensity of other substances, a phenomenon referred to as cross-adaptation. It has been assumed that if adaptation to one substance lowers the perceived intensity of another substance, both substances might act on the same receptors. Thus, cross-adaptation has been used in attempts to determine the specificity of taste receptors. It has been found that cross-adaptation takes place between several different acids, thus implying that they are all mediated by a common kind of receptor. On the other hand, cross-adaptation does not take place between all bitter-tasting substances, and there is no cross-adaptation between a number of different salts.

ELECTROPHYSIOLOGY OF TASTE RECEPTORS AND FIBERS

A more direct approach to the problem of receptor specificity has been made in investigations of electrical responses of taste cells. Kimura and Beidler (1961) introduced microelectrodes into the taste buds of rats and hamsters and recorded what are presumably receptor potentials from individual taste cells in response to taste solutions flowing over the tongue. These investigators described slow, graded potentials which increased as the concentration of the stimulating solution increased. They found that the receptor potential from each cell is elicited by a variety of substances, which differ, apparently, for each receptor. However, it appears that each sensory cell is differentially sensitive to different substances, and responds best to one particular substance. Since there are apparently no taste receptors which code only one quality, it appears that the taste system, like the olfactory system, codes different stimuli in terms of patterns of discharge in many fibers.

While attempts to record the electrical activity of taste receptors are still in an initial exploratory stage, more progress has been made in recording electrical discharges from taste fibers in response to stimulation of the tongue. Pfaffmann (1941) found that in the cat some taste fibers respond only to an acid solution; others respond to both acid and salt, and still others respond to both bitter and acid substances. Thus, each fiber can apparently convey information concerning different taste qualities; which particular quality is signalled depends upon activity in other fibers. In other words, it appears that taste quality is coded by the pattern of excitation in a number of different fibers, as one might expect from the analysis of receptor coding, mentioned above. The same principle seems to apply to discharges of taste fibers in the rat (Pfaffmann, 1955). Like those in the cat, these fibers respond to more than one substance stimulating the tongue. As seen in Figure 4.24, Fiber A responds to both salt and sugar and increases its rate of firing as both concentrations increase. However, it is relatively more sensitive to salt than to sugar. The relative sensitivity of Fiber B to these two substances is the opposite to that of Fiber A. When salt in any concentration stimulates the tongue, Fiber A will fire more than Fiber B; when sugar in any concentration stimulates the tongue, Fiber B will fire more than Fiber A. Thus, information concerning salt or sugar stimulation seems to be specified by the relative discharge rates in two sets of fibers.

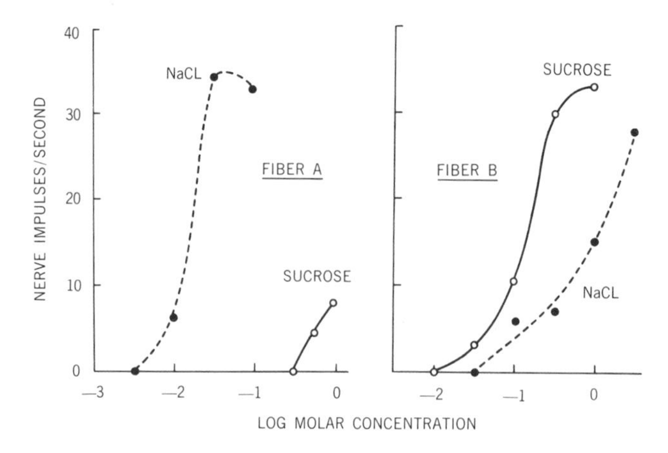

Figure 4.24

Nerve impulse frequency of two fibers innervating the rat tongue as a function of concentration of NaCl and of sucrose solution on the tongue. Note that while both fibers respond to both solutions, FIBER A *is relatively more sensitive to NaCl, while* FIBER B *is relatively more sensitive to sucrose. From Pfaffmann, C., Gustatory nerve impulses in rat, cat, and rabbit, Figure 11, page 438.* J. Neurophysiol., *1955,* 18, *429–440.*

CENTRAL MECHANISMS OF TASTE

As shown in Figure 4.25, the nerves which carry taste impulses enter the brain stem and terminate in the nucleus of the solitary tract. From this nucleus arise fibers which may ascend in the medial lemniscus (the brain-stem pathway of the lemniscal system) and project to a portion of the thalamus which also receives impulses from the facial region. (There is evidence that some of these central structures may exert efferent control over neural activity in peripheral taste fibers. Electrical responses of peripheral taste fibers to certain substances on the tongue are altered in frequency when the stomach is distended with a balloon. These effects of stomach distension are abolished if the lower brain stem is destroyed [Esakov, 1961].) From the thalamus, gustatory impulses are conveyed to an area of the cerebral cortex, near the tactile projection area of the tongue, and to adjacent areas, including the insula. Electrical recordings with microelectrodes in cells of the gustatory pathway indicate that these neurons, like those in the peripheral taste nerve, respond to several different kinds of solutions stimulating the tongue (Pfaffmann, Erickson, Frommer, and Halpern, 1961). There is no indication from these studies whether or in what way taste information may be recoded in these central structures.

Destruction of the thalamic taste area in animals produces a marked increase in preference and aversion thresholds for substances such as sucrose and quinine, presumably reflecting a loss of taste discrimination. Similar alterations have been observed following lesions of the cortical taste area in animals (Oakley and Benjamin, 1966). Impairments in taste discrimination are also found when the comparable areas are damaged in man.

It appears that the evaluative, or preference-aversion aspect of taste is not coded by the taste receptors or their fibers. Figure 4.26 shows that the neural discharges from taste fibers continuously increase over a range of increasing concentrations of salt solution. Over the same range, behavioral preference for salt first increases, then decreases, and finally is replaced by aversion. It appears, then, that the neural correlates of the motivational aspects of taste would be found in the brain structures to which the taste system projects. In fact, one of these structures, the insula, is part of a neural system (referred to as the limbic system) which is involved in motivational processes (as described in Chapter 7). Electrical stimulation of this system produces physiological and behavioral signs of arousal (Kaada, 1960). Even more significant is the observation that damage to this system produces striking changes in preferences and aversions as related to feeding, sexual behavior, and

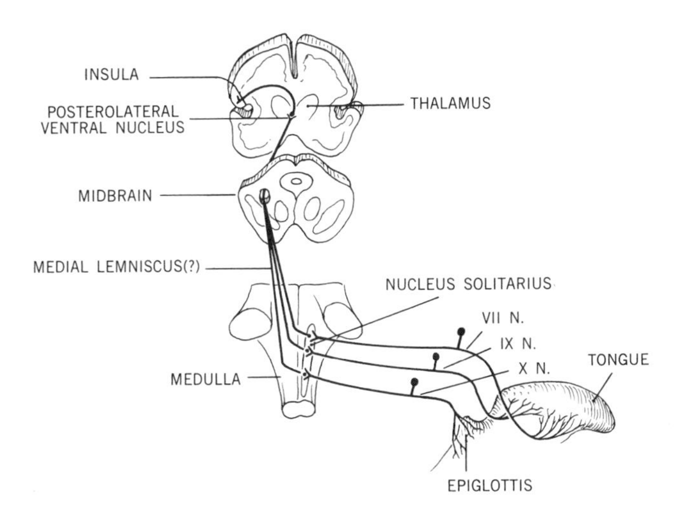

Figure 4.25

Diagrammatic view of the taste system, including peripheral nerve pathways and central pathways. From Peele, T., The neuroanatomic basis for clinical neurology, *2nd ed., Figure 20–1, page 471, and Figure 20–2, page 472. New York: McGraw-Hill, 1961.*

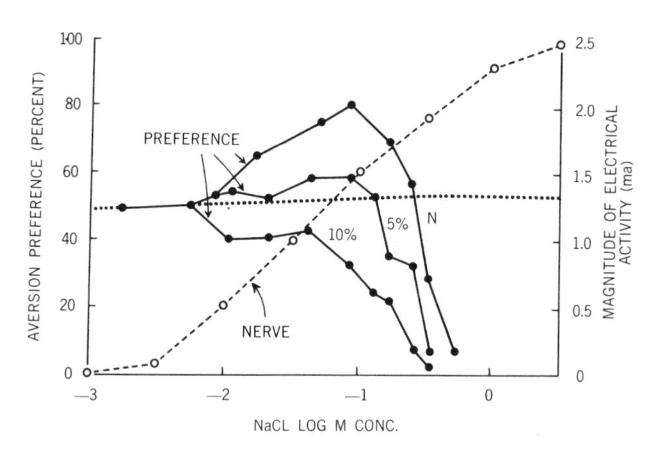

Figure 4.26

Graph showing magnitude of electrical activity (summated nerve impulses) in taste fibers from the rat tongue as a function of NaCl concentration on the tongue. Plotted on the same graph are percent preferences and aversions of rats for NaCl solution taken from an experiment in which rats were offered a choice between NaCl solutions and water. Preference-aversion curves were obtained from three different groups of rats: rats with normal diet (N), *rats with 5% additional salt in the diet* (5%), *and rats with 10% additional salt in the diet* (10%). *From Pfaffmann, C., Taste mechanisms in preference behavior, Figure 4, page 145.* Amer. J. clin. Nutrition, *1957, 5, 142–147.*

fear. Thus, following damage to the limbic system, monkeys will accept and put in their mouths not only normally preferred foods but unpreferred foods, such as meat and fish, as well as inedible objects (Klüver and Bucy, 1939). Moreover this change in food preferences is not due simply to a loss of taste discrimination, since lesions involving these structures will change taste preferences without altering taste discrimination thresholds (Weiskrantz, 1960). It appears that through its connections with the insula, the taste system comes into association with mechanisms regulating preferences and aversions.

SUGGESTED READINGS

VISION

Hubel, D. H. The visual cortex of the brain. *Sci. Amer.*, November 1963.
Kennedy, D. Inhibition in visual systems. *Sci. Amer.*, July 1963.

Lettvin, J. Y., Maturana, H. R., McCulloch, W. S., and Pitts, W. H. What the frog's eye tells the frog's brain. *Proc. Inst. Rad. Engin.*, 1959, *47*, 1940–1951.
MacNichol, E. F., Jr. Three-pigmented color vision. *Sci. Amer.*, December 1964.
Miller, W. H., Ratliff, F., and Hartline, H. K. How cells receive stimuli. *Sci. Amer.*, September 1961.
Rushton, W. A. H. Visual pigments in man. *Sci. Amer.*, November 1962.
Wald, G. Eye and camera. *Sci. Amer.*, August 1950.

AUDITORY SYSTEM

Békésy, G. von The ear. *Sci. Amer.*, August 1957.
Rosenzweig, M. R. Auditory localization. *Sci. Amer.*, October 1961.

SOMATIC SENSORY SYSTEM

Livingston, W. K. What is pain? *Sci. Amer.*, March 1953.
Loewenstein, W. R. Biological transducers. *Sci. Amer.*, August 1960.
Woolsey, C. N. Organization of somatic sensory and motor areas of the cerebral cortex. In H. F. Harlow and C. N. Woolsey (Eds.), *Biological and biochemical bases of behavior*. Madison, Wisc.: University of Wisconsin Press, 1958, 63–82.

TASTE AND SMELL

Haagen-Smit, A. J. Smell and taste. *Sci. Amer.*, March 1952.
Hodgson, E. S. Taste receptors. *Sci. Amer.*, May 1961.

MOTOR SYSTEMS 5

As one watches an expert gymnast smoothly performing a difficult feat, one may not recognize that the performance involves the complex coordination of a variety of different movements and postures. For example, in performing a somersault on the parallel bars, the gymnast mounts the bars by first extending the arms and then firmly grasping and pushing down on the bars while raising the trunk and shoulders. Next he swings his body forward at the shoulders so that the trunk is horizontal with the bars and his body is supported by the extended arms. He then lifts his hips to obtain the maximum swing for the somersault while keeping his extended legs together for balance. To execute the somersault, he flexes the neck, trunk, and hips while pushing down on the bars and releasing his grip so that he is propelled upward and over. Near the end of the somersault, the gymnast keeps his arms in a horizontal position at his side so that when he lands, his arms and hands rest on the bars and support the body. The hips are then extended so that the legs are lowered, and he returns to an upright position.

The dazzling somersaults of an expert gymnast can serve to illustrate many of the basic features of all movements. First of all, a somersault is a complex act that consists of a large number of individual movements involving various parts of the body. A careful analysis of these movements reveals that each consists of simpler movements, which themselves are coordinated patterns of activity involving several muscles. This kind of organization, in which simpler elements make up more complex ones, is referred to as hierarchical organization—a characteristic feature of all movement. Moreover, as we shall see in this chapter, there appears to be a corresponding hierarchical organization of the neural structures that mediate muscular movement. That is, lower levels of the CNS (in the spinal cord) control simple movements, while higher levels of the CNS combine these simpler movements into more complex ones.

The coordination, or integration of simple into complex motor acts has two important aspects as we recall: spatial integration and temporal integration. For example, pedalling a bicycle involves a rhythmic sequence of alternate flexion and extension movements of each leg. At any one moment in time, the movements of the two legs are coordinated in a spatial pattern. When one considers the delicate timing and coordination required for the performance of skilled acts, it becomes evident that the neural circuits mediating these acts are intricate and complex to a degree that exceeds any man-made machine.

Furthermore, postural adjustment plays a crucial role in the gymnast's performance, as it does in all movement. Thus, for example, in the act of walking, or even in reaching out for an object, as well as in the performance of a somersault, a number of muscles are brought into play in order to counteract the force of gravity and keep the body properly balanced. As the movement progresses, the body posture concomitantly changes in order that balance is maintained. Thus, movement and posture are closely coordinated in the performance of motor acts. In addition, the initiation of movements is aided by initial postures assumed by the body. These initial postures, such as the lifting of the hips prior to performance of a somersault, prepare the muscles for the proper execution of movement. Moreover, prior to the movement, the muscles involved frequently undergo partial, anticipatory contraction, which serves a kind of "priming" function. In view of these facts, it is not surprising that the control of movement and posture is exerted by common neural mechanisms.

Finally, although it may not be evident to the viewer, the gymnast's stunt, like all movement, is under the control of sensory inputs. Sensory guidance of movement is provided by a variety of stimuli, including visual stimuli, pressure of surfaces against the skin, and the rotation of joints produced by the movement itself. Moreover, other kinds of sensory information, of which we are not ordinarily aware, play important roles in controlling movement: These include sensory messages from muscle receptors, which signal muscle tension, and sensory messages from receptors in the vestibular organ in the inner ear, which signal the position of the head in space and angular acceleration and deceleration of the head. It will be noted that many of these sensory signals are proprioceptive; that is, they arise from changes within the body, some resulting from movement. Thus these proprioceptive signals provide reafference or sensory feedback, which is necessary for the normal performance of movement as well as for the maintenance of posture. As we shall see in the following pages, there is ample evidence that the neural structures mediating motor activity are under the control of afferent systems which conduct sensory information into the CNS.

NEURAL CONTROL OF REFLEX ACTIVITY

GENERAL FEATURES OF REFLEXES

As we noted in Chapter 3, the spinal cord and brain stem control certain body movements and the activity of internal organs. Reactions such as these are generally referred to as reflexes. Reflexes, in contrast to other, more complex kinds of behaviors, are fixed reactions which are consistently and rapidly evoked by appropriate stimuli. Furthermore, reflexes are innate; their performance does not require prior experience. For example, the reflex withdrawal of a child's hand from a hot stove is a direct and immediate response which always occurs in much the same manner without the benefit of past learning. While reflexes are generally of less interest to the neuropsychologist than more complex learned behaviors are, neural mechanisms of reflexes exemplify some of the basic functions of the nervous system.

The neural mechanism mediating a particular reflex response involves several kinds of neurons referred to previously—afferent (together with receptors), internuncial, efferent, and reafferent. Through their synaptic interconnections, these different kinds of neurons form a neural circuit, like the one diagrammatically shown in Figure 2.1 (page 7). The particular synaptic connections between neurons in these circuits permit a particular stimulus (such as heat) to evoke a particular reflex response (such as withdrawal).

While each reflex involves a unique pattern of movement, all reflexes have basic common features: (1) One such feature is adaptiveness; each reflex movement plays a particular role in the adjustment of the organism to its environment. For example, the flexion reflex (a withdrawal movement of a limb) may be described as a movement which aids the animal in escaping from painful stimulation. When the outer part of the dog's footpad is stimulated, the leg is withdrawn and adducted; that is, it is moved toward the body and thus away from the source of stimulation. When the inner part of the footpad is stimulated, the leg is withdrawn and abducted, that is, moved away from the body and thus away from the source of stimulation. (2) It follows from such observations that reflex reactions, like other responses, consist not of a single muscle twitch, but rather of movement patterns which involve the coordinated activity of several groups of muscles. To cite another example of coordinated muscular activity, reflex contraction of a flexor muscle is accompanied by relaxation of antagonists —muscles having an opposite action—in this case, extensor muscles. In addition, reflex contraction of a muscle is often accompanied by the contraction of synergists—muscles whose action enhances or facilitates movements produced by a particular muscle. (3) Finally, it is characteristic of each reflex that it is evoked by a particular stimulus and only by that stimulus, which is referred to as the adequate stimulus for that reflex. For example, the adequate stimulus for reflex scratching in dogs is a tactile stimulus applied to the saddle region of the back. This stimulus will not evoke limb withdrawal, and the adequate stimulus for limb withdrawal, painful stimulation of the paw, will not evoke scratching movements. The fact that the adequate stimulus in each case evokes only the appropriate reflex response emphasizes again the fundamental adaptiveness of reflex organization.

SPINAL REFLEXES: DEFINITION

A variety of reactions, including scratching, limb withdrawal, certain postural adjustments and movements involved in locomotion, were at one time thought to be the products of brain activity because of their purposeful character. Although the brain does modify these movements, it is not necessary for their performance. Rather, these reactions are mediated by neural circuits in the spinal cord; hence, they are referred to as spinal reflexes. In order to study the spinal mechanisms underlying these reflexes without the influences normally exerted by the brain, the spinal cord is transected (cut through) at a high level. Those behaviors preserved following spinal transection are assumed to be normally mediated by neural mechanisms below the level of the transection. On the other hand, behaviors which are completely and permanently missing following spinal transection are assumed to be normally under the primary control of neural mechanisms above the level of the transection.

STRETCH REFLEX

When a muscle is suddenly passively stretched, for example, by sharply tapping the muscle or its tendon, the muscle shows a rapid reflex contraction. This so-called stretch reflex is especially prominent in extensor muscles, such as the quadriceps muscle, which produces the familar knee-jerk when stretched. The reaction is not simply a mechanical one, for it is no longer evoked after nerve fibers to the muscle are severed. Obviously, the reaction is neurally mediated. What, then, is the nature of the sensory event that produces the reaction? The results of a number of experimental investigations indicate that the sensory events triggering the stretch reflex arise from proprioceptors in the muscle itself. The key structure is the muscle spindle, shown in Figure 5.1, which receives afferent fibers. The terminals of these fibers are sensitive to stretch of the muscle spindle, which causes them to discharge impulses. Many of these fibers synapse directly upon spinal motoneurons, as seen in Figure 5.1. These motoneurons give rise to fibers which innervate the stretched muscle and cause it to contract when the motoneurons are activated by impulses from the muscle afferents. Since only one synapse is involved in the reflex circuit shown in Figure 5.1, it is referred to as a monosynaptic reflex. As muscle stretch increases, impulses generated in the muscle spindle afferents increase in frequency, and the muscle shows stronger contraction. However, the response tends to be self-limiting, for contraction itself reduces the tension on the muscle spindle and consequently on the muscle spindle afferent discharge rate. Here is a case, then, of self-regulation through "negative feedback": The effects of the response tend to decrease the stimulus which initially triggered the response.

What is the functional significance of a reflex contraction of extensor muscle to stretching? The answer to this question is straightforward. Under normal conditions, stretching of extensor muscles is produced by the force of gravity, which, acting on the body, would cause the limbs to buckle under and the body to sink to the ground. Thus, reflex contraction of extensor muscles to stretch serves to counteract the force of gravity and maintain an upright posture.

The effectiveness of the stretch reflex in a muscle is further enhanced by the simultaneous inhibition of its antagonist. The neural circuit presumed to mediate this inhibitory effect is also shown in Figure 5.1. According to this scheme, branches of afferent fibers from the muscle spindle synapse upon internuncial neurons in the spinal cord, and fibers from these internuncial neurons form inhibitory synap-

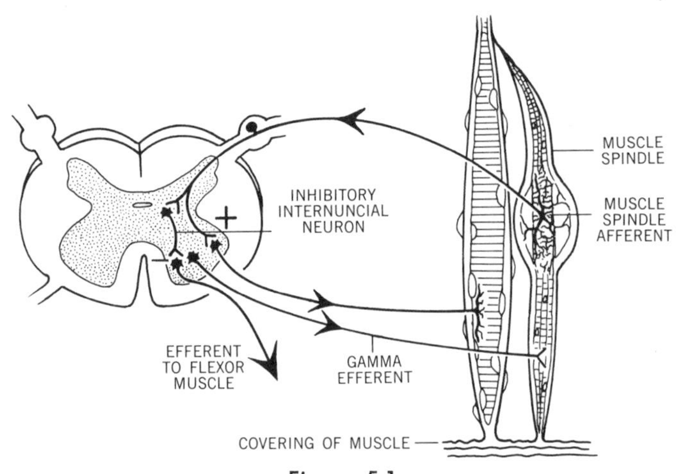

Figure 5.1

Diagrammatic view of the neural circuit mediating the stretch reflex. The afferent terminal in the muscle spindle discharges impulses when the muscle is stretched. Through the excitatory synaptic connection (+) in the spinal cord, motor neurons innervating the same muscle fiber are activated, and the muscle contracts. Simultaneously, the flexor muscle is inhibited by the inhibitory synaptic connection (−) in the spinal cord. The gamma efferent fiber innervates a contractible portion of the muscle spindle and causes the muscle spindle to be stretched when it fires nerve impulses. From Ruch, T. C., Patton, H. D., Woodbury, J. W., and Towe, A. L., Neurophysiology, *2nd ed., Figure 12, page 191. Philadelphia: Saunders, 1965.*

tic connections upon motoneurons—those which supply an antagonist. Thus, we see that even simple reflex reactions involve coordinated activity (in this case, spatial integration) of different muscles.

The reflex contraction of a stretched muscle is not adaptive under all conditions; if a very strong load is placed on the muscle, it might be damaged if contraction were to take place. There appears to be a mechanism which prevents the muscle from incurring this kind of damage. If a muscle is subjected to undue stretch, it no longer contracts, but, instead, suddenly relaxes. This so-called "lengthening reaction" is a reflex response which is triggered by sensory endings in the muscle tendon. Afferent fibers from these tendon receptors form inhibitory synapses via internuncial neurons with the motoneurons which supply the stretched muscle. Through this inhibitory reflex, the muscle is protected against the damaging effects of heavy loads.

One of the most important discoveries in recent years is that the muscle-spindle afferents are controlled not only by the degree of muscle stretch, but also by the action of efferent fibers, referred to as gamma fibers. These gamma efferent fibers originate from the gamma motoneurons of the spinal cord (see Figure 5.1). Unlike the efferent fibers mentioned previously, which innervate other portions of the muscle, the gamma fibers do not produce contraction of the muscle. Rather, they cause the contraction of only the muscle fibers to which the spindle is attached. Because these fibers are located on either end of the muscle spindle, as shown in Figure 5.1, their contraction and shortening stretches the muscle spindle. Consequently, the muscle spindle afferents increase their rate of discharge, which, in turn, causes the muscle to reflexly contract. What functional role do the gamma efferents play in the control of reflex activity? It appears that the gamma efferents regulate the sensitivity of the muscle-spindle afferents so that their discharge (and the consequent reflex contraction of the muscle) is not simply dependent upon the degree to which the muscle is lengthened or shortened. Without the gamma efferent control of the muscle spindle, the muscle would reflexly contract only when it is lengthened and never when it is already shortened through contraction, even though external stretch may be imposed on the muscle. The gamma efferents, by activating the muscle-spindle afferents, may serve to adjust the stretch reflex to varying degrees of stretch independently of the muscle's state of contraction. Thus, it appears that the stretch reflex becomes more flexible through gamma efferent control and thus postural adjustment is more effective.

FLEXION REFLEX

The flexion reflex, as mentioned previously, consists of a withdrawal movement of a limb that is painfully stimulated. Unlike the stretch reflex, which involves but one muscle and its receptors, the flexion reflex involves many muscles and is triggered by stimulation anywhere within a large area of skin covering the limb. The withdrawal movement involves muscles flexing the ankle and hip as well as those flexing the knee. Acting together, these several flexion movements increase the effectivness of the withdrawal movement and thus its protective value. Concurrent with the flexion movement, a reflex extension of the opposite limb takes place. This movement aids in supporting the weight of the body and maintaining an upright posture when the stimulated leg is lifted. Thus, here at the spinal level, movement and postural adjustment are integrated. The widespread spatial integration, characteristic of muscles that are participating in the flexion, suggests that its neuronal pathways are much more complex than those mediating the stretch reflex and involve multiple synapses, both excitatory and inhibitory. The kinds of neural circuits which presumably underlie the flexion reflex are shown diagrammatically in Figure 5.2.

REFLEX STEPPING

So far we have considered the spinal mechanisms involved in posture and withdrawal movements. Locomotor movements are also integrated in a rudimentary fashion by the spinal cord; reflex stepping movements of the hind limbs can be elicited in animals in which the spinal cord is severed. These movements can be induced by tactile stimulation of the footpads or by stretching the extensor muscles of the leg. Since stepping movements involve alternate flexion and extension of the limb, the neural circuits mediating this reflex, like that involved in scratching, are complex, involving temporal and spatial patterning of excitatory and inhibitory effects on motoneurons controlling a number of different muscle fibers.

DYNAMIC PROPERTIES OF SPINAL REFLEXES

Spinal reflexes are not merely static responses which occur always in the same manner. Rather, they show certain dynamic features—that is, they change in strength under varying conditions of stimulation. The results of many experiments, too detailed to describe here, indicate that many of these dynamic properties of reflexes can be understood in terms of the neuronal processes described in Chapter 2.

We know that the strength of a reflex response tends to increase as the intensity of stimulation increases. This stimulus-response relationship can be understood in terms of the following events: Increasing the intensity of stimulation increases both the frequency of discharge in afferent fibers and the number of fibers discharging. Both of these changes would tend to fire more of the motoneurons innervated by the afferent fibers, because increased frequency of stimulation will produce temporal summation of excitatory postsynaptic potentials in these

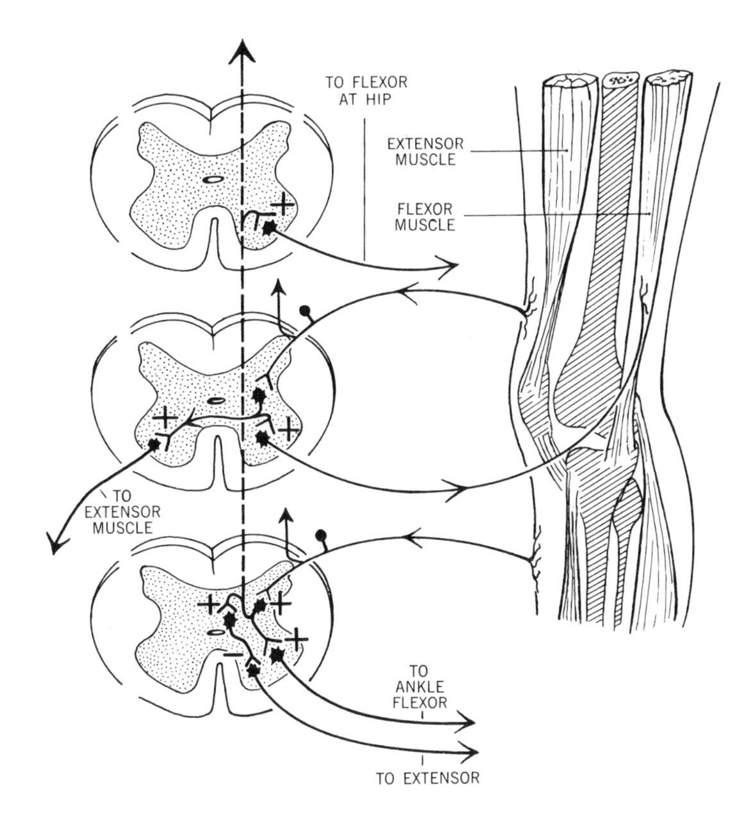

Figure 5.2

Diagrammatic view of the neural circuits presumed to mediate the reflex flexion of a limb to painful stimulation of the skin. Note that through synapses with internuncial fibers the "pain message" from cutaneous nerve endings produces reflex contraction of several flexor muscles, together with the inhibition of antagonists (extensors of the limb) and contraction of extensor muscles in the opposite limb (crossed extension reflex). Excitatory synapses are indicated by plus signs; inhibitory synapses by minus signs.

motoneurons, thus increasing the likelihood of their firing nerve impulses. Also, an increase in the number of afferents firing will increase the excitation of each motoneuron and bring into play larger numbers of motoneurons (see Figure 5.3A). The larger the number of motoneurons firing, the more muscle fibers are contracted, and, consequently, the greater the degree of contraction of the whole muscle.

It is also known that reflex responses, such as flexion and scratching, may continue for a short time after stimulation has terminated.

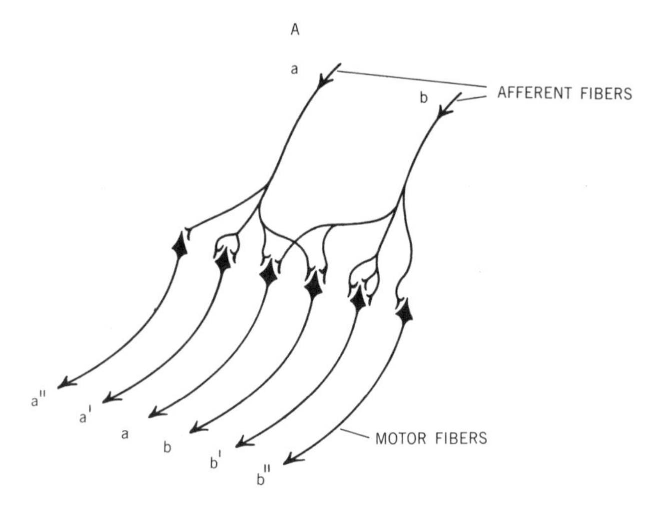

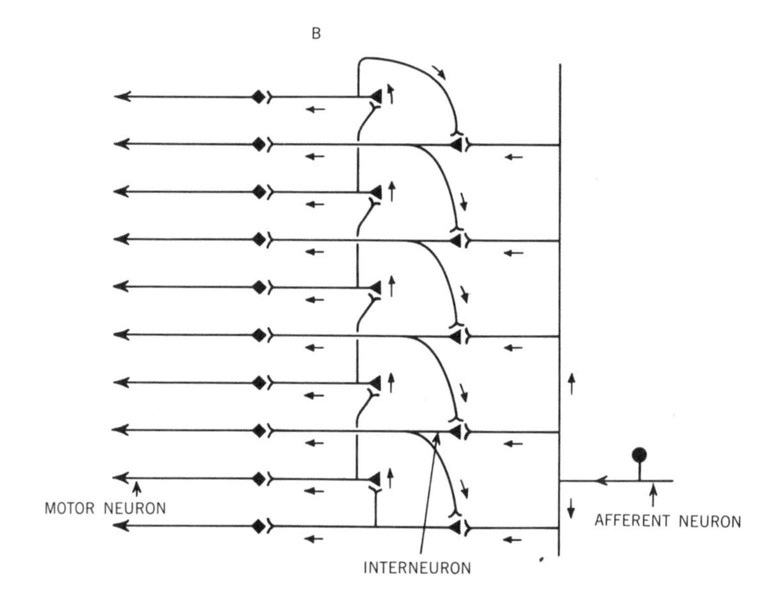

Figure 5.3

(A) *Diagram of synaptic connections between afferent and efferent fibers, illustrating how simultaneous activity of afferent fibers facilitates motor fiber discharges. Afferent Fiber* a *strongly excites Motor Fiber* a′ *but only weakly excites Motor Fibers* a *and* b. *Afferent Fiber* b *strongly excites Motor Fiber* b′ *but only weakly excites* a *and* b. *However, the combined activity of Afferent Fibers* a *and* b *will produce strong excitation of Motor Fibers* a *and* b. **(B)** A

This phenomenon, known as afterdischarge, may be accounted for by the reverberation of electrical activity in closed chains of interneurons within the spinal cord. Through these pathways, motoneurons continue to be excited after afferent activity ceases (see Figure 5.3B).

REFLEX MECHANISMS OF THE BRAIN STEM

The basic reactions of posture and locomotion (such as the stretch reflex and reflex stepping) are mediated by the spinal cord. However, the animal (or human) that has use only of the spinal cord lacks the ability to integrate these movements into the more complex patterns of postural and locomotor movements shown by the normal, intact animal and cannot react appropriately to many of the proprioceptive and exteroceptive stimuli which impinge on it. These complex patterns of behavior require the activity of higher brain mechanisms.

REFLEX MECHANISMS OF THE MEDULLA

If the brain stem of an animal, such as a cat, is transected just above the medulla, so that only the medulla and spinal cord can influence its movements, the animal shows several kinds of postural reactions not found when the spinal cord alone controls movement. Many of these reactions are evoked by proprioceptors in the neck muscles signalling the position of the head in relation to the body. For example, when the jaw of the animal is rotated to one side, the extensor muscles of the limbs on that side tend to contract, while those on the other side relax. The adaptive value of this postural adjustment is not difficult to envisage. When a cat's head turns to the right in response to some event coming from that direction, the extended limbs on that side and relaxed limbs on the opposite side provide body support necessary for a leap to the right. Other similar postural reactions present in the animal with medulla intact are under the control of the vestibular organs, which contain receptors sensitive to changes in the position of the head in space (see Figure 5.4).

REFLEX MECHANISMS OF THE HIGHER BRAIN STEM

While the animal with medulla intact shows postural reactions not present in the animal that has use only of the spinal cord, it still does not right itself, stand, or walk spontaneously. On the other hand, the cat or dog with midbrain intact does show these behaviors. There are several kinds of righting reflexes, some acting on the head, some on the body. For example, if the animal's body is rotated up or down,

---

schematic view of neural circuitry which might be involved in afterdischarges. From Ranson, S. W. and Hinsey, J. C., Reflexes in the hind limbs of cats after transection of the spinal cord at various levels. Figure 12, page 491. Amer. J. Physiol., *1930,* 94, *471–495.*

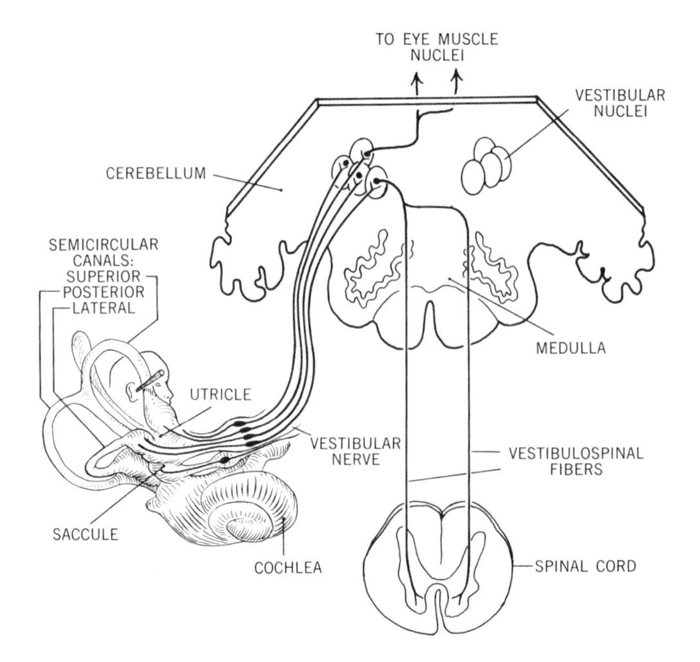

Figure 5.4

The vestibular organs together with a schematic diagram of their connections with the brain. The semicircular canals contain receptors which respond to rotary acceleration of the head, while receptors in the utricle respond to gravitational forces on the head and to linear acceleration. The function of the saccule is not known. Nerve fibers innervating sensory cells of the vestibular organs travel in the vestibular nerve to the vestibular nuclei of the medulla. Here they synapse upon neurons which go to centers controlling eye muscles and neurons in the spinal cord controlling body movements for appropriate postural reactions. From Hardy, M., Observations on the innervation of the maculi sacculi in man, Figure 7, page 412. Anat. Rec., *1934,* 59, *403–417. And from Crosby, E. C., Humphrey, T., and Lauer, E. W.,* Correlative anatomy of the nervous system, *Figure 130, page 153. New York: Macmillan, 1962.*

the head maintains a horizontal position. This reflex is dependent upon sensory input from the vestibular organs. When the neck is turned in response to this reflex, the body is then turned so that it also assumes a horizontal position. This movement is evoked by sensory input from proprioceptors in neck muscles. It is apparent that reactions such as these, as well as standing and walking, require the complex coordination of a variety of simpler reflexes mediated by the spinal cord and lower portions of the brain stem. Thus, the motor control mechanisms of the spinal cord and brain stem form a heirarchically organized system in which processes at higher levels control those at lower levels.

RETICULAR CONTROL OF MOTOR ACTIVITY

The reticular formation of the brain stem is critically involved in the control of spinal reflexes and the coordination of muscular activity during movement. This structure, which runs through the central core of the brain stem, consists mainly of neurons with short fibers which form a diffuse network (see Figure 5.5). The reticular formation also includes neurons with long fibers extending downward toward the spinal cord. Thus, possibilities for both slow, diffuse conduction and rapid conduction exist in this structure. The reticular formation receives a variety of inputs via collaterals from many of the afferent pathways. Its outputs include fibers which descend down to the spinal cord, as shown in Figure 5.5. Through these descending fibers the reticular formation controls spinal motor mechanisms.

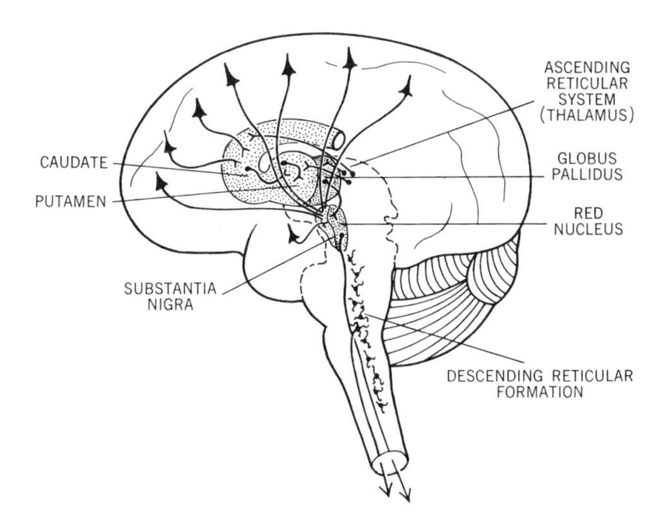

Figure 5.5

Diagrammatic view of the structures forming the extrapyramidal system, and their connections, together with the descending reticular formation of the brain stem and the thalamic portion of the ascending reticular activating system. From Everett, N. B., Functional neuroanatomy, *5th ed. Philadelphia. Lea and Febiger, 1965.*

These reticular influences are apparently quite powerful, for electrical stimulation of the reticular formation exerts strong facilitation or inhibition of motor activity which is induced by various means. Furthermore, it appears that the reticular formation produces these effects primarily through its control of gamma motoneurons. The gamma efferent fibers, it will be recalled, control the discharge of muscle spindle afferents. They appear to influence the degree to which muscles contract (stretch reflex) by adjusting the afferent inflow from the muscle. Stimulation of the reticular formation at sites which facilitate movement also increases the discharge of muscle spindle afferents via the gamma route, whereas suppression of muscle spindle discharges is produced by stimulating regions of the reticular formation which inhibit movement (Eldred, Granit, and Merton, 1953). Moreover, the reticular control of gamma efferents is exerted via slow-conducting, diffuse pathways as well as via fast-conducting, direct pathways (Granit, Holmgren, and Merton, 1955). Thus, it appears that the reticular control of gamma motoneurons is utilized both for facilitating slow, tonic (i.e., long-lasting) contraction of muscles involved in the maintenance of posture (as in standing) as well as the rapid, phasic (i.e., rapid and short duration) contractions of muscles involved in the control of movement. In fact, the fast-conducting pathway provides for even more rapid conduction than occurs over pathways directly innervating motoneurons which contract muscles. Through this fast pathway, the reticular formation may play a central role in "priming" or preparing muscles for the postural adjustments which aid in initiating movement and in organizing sequences of movements (Jung and Hassler, 1960).

The reticular formation also provides an important coordinating mechanism for several kinds of reflexes, such as the righting reflexes described previously, and optovestibular reflexes which coordinate the position of the eyes with that of the head. Furthermore, the red nucleus, whose functions appear to be closely related to those of the reticular formation, is thought to control locomotor movements (see Figure 5.5). Thus, electrical stimulation of its efferent pathway to the spinal cord elicits upward movements of the head and also elicits the body posture associated with this movement (Hess, 1957). Stimulation of this structure in monkeys produces not only these postures, but also bipedal locomotion (Delgado, 1964). Experimental findings such as these suggest that reticular mechanisms regulate postural adjustments and coordinate them with movements in order to produce effective motor performance.

THE EXTRAPYRAMIDAL MOTOR SYSTEM

The descending reticular formation actually constitutes one portion of the extrapyramidal system, a major neural system controlling both voluntary movement and posture. As seen in Figure 5.5, this system includes structures in the upper part of the brain stem, the basal ganglia within the cerebral hemispheres, as well as various regions of the cerebral cortex.

A great deal of attention has been focussed on the basal ganglia and their role in motor performance. Despite these efforts, however, the contributions of these structures to motor performance is far from thoroughly understood. The basal ganglia have two major inputs; one of these is the ascending reticular formation (described in Chapter 6); the other is the frontal areas of the cerebral cortex. These cortical areas include regions which also contribute to the pyramidal system—another major motor system (see Figure 5.6). One major output of the basal ganglia consists of a pathway which descends through the thalamus and establishes connections with diencephalic and midbrain structures, including the reticular formation. Through this latter pathway, the basal ganglia can influence spinal motor mechanisms. Another efferent pathway terminates in a portion of the thalamus which projects upward to the cerebral cortex. Through this anatomical pathway, the basal ganglia can modulate the activity of the pyramidal system, to be discussed below. The basal ganglia appear to be involved in the facilitation and suppression of a variety of motor movements. Electrical stimulation of the globus pallidus enhances reflex movements as well as movements produced by electrical stimulation of the cerebral cortex. Perhaps the most dramatic demonstration of the general activation exerted by this structure is the finding that human patients under general anesthesia will awake and show orienting movements when this structure is electrically stimulated during surgery (Jung and Hassler, 1960). Conversely, lesions of the globus pallidus in animals results in a loss of spontaneous movements, somnolence, and a curious tendency to remain in unusual postures into which they are placed (Mettler, 1954). The caudate nucleus, on the other hand, seems to be more involved in suppression of movements and excitatory processes in the cerebral cortex. Thus, in some experiments with animals, caudate stimulation produces suppression of ongoing movements (Hunter and Jasper, 1949; Mettler, Ades, Lipman, and Culler, 1939); while, in other experiments, somnolence and electrical patterns of activity associated with sleep have been found (Hess, 1957). By contrast, caudate lesions produce abnormally heightened locomotor activity which in its most dramatic form is manifest as "obstinate progression" in which the animal continuously walks straight ahead, bumping into objects and continuing its movements even when coming up against a wall (Mettler and Mettler, 1942). Learned responses are also affected; animals with caudate lesions are impaired in suppressing incorrect responses in problem-solving and discrimination-learning situations (Battig, Mishkin, and Rosvold, 1962). These effects of caudate lesions are referred to as "positive symptoms" as opposed to the "negative symptoms" or losses in behavior frequently seen following lesions in other brain regions. The presence of these positive symptoms implies that the lesioned structure normally exerts suppressive control over other structures whose activity is now "released" or unchecked.

Such signs of release are seen most frequently in cases of damage to the basal ganglia in humans. Disease of the basal ganglia, and especially of the caudate and putamen, characteristically produces a state of hyperkinesis, or abnormally increased motor activity, over which the patient has no control. The heightened activity may appear as slow, wormlike, and spasmodic movements (athetosis) or jerky, repetitious movements (chorea) or, frequently, combinations of these two types of disorders. In such patients the maintenance of normal posture is impaired and normal movements are severely disturbed; the intention to carry out a movement is sometimes interfered with by conflicting movements. According to Denny-Brown (1959), these disorders often take the form of alternating or conflicting approach and withdrawal movements, which are seen in an exaggerated form when a limb is stimulated. Thus, lesions of the basal ganglia seem to disrupt the balance between approach and avoidance reactions and the postural adjustments with which they are associated. It is likely, then, that the basal ganglia integrate motor control mechanisms in the brain stem to achieve complex patterns of behavior. Moreover, it is probably significant that the hyperkinetic symptoms of basal-ganglia disease are heightened by sensory stimulation or arousal and disappear during sleep. These facts suggest that the disrupted activity of the basal ganglia is triggered by inputs from the ascending reticular formation, which is critically involved in arousal and wakefulness.

Parkinson's disease is another disorder of the extrapyramidal system. Persons afflicted with Parkinson's disease have rigid muscles which show resistance to passive movement, hypokinesis (i.e., loss of movement), and tremor. Although there is disagreement as to the cause of Parkinsonism, it is probably due to damage to the substantia nigra, a brain-stem structure which is part of the extrapyramidal system (see Figure 5.5). It appears that the muscular rigidity and tremor are due to unchecked facilitatory mechanisms involving the globus pallidus, for surgical destruction of this portion of the basal ganglia leads to their disappearance.

As mentioned previously, the extrapyramidal system is under the control of the cerebral cortex. As seen in Figure 5.5, the motor areas of the frontal lobe project to the basal ganglia. In addition, widespread regions of frontal, parietal, and temporal cortex project to the lower divisions of the extrapyramidal system, including the reticular formation. These regions participate in the control of movement via extra-

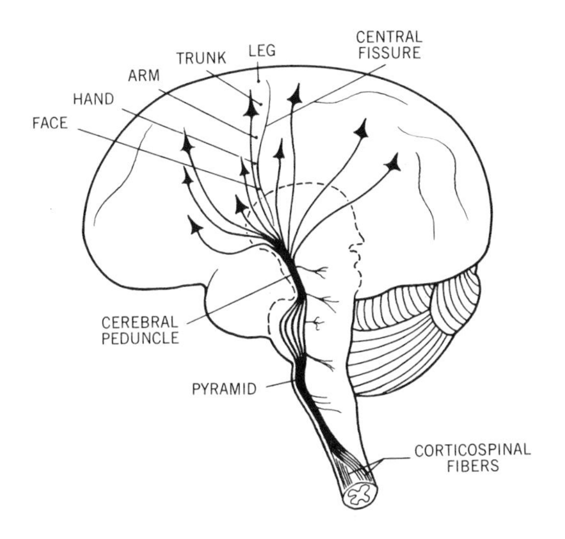

Figure 5.6

Diagrammatic view of the pyramidal system, showing the cortical areas whose neurons contribute to the system, and the representation of body parts in the precentral gyrus. The fibers ending in the brain stem terminate in cranial nerve nuclei which control movements of the head and eyes. From Everett, N. B. Functional neuroanatomy, *5th ed. Philadelphia: Lea and Febiger, 1965.*

pyramidal projections. For, following interruption of the pyramidal pathways, stimulation of the cortex gives rise to organized movements.

THE PYRAMIDAL SYSTEM

The cerebral cortex also gives rise to fibers which bypass the basal ganglia and other extrapyramidal structures and terminate directly in the spinal cord and motor nuclei of the brain stem (see Figure 5.6). These fibers of the pyramidal system, then, have direct access to spinal motor mechanisms, and they arise from many cortical areas. Perhaps the most intensively studied of these areas is the precentral gyrus (see Figure 5.6), which is centrally involved in the functions of the pyramidal system. Electrical stimulation of this region gives rise to fragmentary movements of muscles or groups of muscles in parts of the body as shown in Figure 5.6.

There are two important features of this motor area. First, as seen in Figure 5.6, the movements of various body parts are spatially represented in an organized manner—adjacent body regions are represented in adjacent cortical regions, although there is also considerable overlap of representation. Secondly, those parts of the body which engage in a variety of skilled and complex movements (such as the hands and mouth) have proportionally greater areas of representation than do less articulate parts (such as the muscles of the trunk). Unlike the effects of extrapyramidal damage, damage to the pyramidal system produces primarily negative signs, that is, a loss of movement. While movements may eventually return following damage, they are usually clumsy and unskilled, especially those involving the hands and fingers. Although the ability to perform skilled movements is severely impaired following removal of motor cortex, goal-directed movements are not lost. Thus, following removal of the precentral gyrus, monkeys trained prior to the operation to open boxes to obtain food still show clumsy attempts (sometimes successful) to open the boxes (Pribram, Kruger, Robinson, and Berman, 1954). In a pioneering study, Jasper, Ricci, and Doane (1958) recorded discharges from single neurons in motor cortex of monkeys while they were performing conditioned avoidance responses. Varying patterns of neuronal discharges were found. Some neurons showed accelerated discharges just before and during avoidance movements, while others showed suppression of firing during such movements. However, very few neurons showed changes in discharge in anticipation of movement. This finding suggests that the neuronal events directing skilled movement are not initiated in motor cortex, but perhaps in other regions which provide inputs into motor cortex. Since incising motor cortex or isolating it from surrounding cortical regions does not seriously disrupt skilled movement (Sperry, 1947), subcortical structures (such as the basal ganglia) may provide the inputs necessary for initiating movement.

Stimulation of many cortical regions other than precentral motor cortex gives rise to movements. Unlike those elicited by precentral stimulation, these movements involve many muscles acting in a synergistic manner. For example, stimulation of the region in front of the precentral gyrus gives rise to gross movements involving the trunk and head. Further forward in the frontal lobes, electrical stimulation within a restricted region produces eye movements. Stimulation of a region on the medial wall of the frontal lobes reveals a bilateral representation of the body parts. It is not clear to what extent the movements elicited by stimulation of these various cortical regions is mediated by the pyramidal or extrapyramidal system. Undoubtedly, the extrapyramidal system is involved to some extent, for many of these movements can be evoked after the pyramidal tract is interrupted. Apparently many, if not all, cortical areas give rise to both pyramidal and extrapyramidal fibers. In view of this, it is unwise to consider any one cortical region as "the" motor cortex.

THE CEREBELLUM

The cerebellum, located atop the brain stem, is a complex organ which shows many of the features of the cerebrum, as mentioned in Chapter 3 (see Figure 5.7). Its cortical surface, which contains cell bodies and ascending fibers, is deeply infolded so that the whole structure is divided into several lobes which, in turn, are divided into a number of lobules. Beneath the cortical surface is found the white matter of the hemispheres, which consists of input and output fibers along with several nuclei.

The cerebellum receives a variety of inputs—cutaneous, proprioceptive, and vestibular afferents, as well as afferent fibers from the visual and auditory systems. In addition, the cerebellum receives many descending projections from the cerebral cortex via the nuclei of the pons. Efferent pathways from the cerebellum arise from cells in the overlying cortex, many of which terminate in the cerebellar nuclei. From these nuclei arise fibers which are directed to brain-stem structures of the extrapyramidal system as well as to the vestibular nuclei. Other efferent fibers ascend to the thalamic nucleus which projects to motor

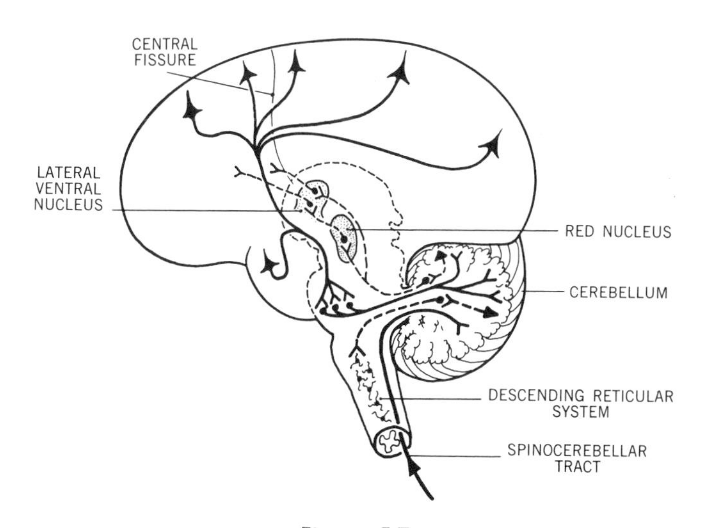

Figure 5.7

The cerebellum and its afferent and efferent connections with other structures. Afferent pathways to the cerebellum are indicated by solid lines while efferent pathways from the cerebellum are indicated by broken lines. The spinocerebellar pathway contains proprioceptive fibers.

areas of the cortex thus reciprocating the cerebro-cerebellar pathway described above (see Figure 5.7).

A good deal of evidence suggests that the cerebellum does not directly initiate movement, but rather modulates executive mechanisms so that temporal integration is achieved. Electrical stimulation of certain portions of the cerebellum inhibits movements arising from reflex stimulation, from cortical stimulation, and spontaneous movements. Apparently, these suppressive effects are exerted via descending extrapyramidal pathways on gamma efferents as well as on motoneurons directly controlling muscular contraction. From the same regions of the cerebellum, stimulation at specific frequencies facilitates motor movements (Moruzzi, 1950). Other portions of the cerebellum exert their effects on cerebral motor mechanisms. Stimulation of these regions can facilitate or inhibit motor responses induced by cortical stimulation.

The effects of cerebellar damage in animals and in humans also supports the view that this structure modulates motor activity. Total

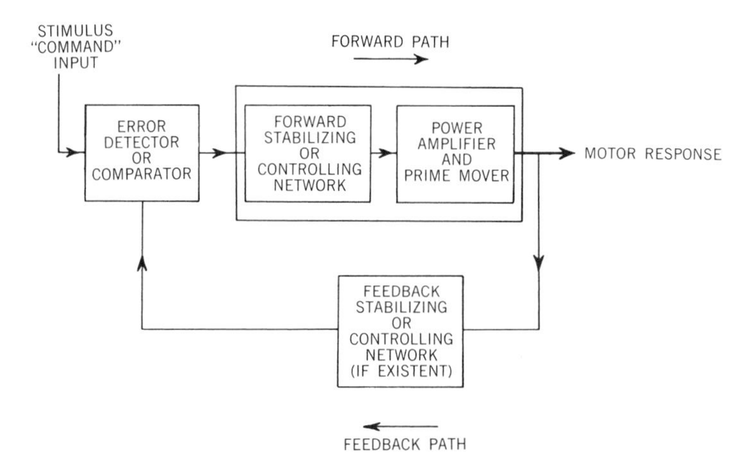

Figure 5.8

Diagram showing a control system for detecting and correcting errors. With regard to the nervous system, the stimulus command might be an object viewed by the eye, and the forward path might be the pyramidal system. Through the feedback network, which might involve proprioceptive inputs via the spinocerebellar pathway, the cerebellum could detect discrepancies between the path of the ongoing movement and the goal (grasping the object) and then correct the error through its projections to the cerebral cortex. From Frank, L. K., Hutchinson, G. E., Livingston, W. K., McCulloch, W. S., and Wiener, N., Teleological mechanisms, Figure 1, page 192. Ann. N.Y. Acad. Sci., *1948,* 50, *187–278.*

removal of the cerebellum in animals produces overactive reflexes, a finding which suggests that inhibitory control mechanisms are disturbed. The timing and coordination of movement are also severely disturbed, a condition referred to as ataxia. Disequilibrium, which produces swaying and falling, is also produced by lesions of the cerebellum. Another characteristic effect of cerebellar damage is tremor, which interferes with the performance of skilled movements. Disturbances in coordinated movements are clearly seen in patients with cerebellar lesions. Usually, such a movement (such as reaching out to touch an object) is slow to start, suggesting the loss of facilitatory influences involved in initiating movement. Errors in the direction of the movement cannot be corrected at the appropriate time so that the hand underreaches or overreaches. Furthermore, errors in the direction of movement tend to be overcorrected so that wild, swinging movements may result.

These disturbances in the performance of movements have suggested that the cerebellum is involved in the kind of neural loop circuit illustrated in Figure 5.8. During the course of movement, the cerebellum receives information from proprioceptive and exteroceptive senses concerning the position of the limb (reafference). It also monitors the activity in the cerebral motor areas which provides information about the direction and amplitude of projected movement. When the limb deviates from the intended pathway, the cerebellum produces the appropriate readjustments through its connections with cerebral and brain stem motor mechanisms. Thus, according to this scheme, the cerebellum acts as a comparator of efferent and reafferent signals, adjusting motor activity so that the two sets of signals coincide.

SUGGESTED READINGS

Galambos, R. *Nerve and muscle.* Garden City, N.Y.: Doubleday, 1962.

Gardner, E. *Fundamentals of neurology,* 4th ed., Chapters 8, 9, and 10. Philadelphia: Saunders, 1963.

Sherrington, C. *The integrative action of the nervous system,* 2nd ed. New Haven, Conn.: Yale University Press, 1947.

Snider, R. S. The cerebellum. *Sci. Amer.,* August 1958.

Woolsey, C. N. Organization of somatic sensory and motor areas of the cerebral cortex. In H. F. Harlow and C. N. Woolsey (Eds.), *Biological and biochemical bases of behavior.* Madison, Wisc.: University of Wisconsin Press, 1958, 63–82.

NEURAL MECHANISMS OF WAKEFULNESS AND SLEEP 6

A sleeping cat is aroused by approaching footsteps in the night; its eyes open, the pupils dilate, it crouches in preparation for the intruder. Hours later, the sun rises and, as if in response to this beginning of a new phase of the celestial cycle, we are roused from sleep. Once again we see and hear the events around us and begin our daily activities. So common are these daily occurrences that we take them for granted, like the rising and setting of the sun, and do not search for explanations. And yet these facts do present us with puzzling problems: What is wakefulness, and how is it initiated and maintained?

We do not customarily think of wakefulness as a process, like coding of sensory information or motor integration. However, it is clear that wakefulness provides a necessary background for many of these processes. Perception, attention, and organized movements normally occur only when we are awake. Thus wakefulness may be thought of as a state of the organism—one which influences our tendencies to detect stimuli, to engage in cognitive activity, and to respond. In this sense wakefulness is closely related to degree of alertness or attention.

Sleep in many ways appears to be the converse of the waking state. During sleep, consciousness is altered, reactivity to external stimuli is greatly reduced, and (it is thought) events are not recorded into memory. Moreover, many body functions, including metabolic activity, are slowed down. Some functions, however, such as digestion, proceed with little or no change. These facts suggest that sleep permits energy conservation; it may also prevent the deleterious effects of fatigue that would accumulate during prolonged wakefulness.

THE SLEEP-WAKEFULNESS CYCLE

The rhythmic alternation of sleep and wakefulness is a fundamental biological cycle, which is closely related to other natural rhythms, such as hunger. Moreover, this periodic waxing and waning of activity is normally geared to the day-night cycle. The activity of some species is greatest during the daytime and least during the night. For other species (the nocturnal animals) the activity cycle is reversed. As Murray (1965) has pointed out, animals that are not biologically equipped to perform activities during a particular period (such as nocturnal animals during the daytime) must expend as little energy as possible during this period, because they cannot take in energy. Thus, the periodic alternations of activity and rest provide a regulatory mechanism for energy expenditure.

Within either portion of the sleep-wake cycle, behavioral and cognitive activity vary considerably. During our waking hours, our degree of alertness may vary from states of quiet daydreaming through degrees of relaxed alertness to intense arousal. Depth of sleep also varies considerably throughout the night. The sleeping hours of many animals, as well as humans, are regularly punctuated by periods when the brain is in a state resembling wakefulness.

In recent years there has been a great increase in investigations of biological mechanisms controlling wakefulness and sleep. The results of these investigations have considerably changed our views of these processes and have raised many new problems.

NEURAL MECHANISMS OF WAKEFULNESS AND AROUSAL

THE ELECTROENCEPHALOGRAM AND WAKEFULNESS

The Austrian psychiatrist Berger demonstrated in 1929 that the electrical activity of the human cerebral cortex can be recorded from the scalp. Ever since Berger's pioneering discovery, investigators have shown that the pattern of electrical activity (referred to as the electroencephalogram, or EEG) varies with states of alertness. As shown in Figure 6.1, slow, high-voltage waves are found during deep sleep, while in light sleep these waves are interrupted by higher frequency spindles. In a state of relaxed wakefulness, rhythms of approximately ten per second are typically found; but during alertness, induced for example by external stimulation, these waves are replaced by fast, low-amplitude waves. Because these waves, unlike those correlated with relaxed wakefulness, are irregular, this pattern of electrical activity is referred to as the desynchronized pattern. Thus, the continuum of consciousness ranging from deep sleep to intense arousal is paralleled by an EEG continuum of increasing frequency of cortical rhythms.

The EEG pattern, then, has been used as an index of behavioral wakefulness and arousal. By inference, it has also been used as an index of cortical excitability, or "activiation." An understanding of the neural mechanisms mediating these behavioral and electrical states has been gradually emerging from the following studies.

THE ROLE OF SENSORY STIMULATION IN WAKEFULNESS

Over thirty years ago, Bremer conducted a significant and pioneering series of experiments on the neurophysiology of the state of wake-

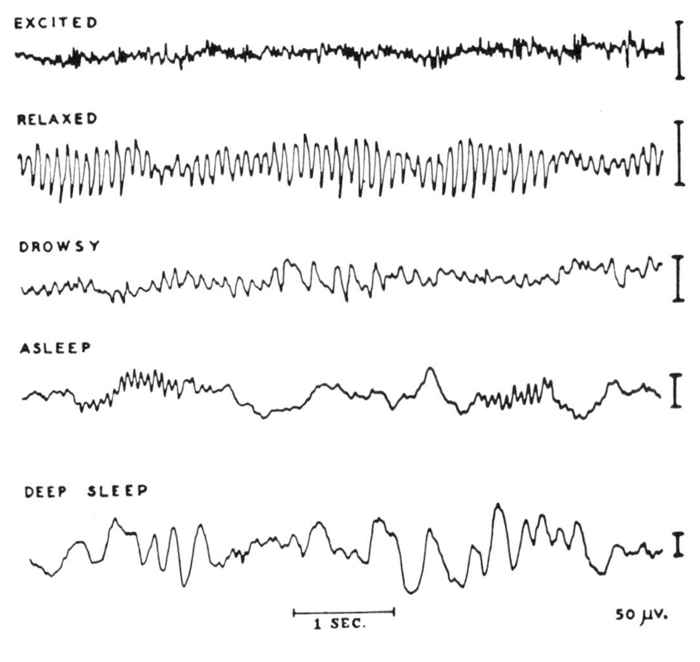

Figure 6.1

Electroencephalogram (EEG) patterns characteristic of different states of consciousness in man. The vertical marker beside each tracing indicates an amplitude of 50 microvolts (μv) or millionths of a volt. The horizontal marker indicates the passage of one sec. From Jasper, H. H., Electroencephalography, Figure 121, page 401. In Penfield, W., and Erickson, T. C., Epilepsy and cerebral localization. *Chapter 14. Springfield, Ill.: C. C. Thomas, 1941.*

fulness in animals. In one study he made the important observation that sensory stimulation, even in only one modality, has a generalized activating effect on the cortex; that is, it produces the desynchronized waking EEG pattern throughout the cerebral cortex (Bremer, 1936, cited in Magoun, 1963).

In a later study, which is described below, Bremer (1937) further concluded that sensory stimulation is necessary for the maintenance of wakefulness. He found that after the brain stem of a cat is transected (that is, cut through) at a high level (the midbrain), the animal's EEG shows only the slow, synchronized waves associated with the sleeping state (see Figure 6.2). On the other hand, when the brain stem is transected at a lower level (near its junction with the spinal cord), then the EEG shows fast, desynchronized waves alternating periodically with slow waves—a pattern found in the normal animal (see Figure 6.2).

Bremer inferred that this activiation of the cortex depended upon a sensory input to the cortex from the cranial nerves. These nerves, he reasoned, were prevented from exerting their excitatory effect on the cortex by the high brain-stem transection. In the absence of sensory inflow to the cortex, Bremer argued, sleep ensues.

THE ASCENDING RETICULAR ACTIVATING SYSTEM (ARAS) AND AROUSAL

Bremer assumed that cortical activation is mediated by the specific sensory pathways—those pathways which project to the cortex through specific thalamic nuclei, as described in Chapter 4. However, the experiments of Moruzzi and Magoun (1949) indicate that the activating effects of sensory stimulation are not mediated by sensory pathways to the cortex; rather, they are mediated by a portion of the reticular formation of the brain stem which they refer to as the ascending reticular activating system (ARAS) (see Figure 6.3).

As described in Chapter 3, the reticular formation consists of a diffuse collection of cells and fibers in the central core of the brain stem. Moruzzi and Magoun found that electrical stimulation of the

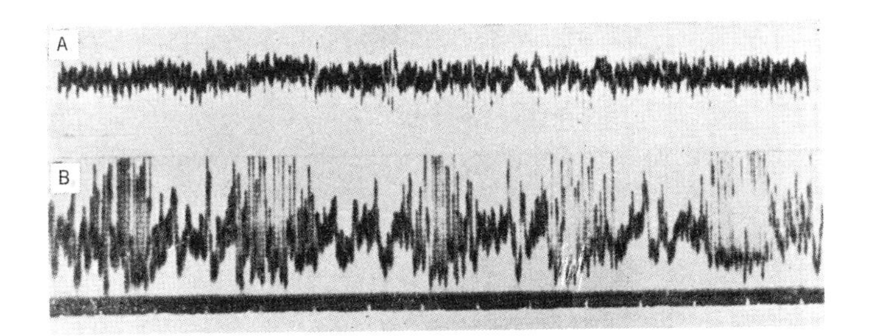

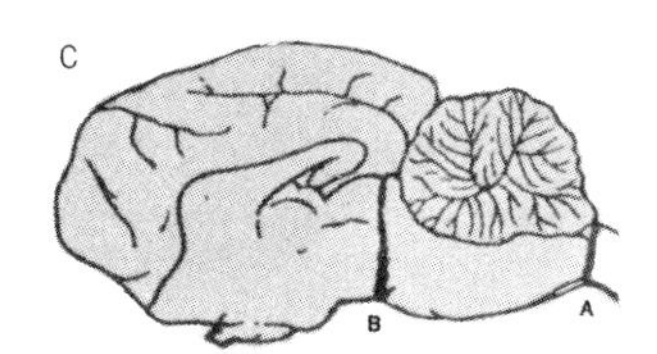

Figure 6.2

The effects of brain transections on cortical EEG patterns in cats. **(A)** *The normal waking pattern seen following transection at the junction of the brain stem and spinal cord, as shown by Line* A *in* **(C)**. **(B)** *Slow waves characteristic of sleep seen following transection of the mesencephalon, as shown by Line* B *in* **(C)**. *From Bremer, F., L'activité cérébrale an cours de someil et de la narcose, Figures 1, 4, 9, and 11.* Bull. Acad. Roy. Med. Belgique, *1937,* 2 *(6th series), 68–86.*

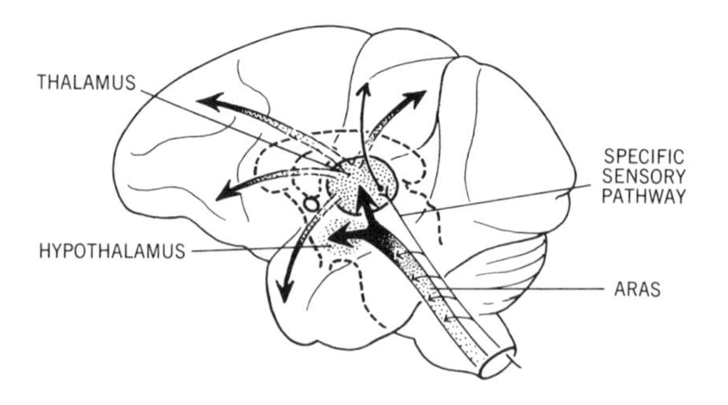

Figure 6.3

The ascending reticular activating system (ARAS) showing its inputs from collaterals of sensory tracts in the brain stem and its projections to the posterior hypothalamus and unspecific nuclei of the thalamus, which, in turn, diffusely project to the cerebral cortex. From Magoun, H., The ascending reticular system and wakefulness, Figure 10, page 13. In J. F. Delafresnaye (Ed.), Brain mechanisms and consciousness. *Oxford: Blackwell, 1954.*

ARAS (especially at high frequencies) produces the desynchronized EEG pattern of activation throughout the cortex. Furthermore, electrical stimulation of the ARAS through electrodes permanently implanted in freely moving animals produces awakening and arousal, like that seen in animals aroused by environmental stimuli (Segundo, Araña-Iniquez, and French, 1955). These findings, then suggest that the ARAS plays a crucial role not only in activating the cortex but also in producing behavioral arousal.

Moreover, following destruction of large portions of the ARAS, animals remain in a comatose state; and they show only slow, synchronous waves in the EEG for several weeks following surgery. During this period they can be aroused only momentarily by sensory stimulation. When stimulation ceases, they fall back into the comatose state (French and Magoun, 1952). But as time progresses, animals with extensive ARAS destruction are more readily aroused and can eventually maintain wakefulness (Sprague, Chambers, and Stellar, 1961). This finding suggests that more rostral parts of the ARAS are capable of functioning in the absence of the midbrain ARAS. On the other hand, destruction of the specific sensory pathways in the brain stem does not interfere with behavioral or EEG signs of wakefulness (Lindsley, Schreiner, Knowles, and Magoun, 1950), although these lesions do produce behavioral abnormalities (Sprague, Chambers, and Stellar, 1961). Thus, these experiments employing lesions, like those using electrical stimulation, indicate that the ARAS is involved in cortical activation and arousal. Apparently, then, the loss of cortical activation that Bremer observed following midbrain transection was due to disruption of ARAS activation of the cortex.

ARAS INPUTS

The cortical arousing effects of the ARAS depend on two processes: The afferent inflow into this structure from sensory pathways and the excitatory projections of the ARAS to the forebrain (see Figure 6.3). With regard to sensory inflow into the ARAS, various sensory systems ascending through the brain stem contribute collateral fibers to this structure as shown in Figure 6.3. When different sensory pathways (such as somatosensory or auditory) are electrically stimulated, evoked electrical discharges are recorded within the ARAS (French, Verzeano, and Magoun, 1953), sometimes at the same site. Furthermore, individual neurons within the ARAS respond to sensory information from several modalities. For example, ARAS neurons discharging to tactile, visual, and auditory stimuli have been reported (Amassian and Waller, 1958). Apparently, information from different sensory systems converges within the ARAS, where it is pooled in diffuse, multisynaptic networks. Thus, the ARAS, independent of the source of stimulation, produces excitatory effects on the cortex. Through this mechanism, the organism can be awakened or aroused by various stimuli.

ARAS PROJECTIONS

By stimulating at various points in the brain stem and forebrain, Moruzzi and Magoun showed that the cortical activating effects of ARAS stimulation are mediated by several ascending pathways. One of these pathways involves a route through the so-called unspecific nuclei of the thalamus (see Figure 6.3). The unspecific nuclei of the thalamus, unlike the specific thalamic nuclei, receive little direct sensory input. Their afferent inflow comes mainly from the ARAS and from the specific thalamic nuclei. High-frequency stimulation of the unspecific nuclei produces cortical activating effects similar to those produced by ARAS stimulation. Hence, these structures are sometimes referred to as the thalamic portion of the ARAS.

The arousal effects mediated by the ARAS and the thalamic reticular structures are not identical. They differ with regard to several important characteristics; this suggests that they mediate somewhat different functions. For example, Sharpless and Jasper (1956) concluded from their experiments that the thalamic portion of the ARAS mediates brief, rapid cortical activation and is highly sensitive to changes in sensory stimulation. In other words, this portion of the reticular system appears to regulate alertness to rapid fluctuations in environmental stimulation.

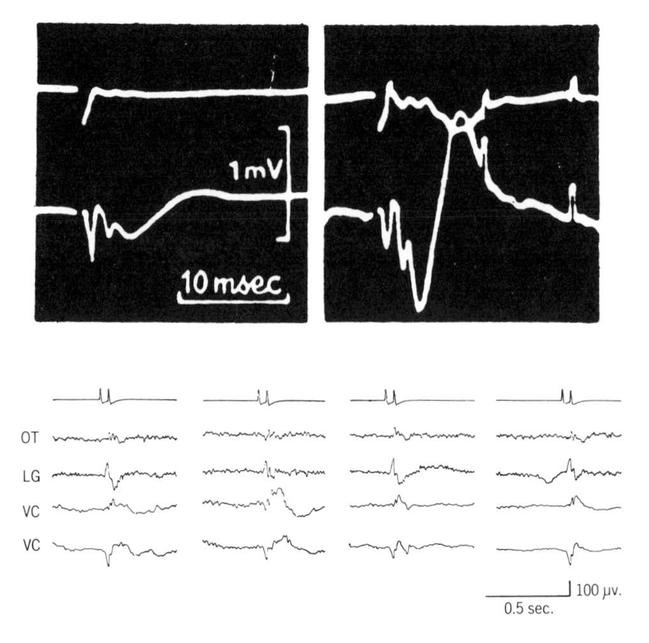

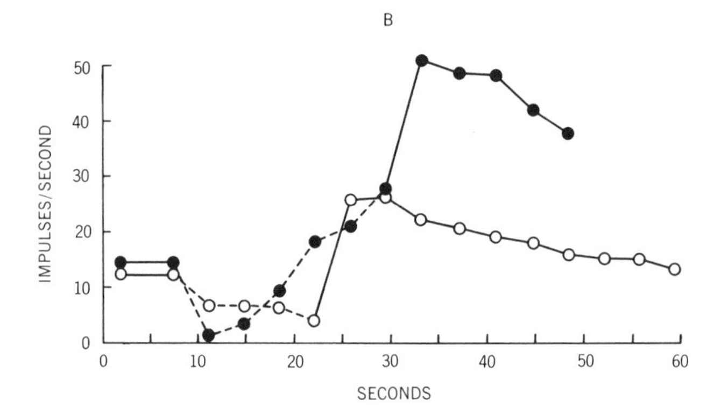

Figure 6.4

Effects of reticular stimulation on afferent transmission. **(A)** *The tracings in the upper half show the effects of reticular stimulation on evoked potentials recorded in visual cortex of cat to electrical stimulation of the lateral geniculate nucleus. In the left panel, the upper trace shows the stimulus to the lateral geniculate while the lower trace shows the cortical evoked potential. In the right panel, the amplitude of the evoked potential is enhanced as a result of reticular stimulation. From Bremer, F., and Stoupel, N., Facilitation et inhibition des potentials évoques corticaux dans l'eveil cérébral, Figure 3, page 246.* Arch. int. Physiol., *1959, 67, 240–275. The tracings in the lower half of* (A) *show the effects of reticular stimulation on evoked potentials in visual*

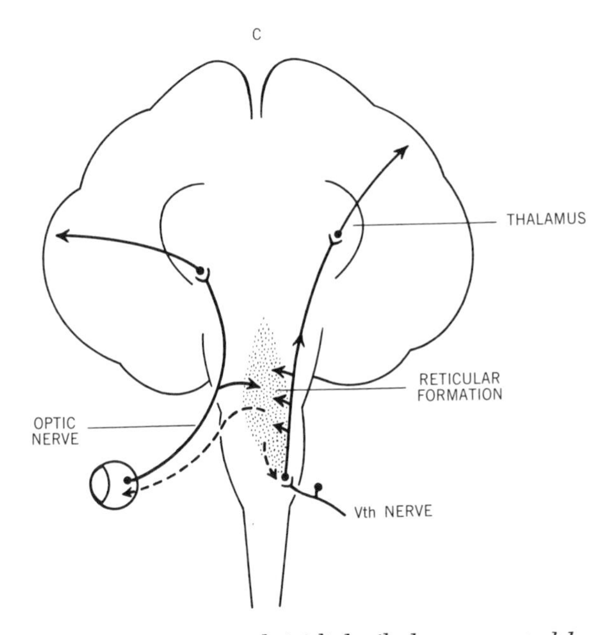

*cortex of cat to two brief light flashes, separated by 50 msec. Tracings in the column at far left were taken before reticular stimulation; those in the second column, during reticular stimulation; those in the third column, 0–10 seconds after reticular stimulation; and those in the last column, 10–12 seconds after reticular stimulation. Note that the two closely spaced light flashes shown in the top row are responded to as one by evoked potentials in visual cortex (*VC, *lowest tracing). However, for 10 seconds following reticular stimulation,* each *of the two flashes produces an evoked potential in visual cortex.* (OT: *optic tract.* LG: *lateral geniculate.) From Lindsley, D. B., The reticular system and perceptual discrimination, Figure 7, page 525. In Jasper, H. H., Proctor, L. D., Knighton, R. S., Noshay, W. C., and Costello, R. T. (Eds.),* Reticular formation of the brain. *Boston: Little, Brown, 1958.* **(B)** *The effect of reticular stimulation on impulse discharges of a ganglion cell in cat retina to light. Following reticular stimulation, which is indicated by the broken lines, there is an increase in the ganglion cell's frequency of discharge. (Filled circles: reticular stimulation with pulses of 49/sec. Open circles: reticular stimulation with pulses of 107/sec.) From Granit, R.,* Receptors and sensory perception, *Figure 44, page 106. New Haven, Conn.: Yale University Press, 1955.* **(C)** *Diagrammatic representation of possible efferent pathways from the reticular formation to nerve cells in the retina and to synapses of the Vth nerve in the brain stem, illustrating how the reticular formation might gate sensory inputs. From Hernández-Péon, R., Reticular mechanisms of sensory control, Figure 12, page 516. In W. Rosenblith (Ed.),* Sensory communication. *New York: Wiley, 1961.*

On the other hand, the brain stem portion of the ARAS seems to be involved in longer-lasting states of arousal—the kind that may underlie the maintenance of wakefulness.

RETICULAR CONTROL OF SENSORY TRANSMISSION AND ATTENTION

Stimulation of the reticular structures in the brain stem not only produces arousal, it also affects the transmission and processing of sensory information, both at the cortex and in the lower sensory pathways. For example, reticular stimulation increases the amplitude of evoked potentials in visual cortex; it also facilitates the excitability of visual cortex to repetitive light stimulation (see Figure 6.4A). With regard to its influences on lower portions of the sensory pathways reticular stimulation can, for example, alter the excitability of ganglion cells in the retina (see Figure 6.4B).

Thus, the reticular system may control alertness not only by changing cortical excitability but also by gating, or selecting, sensory information. This selection of sensory information is probably accomplished through efferent projections of the reticular system to lower sensory pathways (see Figure 6.4C). Through this efferent mechanism, the reticular system can determine which messages are allowed through to higher levels of the sensory systems for further processing. In other words, the reticular system seems to be involved in selective attention. Through this process particular stimuli are at various times selected for further perceptual coding; others are not. It is of interest in this regard that attention affects evoked potentials in a manner similar to ARAS stimulation. When human subjects attend to visual stimuli, evoked potentials, which are recorded from the scalps of the subjects, increase in amplitude (Haider, Spong, and Lindsley, 1964). The role of the reticular system in attention is also suggested by the finding that reticular stimulation enhances the ability of monkeys to discriminate between visual stimuli that are exposed for short durations (Fuster, 1958).

CORTICAL MODULATION OF RETICULAR ACTIVITY

Not only can the ARAS influence the excitability of the cortex, but, conversely, the cortex itself can also influence the activity of the ARAS. Several cortical areas send fiber projections to the ARAS (French, Hernández-Péon, and Livingston, 1955); through these projections the cortex can increase the excitability of the ARAS and thus produce EEG activation (Bremer and Terzuolo, 1953). Furthermore, the cortex can also suppress reticular activity; for, in the absence of cortical influences, the reticular system exerts more powerful effects on reflexes (Hugelin and Bonvallet, 1957a and b). This latter finding is significant, for it suggests the operation of a feedback loop whereby the cortex, once activated by the ARAS, in turn suppresses ARAS activity (see Figure

6.5). It appears, then, that the cortex provides a kind of physiological brake on arousal processes. Through this feedback loop, cortical mechanisms that mediate such complex processes as perception and thinking could modulate reticular activation. Thus, these mechanisms could maintain a level of arousal that is optimal for efficient functioning of these complex processes (Hebb, 1955).

NEURAL MECHANISMS OF SLEEP AND DREAMING

INHIBITORY MECHANISMS OF SLOW-WAVE SLEEP: THALAMIC RETICULAR SYSTEM

Investigations of the ARAS have suggested a neural theory of sleep as well as a neural theory of wakefulness. According to this view, sleep and its concomitant EEG pattern are simply consequences of a diminution in sensory stimulation. A decrease in sensory stimulation lowers excitation in the ARAS which, in turn, leads to a diminution in cortical excitability. This idea that sleep is due simply to a "deafferentation" of the cortex appears reasonable in light of the common experience that sleep often ensues when environmental stimulation is reduced. Moreover, we seek this reduction in stimulation when we wish to sleep.

On the other hand, there is evidence that sleep is not entirely a passive process but is produced by active inhibitory mechanisms—mechanisms whose action is opposed to the excitatory influences of the ARAS. The evidence that active mechanisms produce sleep derives from observations that electrical stimulation of certain neural structures leads to EEG and behavorial signs of sleep (see Figure 6.6). Surprisingly, some of these neural structures are the same ones that can produce activation and arousal. The critical factor which determines whether sleep or arousal is evoked from these structures is the frequency of stimulation. Thus, arousal is triggered by high-frequency stimulation of the thalamic reticular structures; while low-frequency stimulation of these structures produces cortical slow waves, synchronized to each stimulation pulse, and spindles like those found in natural sleep (see Figure 6.6).

Behavioral sleep also has been produced by low-frequency stimulation of these structures in cats (Hess, 1957). This finding is striking, for stimulation induces the acts that customarily precede sleep. These acts include circling, curling up and yawning, as well as sleep itself. The very naturalness of these evoked behaviors suggests that a neural system involved in sleep is being activated.

INHIBITORY MECHANISMS OF SLOW-WAVE SLEEP: THE MEDULLA

Apparently the thalamic reticular system is just one link in a larger neural system mediating sleep. For, stimulation of the caudate nucleus

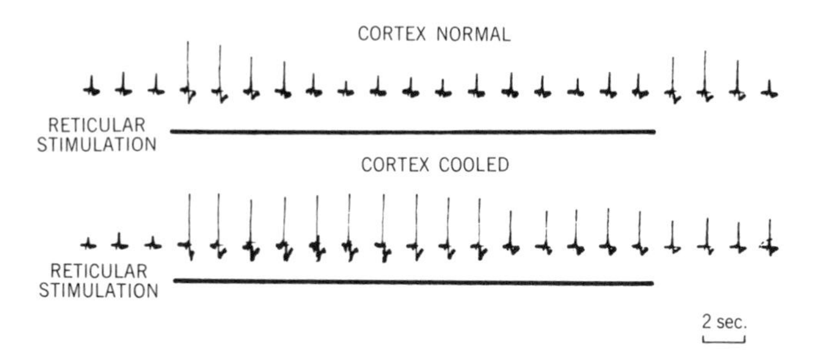

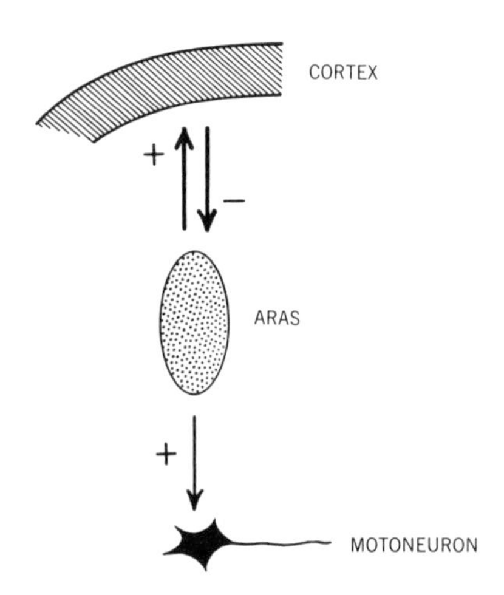

Figure 6.5

Inhibitory influence of the cortex on the reticular system. Tracings in the top of the figure show the effects of cortical depression (produced by cooling the cortex) on reticular facilitation. In the first row of tracings, reticular stimulation initially enhances the amplitude of a reflex response, shown by the increased height of the recording, but the amplitude of the response soon returns to normal. When the cortex is depressed, the reticular enhancement effect persists for a long time. The bottom of the figure contains a diagrammatic representation of the reticulo-cortical-reticular feedback loop: the ARAS excites the cortex, which in turn suppresses the ARAS. From Hugelin, A., and Bonvallet, M., Tonus cortical et controle de la facilitation motrice d'origine reticulaire, Figure 3, page 1178. J. de Physiol. *(Paris), 1957, 49, 1171–1200. And from Hugelin, A., and Bonvallet, M., Étude experimentale des interrelations reticulo-corticales. Proposition d'une théorie de l'avertissement reticulaire à un système diffus cortical, Figure 5, page 1208.* J. de Physiol. *(Paris), 1957, 49, 1201–1223.*

and of the preoptic area also produces EEG and behavioral signs of sleep. Moreover, it appears that regions of the medulla (in the lower brain stem) provide a mechanism for initiating slow waves in the cortex. If the brain stem is transected at the level of the pons, so that the medulla cannot exert its effects on the cortex, then slow waves are no longer found in the cortex. Only the fast waves associated with wakefulness are seen (Batini, Moruzzi, Palestini, Rossi, and Zanchetti, 1959). Furthermore, when a barbiturate (a central depressing drug) is injected directly into the artery supplying the medulla, slow waves in the EEG disappear and the waking EEG pattern takes their place (Magni, Moruzzi, Rossi, and Zanchetti, 1959). This finding implies that the drug is depressing the activity of a slow-wave generating mechanism in the medulla, thus allowing ARAS excitatory influences to predominate. Finally, as seen in Figure 6.7, electrical stimulation at low frequencies within the medulla can trigger slow synchronous waves in the cortex (Magnes, Moruzzi, and Pompeiano, 1961).

There are at least two alternative ways in which the slow-wave triggering mechanism in the medulla might act on the cortex. It might directly stimulate the thalamic reticular structures and cause them to trigger slow waves in the cortex. Or it might inhibit the excitatory ARAS and thus allow thalamic or other slow-wave generating structures to predominate. Some evidence favoring the latter alternative is that lesions of the medulla produce unstable patterns of ARAS cortical activation (Bonvallet and Allen, 1963).

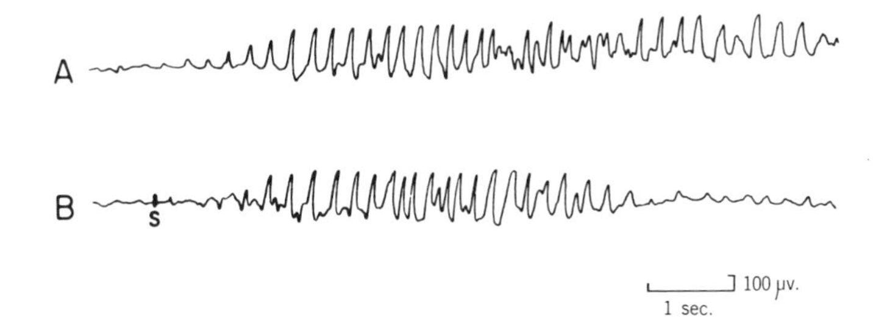

Figure 6.6

Spontaneous spindle burst recorded from cerebral cortex of cat **(A)** *and a spindle burst* **(B)** *in the same cortical area produced by electrical stimulation of thalamic reticular system at* (S). *Note the similarity between the two tracings. From Jasper, H. H., Unspecific thalamocortical relations, Figure 1, page 1308. In J. Field (Ed.),* Handbook of physiology. *Vol. II. Wash.: American Physiological Society, 1960. 1960.*

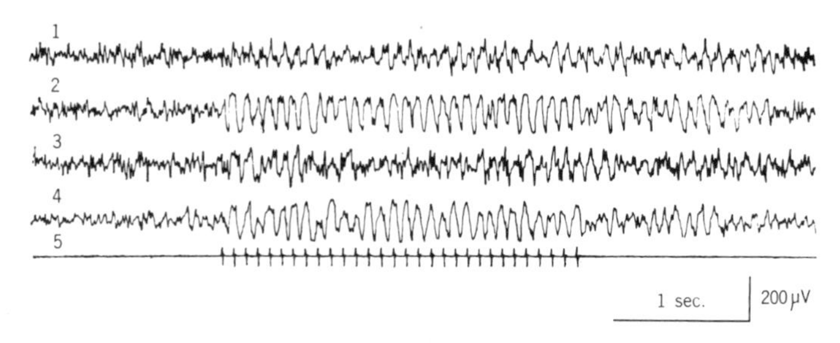

Figure 6.7

Sleep-like slow waves produced in cerebral cortex of cat by electrical stimulation of medulla. Note that slow waves are synchronized to each electrical pulse. (1: right parieto-temporal area; 2: right temporo-occipital area; 3: left parieto-temporal area; 4: left temporo-occipital area; 5: stimulus marker.) From Magnes, J., Moruzzi, G., and Pompeiano, O., Synchronization of the EEG produced by low-frequency electrical stimulation of the region of the solitary tract, Figure 5, page 44. Arch. Ital. Biol., *1961, Vol. XCIX, 33–67.*

COMMON MECHANISMS OF SLEEP AND WAKING

While low-frequency stimulation of the medulla produces slow waves, high-frequency stimulation produces the waking pattern in the EEG. As mentioned previously, the thalamic reticular system also produces waking or sleeping EEG patterns, depending on the frequency of stimulation. It appears, then, that neural mechanisms of wakefulness and sleep may overlap anatomically; or they may share several structures whose mode of action is frequency-specific. It is conceivable that such "frequency modulation" might be functionally related to conditions favoring sleep or wakefulness. Thus, according to the frequency code described in Chapter 4, intense sensory stimulation would produce high-frequency impulses in the sensory pathways. As a result, the ARAS and thalamic reticular system would be bombarded with high-frequency impulses from collaterals of these sensory fibers and the cortex would be activated. On the other hand, in the absence of sensory stimulation, the slow, spontaneous discharge rates of afferent fibers might provide low-frequency stimulation of the reticular system. On the basis of the results cited above, this kind of stimulation might be expected to activate a mechanism producing slow waves and sleep.

PARADOXICAL SLEEP: NEUROPHYSIOLOGICAL MECHANISMS

Recent physiological investigations have led to a highly important discovery, which has significantly changed our conception of sleep.

There seem to be two different kinds of sleep, each with its own distinctive psychophysiological properties. The fundamental observations were made by Jouvet (1961), who recorded electrical activity in various brain structures and other physiological alterations during natural sleep in cats. He found that as the animal falls asleep, the fast waves in the EEG are replaced by spindles and later by slow waves, as described previously. The slow waves appear first in the cortex and then successively in the diencephalon and midbrain. Muscle activity gradually decreases during this period. Also the threshold of awakening, defined by the minimal intensity of reticular stimulation necessary for arousal, is raised. This is the slow-wave state of sleep, similar to that described in humans.

Quite suddenly, however, the slow waves are interrupted by fast waves, like those seen in the state of wakefulness (see Figure 6.8A). Since the cat remains asleep when these fast waves appear, this state is referred to as paradoxical sleep. During paradoxical sleep distinctive physiological changes occur. Skeletal muscles become completely inhibited, respiration becomes irregular, and rapid movements of the eyes are recorded from electrodes placed over the eye muscles. In addition, during paradoxical sleep the threshold of arousal to external or reticular stimulation is increased 200 to 300 percent compared to the threshold of arousal obtained during slow-wave sleep. Here, then, is another paradoxical aspect to paradoxical sleep: The cortex shows fast waves as in arousal but it is difficult to arouse the animal, more difficult, in fact, than in any other stage of the sleep-wakefulness cycle. The paradoxical phase of sleep in cats lasts ten to fifteen minutes, and it recurs regularly at twenty- to thirty-minute intervals throughout sleep.

Jouvet also has provided evidence that the two states of sleep (slow-wave sleep and paradoxical sleep) depend on different neural structures. After the cerebral cortex is completely removed, cats still show cyclical alterations in sleep and wakefulness. However, when they sleep, they never show slow waves in subcortical structures (see Figure 6.8B). Rather, their sleep is entirely paradoxical sleep, including the EEG and physiological signs seen in normal animals. It would appear, therefore, that the cerebral cortex (as well as structures in the medulla) is necessary for the slow-wave stage of sleep but not for the paradoxical stage.

The paradoxical stage of sleep seems to depend on structures in the reticular formation of the pons. This conclusion is suggested by the following observations of Jouvet. Paradoxical sleep (defined by the respiratory and muscular changes described above) is normal in cats deprived of the cortex and even in those in which the brain has been transected at the level of the midbrain. However, if the brain stem is transected in the posterior part of the pons, there are no signs of paradoxical sleep. Furthermore, if the reticular portion of the pons is

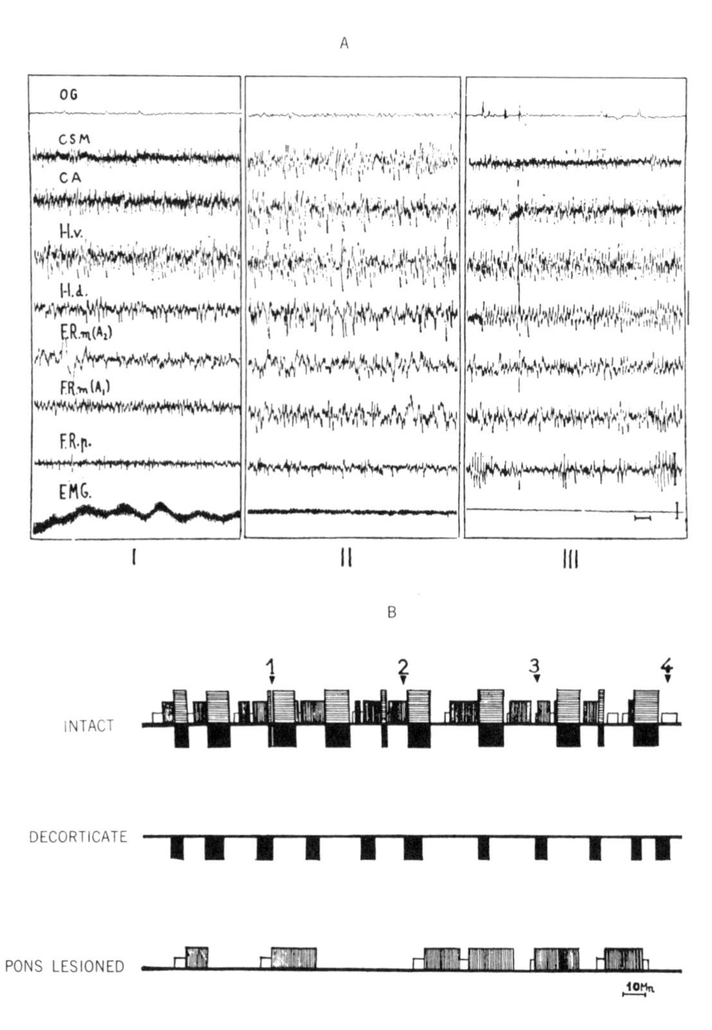

Figure 6.8

(A) *The two phases of sleep in cat.* (I: *arousal;* II: *slow wave sleep;* III: *paradoxical sleep.*) *Note rapid eye movements* (OG), *the low voltage desynchronized pattern in motor* (CSM) *and auditory cortex* (CA), *as well as synchronous waves in the hippocampus* (H.v. *and* H.d.) *and total disappearance of muscular activity* (EMG) *during paradoxical sleep.* (F.R.m. (A_2) *and* F.R.m. (A_1): *mesencephalic reticular formation;* F.R.p.: *pontile reticular formation. Vertical marker: 50 microvolts; horizontal marker: 1 sec.*) *From Jouvet, M., Telencephalic and rhombencephalic sleep in the cat, Figure 1, page 192. In G. Wolstenholme and C. M. O'Connor (Eds.),* The nature of sleep. *Boston: Little, Brown, 1961.* **(B)** *The effects of brain* selectively destroyed, the cat never shows paradoxical sleep but only slow-wave sleep (see Figure 6.8B). Recent experiments of Jouvet indicate that the region of the pons initiating paradoxical sleep is sharply demarcated, and divided into separate subregions mediating EEG activation and muscular inhibition (Jouvet, 1967). Jouvet has also demonstrated that paradoxical sleep, including EEG activation, can be triggered by stimulating this same region of the pontile reticular formation during slow-wave sleep. This fact suggests that paradoxical sleep, like slow-wave sleep, is an active phenomenon. The neural pathways over which the pontile paradoxical sleep mechanism activates the cortex have not yet been determined.

The rhythmic recurrence of paradoxical sleep suggests that it may be mediated by a neurochemical mechanism—that is, it is possible that during sleep a chemical substance may increase in quantity until it is sufficient to excite the neural system mediating paradoxical sleep. Somehow the discharge of the paradoxical sleep mechanism would deplete the substance. In support of this hypothesis is Jouvet's observation that once paradoxical sleep is triggered by electrical stimulation of the pons, the effect cannot be repeated for fifteen to thirty minutes. This suggests that a chemical substance, once depleted, requires time to accumulate again. Recently, a number of attempts have been made to identify chemical substances which induce paradoxical sleep and slow-wave sleep (Hernández-Péon, 1965; Jouvet, 1965). These studies, too detailed to describe here, have not disclosed the nature of the chemical substance triggering paradoxical sleep, but they have identified several substances which may be involved in sleep regulation.

PARADOXICAL SLEEP AND DREAMING

The studies of paradoxical sleep described above have, for the most part, used cats as subjects. A similar phase of sleep has also been discovered in humans, who show periods of increase in EEG frequency and rapid eye movements regularly throughout the night (Aserinksky and Kleitman, 1955a). Moreover, Dement and Kleitman (1957a) have made

---

lesions on the sleep-waking cycle in cats. (The black bars denote periods of paradoxical sleep; horizontal hatching: desynchronized cortical EEG in normal cats; white bars: spindling activity in cortex; vertical hatching: slow wave sleep; horizontal line: arousal.) Note that following pontile lesions, the cat shows slow-wave sleep and spindling but not paradoxical sleep, whereas the reverse is found following decortication. From Jouvet, M., Telencephalic and rhombencephalic sleep in the cat, Figure 2, page 193. In G. Wolstenholme and C. M. O'Connor *(Eds.),* The nature of sleep. *Boston: Little, Brown, 1961.*

the intriguing observation that dreaming takes place during this phase of sleep. When subjects are awakened during the paradoxical phase of sleep, on many occasions they report dreaming. Only very rarely are dreams reported when subjects are awakened during the slow-wave stage of sleep. Furthermore, the frequency and pattern of eye-movement activity seems to be closely correlated with the content of dreams. In eventful dreams, in which much activity is reported, a high frequency of eye movements is recorded. But in uneventful dreams, containing little activity, little eye-movement activity is recorded (Dement and Kleitman, 1957b). Dement (1965) has even reported a subject who, while sleeping, showed a succession of five lateral sweeps of the eyes, each followed by an upward movement. When awakened, the subject reported watching someone ascending five steps of a stairway!

Dement (1960) has also provided evidence for a need to dream. He partially deprived subjects of dreaming on several nights by awakening them when electrical recordings showed that they were dreaming. Subsequently, on a recovery night on which they were allowed uninterrupted sleep, the subjects showed a greater frequency of dreaming than they had prior to dream deprivation. Dream deprivation also proved to have an effect on personality: irritability, restlessness, and even psychotic-like behavior are found following several nights of dream deprivation in normal adult subjects. These effects, including the increase in dreaming, are not simply due to being awakened frequently during the night; when subjects are awakened during the slow-wave stage of sleep, they do not show these changes.

It would appear, then, that the dreaming state of sleep resembles such biological drives as hunger and thirst, which are typically enhanced following deprivation. Moreover, dreaming, like drive activities, follows a cyclical course. Dreaming is an active process, involving the excitatory action of a neural mechanism and producing activation of the brain. In fact, paradoxical sleep is accompanied by as much neuronal activity as is found in a state of wakefulness (Evarts, 1962).

Furthermore, the dreaming phase of sleep, as Jouvet's research suggests, is dependent upon a phylogenetically old portion of the brain that is common to all mammalian species. This anatomical fact points to the biologically primitive nature of this state of sleep.

THEORIES OF SLEEP

If the dreaming phase of sleep does represent the operation of a basic biological process, then one might ask what functions does it fulfill? According to psychoanalytic theory, dreams act as a kind of "safety valve"—that is, they allow drives and impulses that are checked and denied expression in waking life to discharge internally during sleep. Recently, Dement and his colleagues have offered a somewhat different interpretation of dreaming (Roffwarg, Muzio, and Dement, 1966). They present evidence from several sources, that paradoxical sleep constitutes approximately one-half of total sleep in the fetal stage and in newborn infants. As age increases, paradoxical sleep decreases proportionately to total sleep time. By providing large amounts of stimulation to the brain during the early period in life, the paradoxical stage of sleep might facilitate the structural maturation of the brain at a time when its rate of growth is maximum.

But why, then, does paradoxical sleep continue throughout life, long after neural maturation is complete? Is it merely a holdover from an earlier stage of development, or does it actually play some role in the mature organism? A possible clue to the functions of paradoxical sleep is the strong activation of the cortical EEG, resembling arousal, which accompanies this state of sleep. Conceivably, paradoxical sleep mechanisms might provide internal stimulation necessary for the maintenance of normal neural functioning during adult sleep, when external stimulation does not readily activate the brain.

We are also left with the question of the role of non-dreaming (slow-wave) sleep. It has been assumed that sleep contributes to energy conservation and the restoration of body functions. However, it is questionable whether sleep is necessary for the restoration of many body functions; for decrease in body activity also takes place when we lie down and quietly relax. Thus, sleep in itself may not be essential for conserving energy, especially since prolonged sleep deprivation apparently produces only minor effects on body processes. On the other hand, the performance of skilled acts and problem solving deteriorates considerably in prolonged sleep deprivation (Murray, 1965).

These facts suggest that it is the brain rather than the peripheral organs and tissues that requires sleep. This need may arise because the brain is constantly active during the waking hours—processing and storing information and regulating the musculature. Slow-wave sleep, then, might be considered a state which the brain actively initiates (by means of the neural mechanisms described previously) in order to protect itself against the exhaustion of neural processes.

SUGGESTED READINGS

Brazier, M. A. B. The analysis of brain waves. *Sci. Amer.*, June 1962.
French, J. D. The reticular formation. *Sci. Amer.*, May 1957.
Hernández-Péon, R. Reticular mechanisms of sensory control. In W. Rosenblith (Ed.), *Sensory communication.* New York: Wiley, 1961, 495–520.
Jouvet, M. The states of sleep. *Sci. Amer.*, February 1967.
Kleitman, N. Sleep. *Sci. Amer.*, November 1952.
_______. Patterns of dreaming. *Sci. Amer.*, November 1960.

Oswald, I. *Sleeping and waking: Physiology and psychology.* Amsterdam: Elsevier, 1962.
Walter, W. G. The electrical activity of the brain. *Sci. Amer.*, June 1954.
———. *The living brain.* New York: Norton, 1963.

NEURAL MECHANISMS OF INTERNAL REGULATION, EMOTION, AND MOTIVATION

7

Up to this point we have been concerned primarily with neural mechanisms which regulate the organism's adaptation to the external environment. Of even more vital concern to the organism is the regulation of the body's vegetative functions. These functions are necessary for the normal metabolic processes which take place in the body's cells, including the breakdown of foodstuffs and their utilization as fuel in the manufacture of cellular constituents. For these metabolic processes to be carried out, food must first be ingested into the digestive tract and broken down into components which are transported by the blood stream to the body's cells. Cellular metabolism also requires oxygen, which is present in only small amounts within the body. Thus, oxygen must be continuously brought into the blood stream by respiratory mechanisms and pumped through the body by the heart. Water is also necessary for metabolic processes to take place. Internal stores of water must be prevented from escaping through the kidneys, and water must be ingested to compensate for dehydration incurred through evaporation. Finally, metabolic processes are critically dependent upon the maintenance of a constant body temperature.

HOMEOSTATIC MECHANISMS

The vegetative functions described above are regulated by homeostatic mechanisms. A homeostatic mechanism is one which reacts to alterations in a particular body state in such a way that it keeps this state within physiologically normal limits. Homeostasis, then, is a kind of self-regulation, and this self-regulation is accomplished by the processes described in Chapter 2 in the section entitled Stages of Neural Control. One of these processes is stimulus detection, achieved by receptors which are sensitive to shifts in a particular body state away from its normal value. Homeostatic mechanisms also involve effectors, which respond to the sensory signals by producing an appropriate change in the body state—that is, a shift back toward its normal condition. The change in state produced by effectors then feeds back on the sensory cells so that their signals to the effectors are decreased or stopped. As we shall see in this chapter, the sensory and sensory-motor coupling features of homeostatic mechanisms involve the CNS.

THE ENDOCRINES AND INTERNAL REGULATION

The endocrines are internal glands that secrete substances called hormones into the blood stream. Circulating through the body, these hormones exert powerful effects on many internal organs, and contribute to homeostatic regulation. Many internal processes, such as those involved in water balance, internal reactions to stress, and sexual functions, are regulated by hormonal action. Some endocrines (such as the adrenals and the pituitary) are under the control of the CNS. In addition, many endocrines are themselves controlled by another endocrine organ, the pituitary. This tiny gland, located near the base of the brain, secretes hormones which play vital roles in the regulation of a number of endocrines. For this reason, the pituitary is often referred to as the "master gland" of the body.

NEURAL MECHANISMS OF HOMEOSTASIS

The part of the nervous system most directly involved in homeostasis is referred to as the autonomic nervous system (ANS). The ANS is perhaps the most primitive part of the nervous system, and, as described in the following pages, it utilizes reflex controls over peripheral effectors to achieve homeostatic balance. Many of these reflexes are mediated through circuits in the spinal cord and lower brain stem. The hypothalamus, a structure at the base of the brain, also plays a dominant role in homeostatic regulation, as we shall see in this chapter. Moreover, through the influence of a variety of forebrain structures, sensory information from the environment can modify the activity of the hypothalamus.

HOMEOSTASIS AND MOTIVATION

Homeostatic mechanisms often involve overt behavior. This is obvious in the case of food and water regulation, but other aspects of internal regulation may also involve behavior. For example, a drop in environmental temperature produces autonomic responses, such as constriction of blood vessels, which tend to conserve body heat. When the temperature drops, we may also do things that tend to preserve body heat, such as putting on additional clothing or closing windows. Whenever homeostatic regulation involves overt behavior, we speak of that behavior as being motivated. The concept of motivation then, refers to behavioral adjustments which satisfy needs of the body. Corresponding to many internal needs there is assumed to be a particular motive or drive: hunger in the case of nutritional needs, thirst in the case of dehydration, and escape from pain in the case of noxious stimulation. A drive is customarily thought of as an internal state arising from a need and provoking consummatory responses, such as eating or drinking. As we shall see in the following pages, motivated behavior seems to be mediated by the same hypothalamic mechanisms that regulate internal states. Drives can also serve as a basis for learning new responses. Any response will be strengthened if it leads to the consumption of a substance for which there is a need. For example, if the hungry rat, by pressing a lever, causes a pellet of food to be delivered, it is more likely to press the lever in the future when it is hungry.

While motivated behavior may be produced by homeostatic imbalance, all motives may not be necessarily produced in this way. For, if we define motives behaviorally, in terms of persistent, goal-directed behavior, then we must admit that many motives are not apparently due to tissue needs. These include sexual behavior, exploratory behavior, and a variety of social behaviors. Animals and humans persist in these behaviors even though the goals sought do not appear to reduce any drive state. As we shall see in the following pages, some of these "nonhomeostatic" behaviors may involve the hypothalamus as well as other brain structures.

EMOTION

Of all psychological terms, emotion is perhaps the most difficult to define and analyze. Moreover, the term is used in several different ways and has multiple meanings. The one which is most familiar refers to the experience of emotion—emotion as a "state of mind." Feelings such as sadness, joy, hate, and fear are each unique experiences which we can readily identify but which are difficult to describe and analyze.

Another aspect of emotion has to do with autonomic responses, such as changes in heart rate, blood flow, respiration and sweating—all mediated by the ANS. While autonomic responses accompany emotional experiences, there is no evidence that a particular kind of autonomic activity corresponds to each kind of emotional experience. However, in many instances, these autonomic responses do have adaptive value, especially when emotional behavior comes into play.

Overt behavior constitutes another aspect of emotion: Aggression is marked by snarling and attacking; fear, by withdrawal or submission; joy, by exuberance and playfulness. A fundamental feature of emotional reactions like these is that they are directed toward environmental situations or events. When we say that an individual is aggressive, we mean that he has a characteristic way of dealing with his environment. The term emotion, then, refers to certain ways of reacting to the environment. Emotion, it may be noted, is similar to the concept of motivation, described in the previous section, in that both refer to goal-directed behavior. Furthermore, at least some kinds of emotional reactions, like motivated behaviors, are adaptive to external situations. By fleeing, the organism removes itself from a threatening event, such as the presence of a predator, with which it cannot cope in any other way. Aggression and attack offer another possible solution to a threatening situation. And, as we shall see in the following section, the autonomic reactions which accompany emotional states are also adaptive in that they prepare the organism for performing overt reactions such as attacking or fleeing. We shall also see that the hypothalamus provides the mechanisms for integrating autonomic and overt responses into patterns of emotional reactions.

The term emotion refers not only to ways of reacting to the environment, but also to ways of perceiving the environment. Our emotions, we say, "color our view of the world." When we are sad, things appear gloomy; when we are apprehensive or fearful, things may appear threatening or dangerous. In other words, there is an evaluative aspect to emotions. Toward the end of this chapter we shall present evidence that the limbic structures of the forebrain are critically involved in this evaluative aspect of emotion.

THE ANS AND INTERNAL REGULATION

As shown in Figure 7.1, the efferent fibers of the autonomic nervous system arise from cells in the spinal cord and in the motor nuclei of the brain stem. These fibers (with the exception of those that directly innervate the adrenals) synapse upon neurons located in ganglia outside the CNS. These neurons, referred to as postganglionic neurons, in turn innervate effector organs. The ANS is actually composed of two different divisions—referred to as the sympathetic and parasympathetic (see Figure 7.1). These divisions differ in their anatomical organization as well as in the manner in which they control effector organs.

THE SYMPATHETIC DIVISION OF THE ANS

The sympathetic division is responsible for bodily reactions to stressful or threatening situations. It involves homeostatic mechanisms that make available the body's reserves of energy for the exertion of effort and for emotional responses. The autonomic effects of sympathetic activity are diffuse and persist for a long time following the termination of the stimulus. These features of sympathetic activation are accomplished in the following manner.

To cope with emergency situations, the sympathetic system produces an increase in heart rate and respiration. The bronchioles of the lungs are dilated so that more oxygen is brought into the blood stream. Furthermore, blood flow to the muscles and brain is increased, so that these organs can function more effectively. Moreover, bodily processes which do not contribute to preparedness for action, such as digestive and eliminative processes, are inhibited by sympathetic activity.

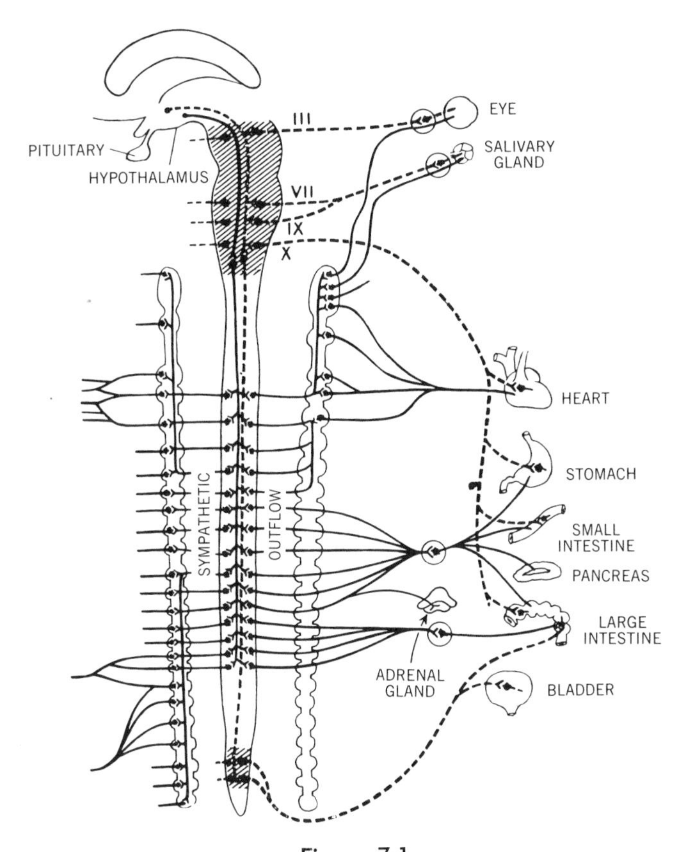

Figure 7.1

The autonomic nervous system (ANS), showing sympathetic outflow through the spinal cord (solid lines), and parasympathetic outflow (shaded area and broken lines) through cranial nerves and through the lowest division of the spinal cord. Some of the organs innervated by the ANS are also shown. From Gardner E., Fundamentals of neurology, *5th ed., Figure 130. Philadelphia: Saunders, 1968.*

These bodily reactions tend to occur together in a diffuse pattern, in part because of the diffuse synaptic connections in the sympathetic ganglia. The widespread nature of sympathetic discharge is also due to activation of the adrenals. As seen in Figure 7.1, these endocrine glands are directly innervated by sympathetic fibers which trigger the release of epinephrine into the blood stream. Epinephrine is a hormone that mimics many of the effects of norepinephrine, the primary chemical transmitter substance at sympathetic synapses with effector organs. Thus, epinephrine circulating in the blood stream augments sympathetic reactions and causes them to persist.

Many of the sympathetic reactions described above are part of reflex circuits involving autonomic afferent fibers which innervate many of the tissues and organs shown in Figure 7.1. Through these autonomic reflexes, homeostatic balance is achieved. For example, accumulation of carbon dioxide in the blood stimulates receptors in arteries leading from the heart. These receptors make reflex connections with centers in the brain stem which in turn produce increased respiration through sympathetic efferents so that carbon dioxide is decreased and oxygen increased.

THE PARASYMPATHETIC DIVISION OF THE ANS

Parasympathetic fibers originate from cells in brain-stem nuclei and from cells in the lowest division of the spinal cord. As seen in Figure 7.1, these fibers synapse in peripheral ganglia on neurons which innervate many of the same organs innervated by the sympathetic division. However, parasympathetic effects on body organs are as a rule quite different from sympathetic effects. The kinds of homeostatic reactions mediated by this system tend to promote the conservation and restoration of the body's energy stores. Thus, parasympathetic activation facilitates digestive processes and the elimination of waste products. Internal reactions involved in the exertion of effort are inhibited: Heart rate and respiration are decreased and the bronchioles of the lungs are constricted.

It will be noted that many of these parasympathetic effects are opposed to those exerted by the sympathetic system. It is not surprising, then, that the parasympathetic system utilizes a different chemical transmitter substance at its synapses with effector organs. This substance is acetylcholine, the same substance which is released at synapses of somatic fibers with skeletal muscles.

HYPOTHALAMIC CONTROL OF MOTIVATIONAL PROCESSES

TEMPERATURE REGULATION

The neural control of body temperature provides a good example of a homeostatic mechanism involving reactions the effects of which feed back on receptors so that self-regulation is achieved. The mechanisms regulating body temperature are in principle analagous to the common home thermostat. However, the body's temperature regulating mechanism is much more complex than this device, for it involves different kinds of sensory devices and several kinds of responses integrated to achieve a remarkable degree of temperature constancy.

Some years ago, Magoun and his colleagues (Magoun, Harrison, Brobeck, and Ranson, 1938) performed an experiment which implicated the hypothalamus in temperature regulation. In this experiment a thermal probe, which produces local heating, was slowly lowered through the brains of anesthetised cats. As long as the thermal probe was in the cortex or the thalamus, no effects were observed; however, as soon as it reached the anterior part of the hypothalamus, the cats began to pant and sweat. This finding implies that the hypothalamus regulates those reflex responses which produce heat loss when the body temperature rises too high. It also suggests that the anterior hypothalamus contains receptors sensitive to increases in temperature. Prior to this finding, it had been assumed that only peripheral receptors are involved in temperature regulation. More recent evidence for central thermal receptors is provided by the finding that heating the anterior hypothalamus causes neurons in this region to discharge impulses (Nakayama, Hammel, Hardy, and Eisenman, 1963). Presumably, under normal circumstances, excessive body heat is communicated to cells in this region by the temperature of the blood stream. Following destruction of the anterior hypothalamus, animals cannot regulate their temperature in a warm environment, as shown in Figure 7.2A (Keller,

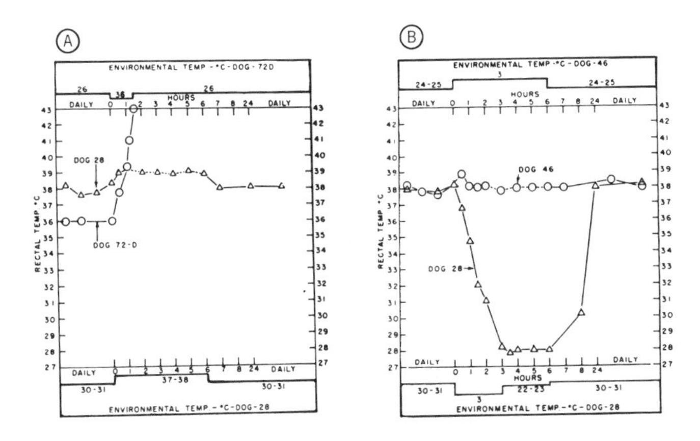

Figure 7.2

Effects of hypothalamic lesions on temperature regulation in dogs. **(A)** *In a warm environment, the dog with posterior hypothalamic lesions* (28) *shows temperature control, whereas the body temperature of the dog with rostral hypothalamic lesions rises. Broken line indicates panting.* **(B)** *In a cold environment, the intact dog* (46) *shows normal temperature regulation accompanied by shivering (broken line), whereas the body temperature of the dog with posterior hypothalamic lesions drops precipitously. From Keller, A. D., The role of circulation in the physiology of heat regulation, Figure 3, page 513.* Phys. Therap. Rev., *1950,* 30, *511–519.*

1950). However, they have no difficulty in maintaining normal body temperature in a cold environment. It appears that another region, in the posterior hypothalamus, is responsible for heat production in cold environments. Following selective destruction of this region, animals fail to show the adequate reflex responses, such as shivering and constriction of peripheral vessels, to cold (Keller, 1950). Consequently, as shown in Figure 7.2B, their body temperature drops.

Through separate homeostatic mechanisms, then, the hypothalamus senses deviations from normal body temperature and throws into action reflex responses which restore normal temperature. It should be noted that many of these reflex responses are mediated by the lower brain stem and spinal cord. However, each of these reflexes involves only local body reactions. The hypothalamus, through its efferent fibers to these reflex mechanisms, integrates them into patterns of reactions so that temperature control of the entire body is achieved.

Behavioral control of body temperature has also been studied experimentally by placing a rat in a cold chamber and allowing it to turn on a heat-producing lamp briefly whenever it presses a lever. In this situation, the rat will learn to press the lever and persists in this behavior as long as the temperature of the chamber is low (Carlisle, 1966a). If the hypothalamus of the rat is cooled, it will continue to press the lever and produce heat, even though the chamber is kept at normal room temperature (Satinoff, 1964). Conversely, if the hypothalamus is heated, the rat stops lever pressing, even when the temperature of the chamber is low (Carlisle, 1966b). Thus, it appears that activation of hypothalamic thermal receptors can control learned responses, even when the information from these receptors is inconsistent with information from peripheral receptors.

WATER BALANCE

There are two aspects to the problem of regulating the body's water supply. First, large amounts of water are passed daily through the kidneys as they filter urea from the blood stream. Thus mechanisms for preventing excessive water loss through the kidneys must be brought into play. Secondly, water is lost through the skin and lungs as a result of normal body activities. In order to compensate for these losses there must be mechanisms for regulating water intake.

Excessive loss of water through the kidneys is prevented in part by the action of a hormone known as the antidiuretic hormone, or ADH. ADH is secreted into the blood stream from the posterior portion of the pituitary, and it acts on the tubules of the kidneys so that they pump water back into the blood stream before it escapes to the bladder (see Figure 7.3). It appears that cells in the hypothalamus manufacture ADH, which then passes down nerve fibers into the posterior pituitary

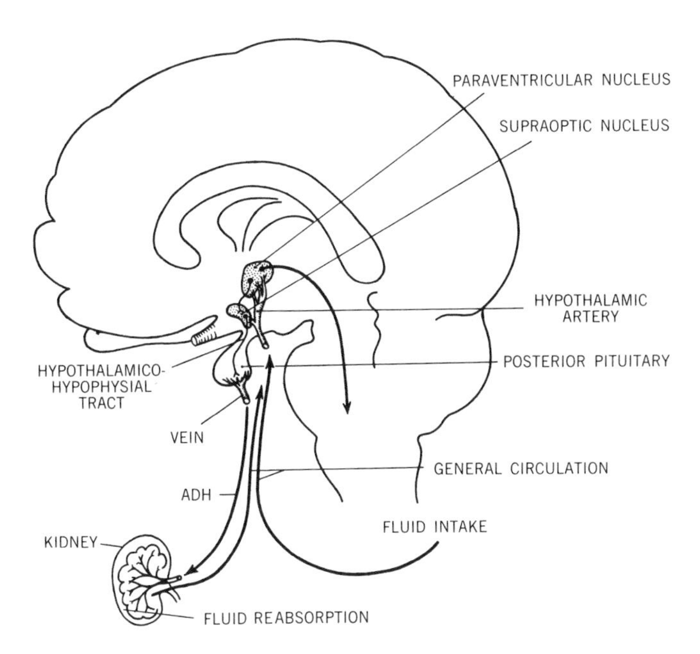

Figure 7.3

Control of water balance. It is thought that ADH is produced by cells of the supraoptic and paraventricular nuclei and then transported to the pituitary. These nuclei may also contain osmoreceptors which receive information concerning amount of water in the blood from arteries. (See text for explanation of other aspects of figure.) From House, E. L., and Pansky, B., A functional approach to neuroanatomy, *Figure 21-13, page 380. New York: McGraw-Hill, 1960.*

where it is absorbed into blood vessels (see Figure 7.3). Damage to these hypothalamic cells or to the fiber pathway to the pituitary leads to diabetes insipidus, a condition in which abnormally large amounts of water are continuously lost through the kidneys.

The amount of ADH secretion is precisely regulated by homeostatic mechanisms so that water loss is prevented when the body is dehydrated, and water is allowed to escape through the kidneys when there is surplus water in the body. In order to regulate water balance effectively, the hypothalamus must be informed about the amount of water in the body. One way in which this may be accomplished is by cells in the CNS that are sensitive to the amount of water in the blood —that is, the degree to which the blood is concentrated or diluted. Since the amount of water in the blood affects the osmotic pressure across cell membranes, it is possible that the detection of water concentration may be accomplished by osmoreceptors, specialized cells sensitive to osmotic pressure. The presence of such receptors in the brain is suggested by the finding that injection into the brain's blood supply of hypertonic saline (saline that has higher salt concentration than does normal blood) increases ADH secretion. Conversely, following injection of hypotonic saline (saline that has lower salt concentration than does normal blood) ADH secretion decreases (Verney, 1947).

The hypothalamus is involved in water intake as well as in the regulation of water loss through the kidneys. Electrical stimulation of the hypothalamus causes animals to drink copious amounts of water (Andersson and McCann, 1955). Further, injections of hypertonic saline directly into the hypothalamus produces drinking (Andersson, 1953), while injection into the hypothalamus of hypotonic saline causes dehydrated animals to stop drinking (Miller, 1961). Thus, hypothalamic control of drinking, like the control of ADH secretion, is apparently regulated by osmoreceptors located in the hypothalamus itself. As is the case with temperature regulation, the hypothalamus exerts its effects on drinking through efferent projections to lower reflex centers controlling movements of the mouth and throat (see Figure 7.3).

Hypothalamic stimulation also elicits responses which have been learned in order to relieve thirst, as the following experiment demonstrates. Andersson and Wyrwicka (1957) first trained goats to place their foreleg on a step in order to obtain water when they were thirsty. After the goats had learned to perform this response regularly, electrodes were implanted in the hypothalamus. The goats were then returned to the experimental situation, this time no longer thirsty, so that they did not perform the learned response. However, as soon as the hypothalamus was electrically stimulated, they performed the learned response and drank water. Thus, activation of hypothalamic drinking mechanisms causes thirst motivation which can serve as a basis for learned responses.

While osmoreceptors in the hypothalamus may control drinking, the hypothalamus might use other, peripheral sources of information to regulate water intake. In fact, some events prior to the ingestion of water, such as sensory messages from the mouth or throat or sensory feedback from the act of drinking, probably do play a role in regulating water intake. This view is suggested by the findings of Adolph (1939), who studied drinking in dogs with esophageal fistulas. That is, he surgically opened the esophagus and attached to one end a tube which led outside of the neck, so that whenever the dog drank, the fluids passed outside and none entered the stomach. Adolph found that these dogs, like normal dogs, drank just enough water to compensate for water losses incurred through dehydration. Apparently, then, both hypothalamic and peripheral receptors are involved in water intake.

HYPOTHALAMIC REGULATION OF FEEDING

Compared to temperature and water regulation, the control of food intake is more complex and involves a variety of factors, for feeding is influenced not only by metabolic needs, but also by taste, odor, the variety of foods available, and learned preferences. The problem of how all these factors influence the CNS control of eating is far from settled, although considerable research has been performed in attempts to understand these mechanisms.

As is the case with temperature and water regulation, the hypothalamus is critically involved in the regulation of food intake. Over 20 years ago, Hetherington and Ranson (1940) found that following damage to the medial hypothalamus, rats consume abnormally large amounts of food and become obese (see Figure 7.4). Apparently, this alteration in feeding is due to a breakdown in the regulation of food intake relative to metabolic needs. Moreover, when an inert substance is added to their diet, normal rats compensate for this change by increasing the total volume they consume. Rats with medial hypothalamic damage, on the other hand, consume less of this mixture compared to their normal, unadulterated diet (Teitelbaum, 1955). It seems, then, that the food intake of the operated rat is determined mainly by what it likes and dislikes (i.e., taste quality), and not by what it needs, for the adulterated diet is less palatable than the normal diet is. Furthermore, while rats with medial hypothalamic lesions take meals no more frequently than normal rats do, the length of their meals is abnormally long (Teitelbaum and Campbell, 1958). What is disrupted in these rats, then, is some mechanism for stopping eating which is normally triggered when satiation occurs. Apparently, this mechanism can be activated by direct electrical stimulation of the medial hypothalamus, which causes animals to cease eating (Smith, 1965b).

The lateral portion of the hypothalamus seems to influence eating in a manner opposite to that of the medial hypothalamus (see Figure 7.4). When this region is destroyed, the food intake of rats markedly decreases and they may cease eating (Anand and Brobeck, 1951). As is the case with the medial lesion, the rat's consumption of food is determined mainly by taste and not by nutritional needs, for the rat with a lateral hypothalamic lesion will often eat highly preferred substances, such as chocolate, while refusing its regular diet (Teitelbaum and Epstein, 1962). Furthermore, electrical stimulation of the lateral hypothalamus elicits eating (Hoebel and Teitelbaum, 1962) and also elicits responses previously learned in order to obtain food rewards (Miller, 1961). Thus, the lateral hypothalamus seems to participate in a hunger mechanism which can motivate the performance of learned behaviors. Furthermore, it has been shown that electrical stimulation of the lateral hypothalamus also causes cats to stalk and attack rats in a typical

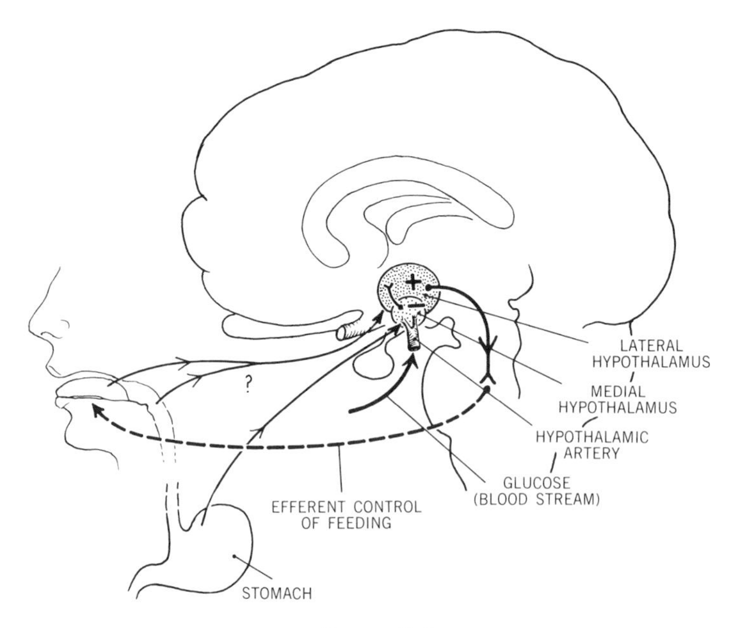

Figure 7.4

Control of food intake. The question mark accompanying arrows from mouth and stomach refers to questionable afferent routes by which these structures regulate feeding. (See text for explanation of figure.)

feline manner (Wasman and Flynn, 1962). Thus, it appears that mechanisms controlling aggression are anatomically related to those controlling feeding, a relationship which is appropriate for a carnivorous animal that obtains food by preying on other animals.

Like the regulatory mechanisms described previously, the mechanism of food regulation seems to involve hypothalamic receptors. These receptors may be sensitive to glucose (a major source of energy for cellular metabolism) circulating in the blood stream (Mayer, 1953). Following administration of glucose in dogs, neurons in the medial hypothalamus increase their rate of impulse discharge, whereas neurons in the lateral hypothalamus decrease their rates of impulse discharge (Anand, Chhina, and Singh, 1962).

These findings are consistent with the following kind of homeostatic mechanism for regulating food intake. When the concentration of glucose in the blood stream is high, glucose-sensitive cells in the medial hypothalamus become active and suppress neuronal discharges in the lateral hypothalamus. As a consequence, the excitatory influences of the lateral hypothalamus on feeding reflexes are reduced, and the animal stops eating. When glucose concentration in the blood stream becomes low (because the animal has not eaten for some time or has expended energy) glucose-sensitive neurons in the medial hypothalamus become less active. Consequently, their suppression of the lateral hypothalamus is lessened, and this structure now exerts its excitatory influences on feeding behaviors (see Figure 7.4).

However, the regulation of food intake probably involves other factors, such as the sensory events accompanying eating (sensations arising from the mouth or stomach or from eating movements) (see Figure 7.4). In fact, it has been shown that "sham feeding" in dogs (achieved by an esophageal fistula) inhibits subsequent eating for a period of time, although not as long as real feeding does (Janowitz and Grossman, 1949).

SEXUAL FUNCTIONS

Sexual activities, unlike those considered so far, do not supply substances vital for normal functions of the body. Furthermore, compared to other drives, sexual activities are more closely controlled by hormonal action. There is a good deal of evidence that these hormonal effects are regulated by the brain. Conversely, brain mechanisms regulating sexual behavior are influenced by hormonal activity. Thus, the regulation of sexual functions involves complex interactions between neural and hormonal factors—interactions which at present are only poorly understood.

The activities of the sexual organs, or gonads, are controlled by hormonal secretions of the anterior pituitary, the so called gonadotrophic hormones (see Figure 7.5). The production of these gonadotrophic hormones is controlled by the hypothalamus. It appears that the hypothalamus manufactures substances which are carried to the anterior pituitary by a system of vessels and there stimulate glandular cells to secrete gonadotrophic hormones as shown in Figure 7.5. While the properties of these hypothalamic substances are unknown, it is thought that a region in the posterior hypothalamus is involved in gonadotrophic regulation, for destruction of this region blocks the release of gonadotrophins, and electrical stimulation in this region induces ovulation normally induced by gonadotrophic hormones (Sawyer and Kawakami, 1961).

In the female, the gonadotrophins trigger a complex chain of reactions involving the production of gonadal hormones by the ovaries and leading to ovulation (see Figure 7.5). These hormones (estrogen and progesterone) stimulate the growth and development of the sexual organs and prepare the uterus for the ovum. Estrogen, as well as the male sex hormone, plays an important role in regulating sexual behavior, as shown by the findings that these substances restore sexual activity in castrated animals (Beach, 1948). Moreover, the gonadal hormones seem to produce their behavioral effects by acting on the hypothalamus. Following lesions in one portion of the hypothalamus, female cats no longer show sexual behavior, even though their anterior pituitary-gonadal system remains normal (Sawyer, 1960). Furthermore, cats in which the ovaries have been removed so that they are no longer sexually receptive toward males do become sexually receptive when estrogen is directly injected into the hypothalamus (Harris, Michael, and Scott, 1958). Apparently certain parts of the hypothalamus are specifically involved in the integration of sexual behavior patterns.

It appears, then, that the hypothalamus contains separate mechanisms for the hormonal regulation of the sex organs and for the control of sexual behavior. However, through feedback systems, these two mechanisms are coordinated (see Figure 7.5). The triggering of gonadotrophic hormones by the hypothalamus stimulates the production of gonadal hormones, which, in turn, act back on the hypothalamus to activate sexual behavior patterns. This complex system also includes negative feedback circuits which regulate the production of hormones. As the level of gonadal hormones in the blood rises, the further production of gonadotrophins is suppressed (Sawyer, 1960). Apparently, the

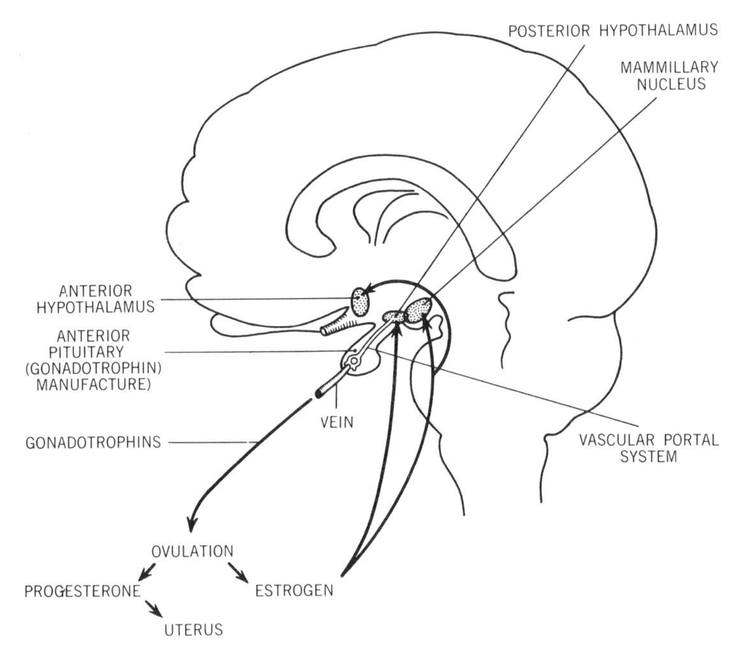

Figure 7.5

Control of sexual functions, including hypothalamic regions that are thought to be involved in the manufacture of gonadotrophic hormones and in the control of sexual behavior.

hypothalamus is involved in this self-regulatory circuit, for estrogen injected into the hypothalamus stops ovulation (Davidson and Sawyer, 1961).

Female sexual behavior, especially in lower mammals, such as rats, is directly under the control of gonadal hormones. On the other hand, the sexual behavior of males depends less on hormones and more on sensory information and past experience. Castration (which leads to a loss of male sex hormones) reduces but does not completely abolish sexual activity in adult male rats (Beach, 1948). Furthermore, while cortical damage leaves female sexual behavior relatively unaffected, it seriously disrupts male sexual behavior (Beach, 1940). More recent findings suggest that the cerebral cortex is involved both in the arousal of sexual activity and in the guidance of copulatory behavior in male rats (Larsson, 1964).

HYPOTHALAMIC CONTROL OF OTHER PITUITARY HORMONES

The hypothalamus also controls the production of several other pituitary hormones. For example, oxytoxin controls lactation and the ejection of milk from the mammary glands. Other pituitary hormones, such as the adrenocorticotrophic hormone (ACTH), indirectly control a variety of effector organs. ACTH activates the production of adrenocortical hormones which prepare the body's organs for stressful situations.

SELF-STIMULATION

In many of the experiments described above, hypothalamic functions were investigated by electrically stimulating this structure in anesthetized animals. If, however, the awake animal is permitted to control stimulation of its hypothalamus by performing some response, a surprising result is obtained: the animal persists in this behavior for long periods of time. Electrical stimulation of the hypothalamus, then, seems to act as external rewards do. Indeed, in some hypothalamic regions, stimulation is even more potent than external rewards; animals will prefer working for this stimulation to working for food, and they will self-stimulate until exhausted (Olds, 1962). While the lateral hypothalamus yields the highest self-stimulation rates, there are a variety of forebrain structures which also yield self-stimulation (see Figure 7.6). In other regions of the brain, electrical stimulation has the opposite effect (see Figure 7.6). Animals refuse to self-stimulate after the first response, and they will learn to shut off the stimulation if it is initiated by the experimenter. Thus, there seems to be a neural system mediating punishment as well as one mediating reward.

The rewarding effects of hypothalamic stimulation are dependent not only upon the site of stimulation, but also upon the drive state of the animal. Frequency of self-stimulation in the lateral hypothalamus increases as the number of hours of food deprivation increases (Olds, 1962). As mentioned previously, electrical stimulation in this same region elicits eating. In fact, it has been shown that at virtually all points in lateral hypothalamus where eating is evoked by electrical stimulation, self-stimulation is also found, whereas in medial regions of the hypothalamus where self-stimulation is weak or not present, eating is not evoked (Margules and Olds, 1962). Moreover, a variety of other drive-regulated responses, such as sexual behavior, aggression and maternal care, are elicited at self-stimulation points. These various findings indicate that there is a close relationship between the rewarding value of hypothalamic stimulation and the evocation of motivational responses. This relationship suggests that what is rewarding is not the reduction of some drive, but the excitation of mechanisms which control consummatory responses. In fact, it has been shown experimentally that the performance of consummatory responses, such as copulation without ejaculation (Sheffield, Wulff, and Backer, 1951) and drinking non-nutritive saccharine solution (Sheffield and Roby, 1950), is rewarding, even though these responses do not reduce drives. That is, in these studies animals engaged in activities (such as running through a maze) to gain the opportunity to perform the consummatory responses.

THE LIMBIC SYSTEM

Among those forebrain regions that influence the hypothalamus, a set of structures referred to collectively as the limbic system play a dominant role. As Figure 3.8 (page 36) shows, these limbic structures are located in the medial and ventral portion of the forebrain, between the cerebral cortex and diencephalon, and they are connected with these regions by a number of fiber pathways. In addition, the structures which comprise the limbic system are interconnected with each other by many fiber systems, some of which are shown in Figure 3.8.

The limbic system, unlike the cerebral cortex, is quite sizeable in lower mammals and is even found in primitive vertebrates lacking a cerebral cortex. Thus these limbic structures constitute the primitive core of the forebrain. The functions of the limbic system seem to be related to the sense of smell in primitive species. While in higher vertebrates many of these limbic areas are not directly involved in olfactory processes, they seem to have retained the motivation functions in which the olfactory system participates.

Perhaps the first clues to the functions mediated by the limbic system were provided by the findings of Klüver and Bucy (1939). These investigators removed the temporal lobes of monkeys and, fol-

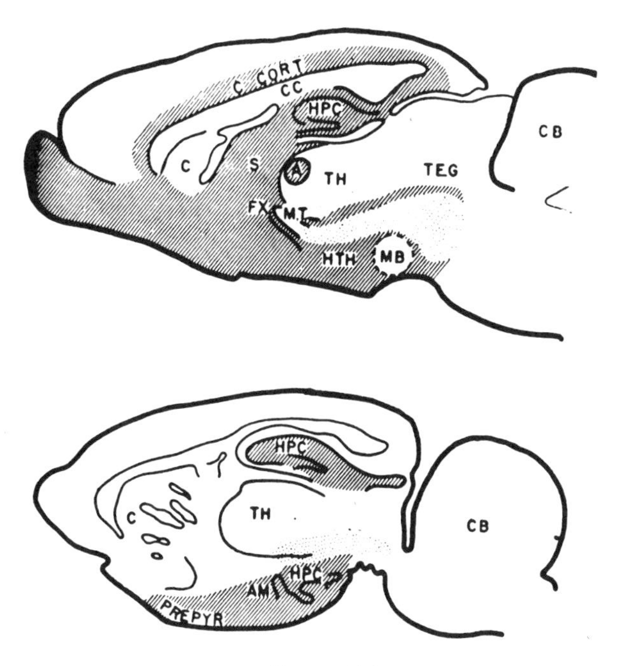

Figure 7.6

Regions of the rat brain yielding positive reinforcement (shaded areas) and those yielding punishment (stippled area). The upper figure shows the rat brain near the midline; the lower figure shows a more lateral view. (C Cort.: *Cingulate cortex;* CC: *corpus callosum;* HPC: *hippocampus;* S: *septum;* C: *anterior commissure;* TH: *thalamus;* FX: *fornix;* MT: *mammillothalamic tract;* HTH: *hypothalamus;* TEG: *tegmentum;* CB: *cerebellum;* PREPYR: *prepyriform cortex;* AM: *amygdala.) From Olds, J., Self-stimulation of the brain, Figure 19, page 324.* Science, *1958,* 127, *315–324.*

lowing surgery, observed striking and dramatic alterations in their behavior. These alterations are collectively referred to as the temporal lobe syndrome. The observed changes included increased oral behavior; following surgery, the monkeys would put non-food objects as well as food in their mouths. These animals also showed increases in sexual activity. Male monkeys would attempt to mate not only with female monkeys but also with animals of other species. Klüver and Bucy also observed emotional disturbances following temporal lobe removal. These animals no longer showed fear of objects, such as snakes or a net, that they avoided preoperatively, and they failed to show normal aggression toward other animals and humans. Subsequent research indicated that these behavioral disturbances are due primarily to removal of limbic structures in the temporal lobes (Pribram and Bagshaw, 1959), and especially the amygdala.

These behavioral disturbances seem to reflect a failure to recognize objects that are rewarding or punishing for the animal (Weiskrantz, 1956). With regard to increases in oral behavior, the operated animal seems to have lost the ability to distinguish food from non-food objects. Similarly, the increases in sexual activity may reflect a loss of the ability to distinguish appropriate from inappropriate mates. With regard to losses in fear and aggression, the monkey with limbic damage seems to be deficient in recognizing objects that are potentially harmful. For the normal monkey, the appearance of a human is usually associated with stressful events, such as being handled or restrained, that provoke fear or aggression. As a result of these experiences, the normal monkey shows emotional responses when confronted with humans. Following removal of limbic structures, the monkey seems to have lost these learned associations and acts "naïve" when faced with threatening events. It is possible that following limbic removal the animal can learn new associations and become either tame or aggressive, depending on how it is treated. Thus, tameness is customarily found in those studies in which the animal is treated postoperatively as a pet. However, when the animal is subjected to provocation and stress (Bard and Mountcastle, 1948) it becomes ferocious.

The effects of amygdala removal on social behavior in monkeys may also be interpreted in a similar manner. Much of the social behavior of rhesus monkeys is determined by a kind of dominance hierarchy, within which each monkey has its own fixed position. Following removal of the amygdala, the most dominant monkey in a group shows a dramatic drop in its social position; it goes from "boss" to "lowest man on the totem pole" (Rosvold, Mirsky, and Pribram, 1954). It is likely that this change in social position is due to a loss of learned associations between social stimuli (such as gestures and vocalizations) and the appropriate social responses. If the amygdala-lesioned monkey fails to exhibit any kind of appropriate social reaction when placed back in the social group after surgery, the other monkeys may sense its lack of responsiveness and, accordingly, dominate it. Thus, postoperatively, the monkey learns to be submissive. In order to test this notion, monkeys with amygdala lesions were placed with a group of young adolescent monkeys after surgery, rather than with the groups in which they had previously been. Since the young monkeys readily yield to domination by an older animal, this would provide the amygdala-lesioned animal the opportunity to relearn the associations involving dominance. The crucial test then involved putting the operated monkey back into the original peer group that it had been in before operation; when this was done, the operated animals did not show a drop in social position (Mirsky, 1960). Apparently, then, the relearning of dominance toward others is possible in amygdala-lesioned monkeys, if the appropriate opportunities for learning are provided.

Thus it appears that the limbic system plays an important role in relating motivational and emotional responses to environmental events —in other words, in the evaluative aspect of emotion. Furthermore, the inappropriate oral and sexual behavior seen following limbic damage suggests that these structures modulate and check motivational systems so that they are elicited only at the suitable time. A number of other findings suggest that the limbic system suppresses motivational systems. If hungry animals are first trained to run to a chamber to obtain food, they will avoid the chamber after receiving a single electric shock there. However, following removal of anterior limbic structures (McCleary, 1961) or the hippocampus (Isaacson and Wickelgren, 1962) animals are impaired in suppressing this food-directed response.

The role of the hippocampus in suppression is also discussed in the following chapter. Removal of the septum produces abnormally strong emotional behavior in animals; rats become vicious, overly aggressive, and show heightened startle responses (Brady and Nauta, 1953). These abnormal behaviors, like those described in Chapter 5, are referred to as release phenomena and imply that other brain mechanisms are operating unchecked, no longer under the modulating control of the destroyed structure. The unchecked mechanisms in the cases described here undoubtedly involve the hypothalamus, which is the major integrating structure for the expression of emotional behavior. In fact, it has been demonstrated that the attack behavior elicited by hypothalamic stimulation (see page 147) is suppressed by simultaneous stimulation of the amygdala (Egger and Flynn, 1962).

SUGGESTED READINGS

Benzinger, T. H. The human thermostat. *Sci. Amer.*, June 1961.
Fisher, A. E. Chemical stimulation of the brain. *Sci. Amer.*, June 1964.
Funkenstein, D. H. The physiology of fear and anger. *Sci. Amer.*, May 1955.
Holst, E. von, and Saint Paul, U. von. Electrically controlled behavior. *Sci. Amer.*, March 1962.
Levine, S. Sex differences in the brain. *Sci. Amer.*, April 1966.
Li, C. H. The ACTH molecule. *Sci. Amer.*, July 1963.
Miller, N. E. Central stimulation and other new approaches to motivation and reward. *Amer. Psychol.*, 1958, *13*, 100–108.
Olds, J. Pleasure centers of the brain. *Sci. Amer.*, October 1956.
Stellar, E. The physiology of motivation. *Psychol. Rev.*, 1954, *61*, 5–22.
Wurtman, R. J., and Axelrod, J. The pineal gland. *Sci. Amer.*, July 1965.

NEURAL MECHANISMS OF LEARNING AND MEMORY 8

Of all neuropsychological problems, the mechanisms underlying learning are perhaps the most difficult to understand. In part, this difficulty arises because there are various kinds of learning, each of which may involve different kinds of mechanisms. One of the most extensively investigated forms of learning is classical conditioning. An example of classical conditioning is the hungry dog that salivates at the sight of food. Salivation is an unlearned or unconditioned reflex (UCR) that is evoked by stimuli such as food in the mouth, which is referred to as an unconditioned stimulus (UCS). A stimulus, such as the sight of food, that is closely followed in time by the UCS will, after a number of such pairings, itself elicit salivation. Such a stimulus is referred to as a conditioned stimulus (CS), and a response such as salivation that is conditioned in this manner is referred to as a conditioned response (CR).

The hungry dog may also learn to sit up and beg for food. This is an example of another kind of learning referred to as instrumental learning. The response of sitting up is learned by making the presentation of the reward (food) contingent upon its occurrence; in other words, the response is instrumental in obtaining food. The termination of an aversive stimulus (such as electric shock) can also serve as a reward and strengthen an instrumental response. Furthermore, by rewarding an instrumental response only when a particular event (such as the verbal command "sit up") takes place, an animal will learn to perform the response only in the presence of this event and not to other events not correlated with reward. When the animal behaves in this manner we say that it has learned to discriminate between these stimuli, and we refer to this event as discrimination learning. Classical conditioning and instrumental learning are discussed in detail in *Conditioning and Instrumental Learning* (Walker, 1967, in this series).

There are other forms of learning about which less is known than classical conditioning and instrumental learning. One of these is the learning of motor skills, such as riding a bicycle. What is initially a series of clumsily executed responses becomes, through practice, a well-coordinated, smoothly executed act. The learning of motor skills is discussed in *Human Performance* (Fitts and Posner, 1967, in this series). Still another form of learning about which little is known is illustrated by the experience of the novice in looking through the microscope for the first time. At first the student reports a confused jumble of ill-defined masses. With more experience he begins to make out definite structures which he can identify and differentiate from other structures. Since this kind of learning seems to involve a change in the way in which something is perceived, it is referred to as perceptual learning. The problem of perceptual learning is treated in *Perception* (Weintraub and Walker, 1966, in this series). All of these forms of learning may be defined in terms of some relatively permanent change in performance due to training or experience. However, they may not necessarily be based upon the same principle; hence, it is possible that the different kinds of learning described above may involve different neural mechanisms.

FACTORS INVOLVED IN LEARNING

Neural mechanisms of learning are also difficult to analyze because what an organism learns depends upon a variety of factors, each of which involves different neural systems. The coding operations of the sensory systems obviously play a role in learning, since different kinds of learning involve some change in the way in which the organism responds to stimuli. Furthermore, investigators commonly assume that motivation is necessary for at least some forms of learning to occur. For example, food is not an appropriate reward for learning an instrumental response if the animal is not hungry. Thus the motivational systems contribute to learning. Also, learning, like other complex behaviors, requires a background of wakefulness and an optimal level of alertness. It seems that the ability of organisms to use stimuli as cues for learned responses is greatly facilitated by attentional processes. Thus, the reticular formation, which is involved in all of these processes, contributes to learning. Finally, a good deal of learning consists in learning to suppress inappropriate behaviors and *not* to respond. As described in the previous chapter, the limbic system seems to be involved in behavioral suppression, and as we shall see in the present chapter, the frontal lobes also appear to be involved in suppression.

THE MEMORY TRACE

The fact that learning takes place implies that some structural change has occurred within the organism. This structural change, which is referred to as the memory trace, presumably mediates the learned associations which are formed in conditioning and other forms of learning. The formation and storage of the memory trace is thought to involve the following sequence of events. First, when some stimulus impinges upon sensory receptors, it is coded in the form of nerve impulses in the sensory pathways. This process takes place very quickly, in a matter of milliseconds. This neural response may then lead to the formation of a temporary memory trace. This process is referred to as short-term memory, which spans a period of minutes or possibly hours, during which a stimulus presented for the first time may be recalled. Finally, the neural representation of the stimulus event may go from short-term memory to permanent memory storage. This process, called long-term memory, may cover a period of days, weeks or years, and it presumably involves some permanent structural change within the nervous system. Experimental investigations of memory suggest that a newly formed memory trace is initially in a fragile state and requires a period of time to become strengthened or consolidated. If this consolidation process is interfered with (by procedures which temporarily disorganize or inactivate the CNS) the memory trace will not be placed in long-term storage, and the stimulus event can no longer be recalled. A discussion of consolidation processes may be found in *Conditioning and Instrumental Learning.*

In this chapter we shall describe some of the research that has been directed toward understanding the neural mechanisms underlying learning and memory. We shall present in turn experiments employing the ablation technique and those employing the methods of electrical recording; and will describe the contributions which each of these methods has made to these problems. Finally, we shall describe some recent studies concerning the role of chemical events in memory.

ABLATION STUDIES OF LEARNING AND MEMORY

THE CONCEPT OF THE CORTICAL REFLEX ARC

During the latter part of the nineteenth century and the first part of the present century, ideas concerning the neural bases of learning and memory were dominated by the concept of the cortical reflex arc. According to this concept, learning and memory involve the kinds of reflex circuitry illustrated in Figure 8.1. It was assumed that sensory information is first projected to cortical reception areas and then conveyed by fibers to nearby non-sensory areas. These non-sensory areas were presumed to provide the associative linkages between different sensory messages that are formed in learning. Hence, these regions have been referred to as the association areas of the cortex. Through their connections with cortical motor areas, the association areas were also thought to provide associative linkages between afferent messages and motor mechanisms controlling responses. It was assumed that these connections, unlike the fixed reflex connections of the spinal cord, are capable of being changed through synaptic growth so that new associa-

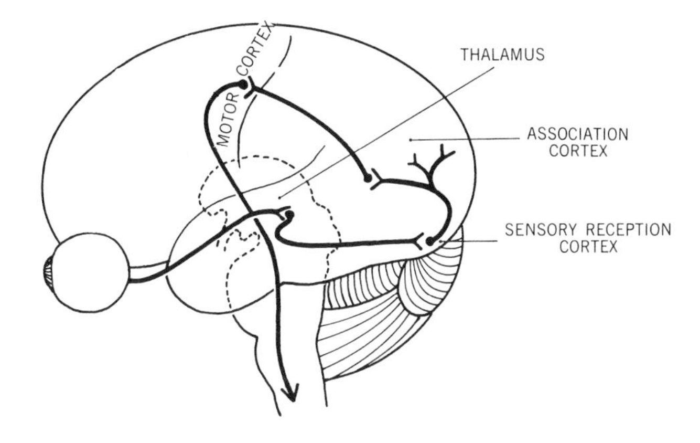

Figure 8.1

The cortical reflex arc. (See text for explanation.)

tions can be formed. The memory trace, according to this view, resides in a particular cortical reflex pathway whose synaptic connections are stable and permanent.

LASHLEY'S CRITIQUE OF THE CORTICAL REFLEX ARC

Over forty years ago, Karl Lashley initiated a series of experiments in order to test the view that memory traces are localized in cortical "reflex" pathways. In one of these experiments he made incisions through the cortex of rats so that the connections between visual and motor cortical areas were severed. According to the cortical reflex concept, these connections are necessary for learning responses to visual stimuli. However, Lashley found that this operation did not affect the rats' ability to learn visual discriminations (Lashley, 1942). Furthermore, removal of the cortical motor areas themselves did not affect learned responses to visual stimuli (Lashley, 1922). Thus, Lashley concluded that memory traces are not mediated by local, cortical reflex circuits.

In another series of experiments, Lashley found that cerebral damage does disrupt learned responses, but not in the manner predicted by the cortical reflex concept. After training rats to run through a maze in order to obtain food in a goal box, Lashley removed varying amounts of cortex and then tested the rats for retention of the maze habit. He found that removal of any one cortical area disrupted the maze habit as much as did removal of any other cortical area, providing that the removals were approximately the same size. He also found that the larger the amount of cortex that was removed, the greater the impairment of the maze habit. On the basis of these findings, Lashley con-

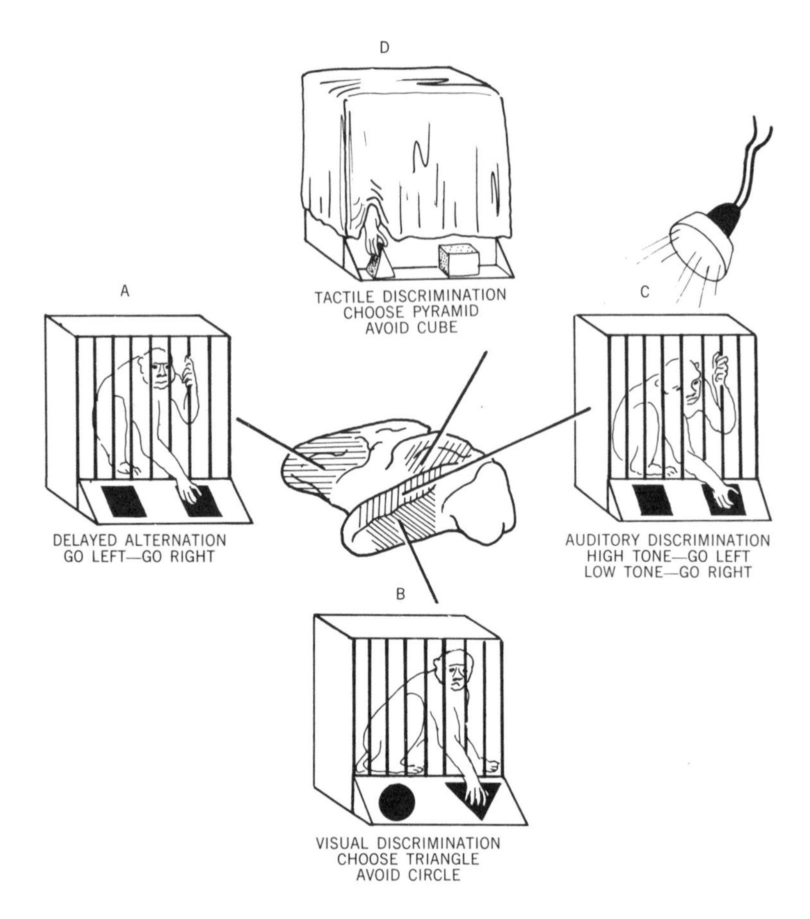

Figure 8.2

Cerebral cortex of monkey (center), showing the association areas whose removal produces selective deficits in particular kinds of learning tasks. In the various tasks depicted, the monkey must displace the correct card or object to obtain a food reward from a food-well directly underneath. Removal of frontal cortex **(A)** *impairs performance on the delayed alternation problem in which the monkey must alternate displacing the left and right cards on successive trials to obtain food (Jacobsen, C. F., Studies of cerebral function in primates: I. The functions of the frontal association areas in monkeys.* Comp. psychol. Monog., *1936,* 13, *3–60). When inferotemporal cortex is removed* **(B)**, *the monkey is impaired in learning to discriminate between forms (Mishkin, M., Visual discrimination performance following partial ablations of the temporal lobe: II. Ventral surface vs. hippocampus.* J. comp. physiol. Psychol., *1954,* 47, *187–193; Chow, K. L., Effects of partial extirpation* cluded that, contrary to the cortical-reflex concept, no one area of cortex is more involved in the memory trace for the maze habit than any other area is. Rather, the memory trace, he argued, must be spread throughout the cortex (Lashley, 1929).

LOCALIZATION OF CORTICAL FUNCTIONS AND LEARNING

However, other interpretations of Lashley's finding have been offered. It has been pointed out that maze learning is a complex habit involving the use of many sensory cues, such as visual, tactile, and olfactory stimuli. Furthermore, in learning the correct path through a maze, rats can use their previous responses (turning a corner) as a cue for the next turn and thus learn response sequences. It is conceivable that each of these factors involved in maze learning depends upon a different area of the cortex. Larger cortical lesions might disrupt maze learning more than smaller lesions do because they interfere with more neural systems, each of which mediates a different kind of cue for the maze habit. Evidence favoring this interpretation comes from the findings of Gross, Chorover, and Cohen (1965). These investigators found that destruction of posterior cortex impairs the performance of rats in sensory-discrimination problems but does not affect their performance of a response-alternation problem, in which the rat is required to learn response sequences. Conversely, removal of frontal cortex impairs performance on the alternation problem but not on the sensory problem.

Furthermore, there is a good deal of evidence that removal of different portions of cortical association areas produces different behavioral impairments in monkeys. Although these findings have not disclosed the neural basis of the memory trace, they provide information about the cerebral control of processes that contribute to learning. As seen in Figure 8.2, removal of a particular cortical region within posterior association cortex impairs the ability of monkeys to learn

---

of posterior association cortex on visually mediated behavior in monkeys. Comp. psychol. Monog., *1951,* 20, *187–217), but when superior temporal cortex is removed* **(C)**, *the monkey is impaired in learning to discriminate between sounds (Weiskrantz, L., and Mishkin, M., Effects of temporal and frontal cortical lesions on auditory discrimination in monkeys.* Brain, *1958,* 81, *406–414). Removal of posterior parietal cortex* **(D)** *retards tactile discrimination performance in which the monkey must discriminate between two objects by touch (Wilson, M., Effects of circumscribed cortical lesions upon somesthetic and visual discriminations in the monkey.* J. comp. physiol. Psychol., *1957,* 50, *630–635.)*

a discrimination within a particular sense modality, either vision, audition, or touch. Each of these regions, then, plays some role in discrimination learning; whether they are involved in the processing of sensory information, in the formation of memory traces, or in some other different kind of function has not yet been established.

On the other hand, removal of the frontal association area does not impair sensory discrimination learning. Rather, following removal of this area, monkeys are impaired in learning the delayed alternation problem, similar to the alternation problem on which rats with anterior cortical lesions are impaired, as described previously. In this problem, the monkey is faced with two alternative responses; as shown in Figure 8.2, it can choose either the left or the right plaque. On successive trials separated by a delay period, the monkey must reverse the choice it made on the previous trial in order to obtain reward. It appears that the monkey with frontal ablation cannot perform this problem because it has difficulty in shifting from the one response to the other; it persists in performing the response rewarded on the previous trial. This difficulty in shifting responses following frontal ablation is also seen in other situations, such as the discrimination-reversal problem (Mishkin, 1964). In the first phase of this problem, the animal is rewarded for choosing one stimulus and not another. After the animal has mastered this discrimination, it is rewarded only for choosing the formerly avoided stimulus in the reversal phase. The monkey with frontal ablation has no difficulty in the first phase and learns the discrimination as quickly as unoperated monkeys do. However, the frontal monkey is impaired in learning to reverse its choice in the second phase of the experiment, and it persists abnormally in choosing the formerly rewarded stimulus. Thus, removal of frontal cortex seems to disturb the ability to alter preferred modes of responding. The ability to alter one's mode of response is a critical factor in almost all complex learning and problem-solving situations in which the rule underlying correct solution changes. For example, when human patients with frontal-lobe damage are required to discover the correct rule for sorting cards into piles, they perform as well as patients with other cerebral lesions do. They can readily learn, for example, to sort cards according to their color through trial and error when the experimenter tells them whether or not each choice was correct. However, when the experimenter changes the rule from sorting on the basis of color to sorting on the basis of some other feature, such as the patterns on the cards, the frontal patient takes many more trials to sort according to this new rule than do control subjects. Like the frontal monkey in the discrimination-reversal situation, the frontal patient persists in the formerly appropriate behavior (Milner, 1964).

While the experiments described in this section have failed to disclose the neural basis of the memory trace, their results suggest that different areas of the cortex participate in functions that are critical for normal learning. Some of these functions are required for sensory discriminations while others are required for shifting the set to respond in a particular way. While the nature of these functions is not known, it is clear from these findings that learning is not simply a matter of joining sensory and motor areas in a reflex circuit, as the traditional view assumed. Rather, it appears that widespread areas of the cortex are involved in learning, and each of these areas seems to contribute something different to the learning process.

INTERHEMISPHERIC TRANSFER OF THE MEMORY TRACE

A different approach to the neural basis of learning and memory is provided by the split-brain preparation, in which the connections between the two cerebral hemispheres are severed. Studies using this technique have given us some valuable clues to the problem of how memory traces are transmitted through the brain.

If a cat learns to discriminate between two visual stimuli with only one eye exposed, then, in a subsequent test with only the other eye exposed, the animal shows transfer of the discrimination. Interocular transfer of this kind is to be expected, since many optic nerve fibers from each eye cross in the optic chiasm and terminate in the opposite side of the brain (see Figure 8.3A). However, interocular transfer also occurs after the optic chiasm is split, so that information from each eye goes only to the cerebral hemisphere on that side, as shown in Figure 8.3B (Myers, 1955). It appears that transfer in this case is mediated by the corpus callosum, the band of white matter interconnecting the two hemispheres, for, if the corpus callosum and the optic chiasm are split prior to training with one eye, interocular transfer does not occur (see Figure 8.3C and D). Apparently the "split brain" animal has two functionally independent hemispheres, in each of which learning processes can proceed normally.

While these findings implicate the corpus callosum in the transfer of memory traces when input is restricted to one hemipshere, they do not indicate the way in which this structure participates in this function. The corpus callosum might convey memory traces from the hemisphere which receives the input to the other hemisphere during initial learning. Or, the corpus callosum might give the untrained hemisphere access to traces stored in the trained hemisphere at the time of testing. It appears that the first alternative is the correct one, for if an animal with split optic chiasm learns a visual discrimination with one eye and the corpus callosum is then cut, he will show interocular transfer (Myers and Sperry, 1953). It thus appears that the corpus callosum mediates transfer between the two hemispheres at the time of learning. In other

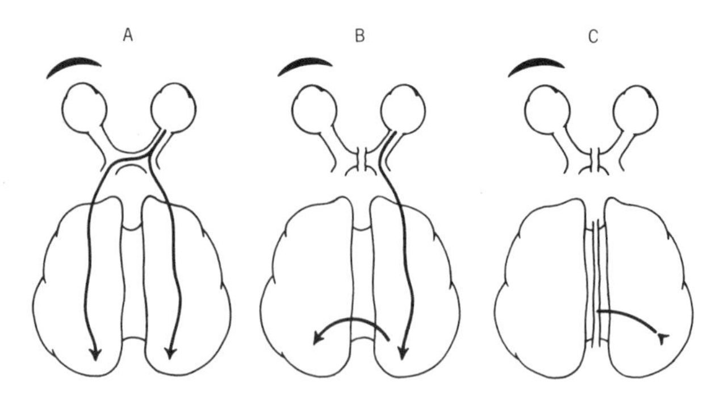

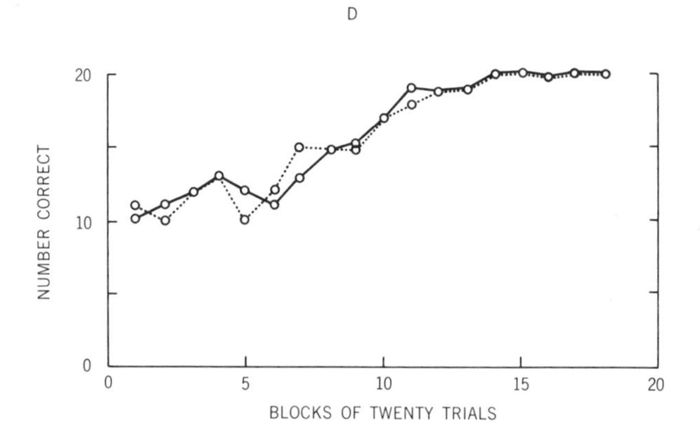

Figure 8.3

The role of the corpus callosum in interhemispheric transfer. In **(A)**, *the intact cat transfers a visual discrimination from the right eye to the left eye, since each eye projects to both hemispheres. But even after the optic chiasm is split* **(B)** *restricting visual input to one hemisphere, the cat shows interocular transfer, presumably because information is transferred from the "trained" hemisphere to the "untrained" hemisphere via the corpus callosum. When the corpus callosum, as well as the optic chiasm is split* **(C)**, *the cat shows no interocular transfer. From Ruch, T. C., Patton, H. D., Woodbury, J. W., and Towe, A. L.,* Neurophysiology, *2nd ed., Figure 5, page 488. Philadelphia: Saunders, 1965. In* **(D)** *visual discrimination learning curves are shown for the left eye and right eye of a cat with split optic chiasm and corpus callosum. Unlike the normal cat, this split-brain cat shows no transfer of a discrimination from one eye to another; the two learning curves are identical. From Sperry, R. W., Stamm, J. S., and Miner, N., Relearning tests for interocular transfer* words, the corpus callosum seems to provide a bridge for duplicating memory traces formed in one hemisphere in the opposite hemisphere. However, this conclusion does not seem to hold for all situations. Thus, difficult discrimination problems show only poor interocular transfer when the corpus callosum is intact (Myers, 1962). And in some simple discrimination tasks animals show interocular transfer even after the corpus callosum is cut (Meikle and Sechzer, 1960). Apparently, the latter memory traces are mediated by subcortical structures. The information in this case may be relayed via efferent fibers from the cortex of the "trained hemisphere" to structures in the thalamus or brain stem, from which it is perhaps further relayed to the paired structure in the opposite "untrained hemisphere."

The split-brain technique has also been used to localize the neural structures involved in the formation of memory traces. Ablation experiments customarily involve removal of cortical tissue in symmetrical regions of both hemispheres. If such bilateral ablations are extensive, they may severely incapacitate the animal or produce various symptoms which make the interpretation of deficits in learned behavior difficult. Many of these difficulties can be avoided by separating the two hemispheres and restricting learning to one hemisphere. Sizable portions of cortex can then be removed from this hemisphere without the devastating consequences seen following bilateral removals of cortex. An example of the use of this technique is provided by the following experiments. If a cat in which the corpus callosum has been severed learns to discriminate between two surfaces of different roughness with one paw, the discrimination does not transfer to the other paw (Stamm and Sperry, 1957). Thus it may be inferred that the memory trace is confined to the hemisphere opposite the paw used in learning, since the afferent fibers from that paw travel in the lemniscal system to the opposite hemisphere. The question can then be asked: Do cortical structures outside of the somatosensory and motor areas play any role in the discrimination? The answer is provided by removing all areas of the trained hemisphere except the somatosensory and motor areas. Following this radical ablation, the cat still shows retention of the discrimination. To be sure that the discrimination is not being mediated by the somatosensory and motor areas of the opposite hemisphere, these must be removed also. Following this ablation, the cat still shows retention of the discrimination (Sperry, 1961). Apparently, then, the memory trace is confined to the remaining sensory and motor cortex of the trained hemisphere, although it is possible that subcortical structures may also play some role in mediating the memory trace.

---

following division of the optic chiasm and corpus callosum in cats, Figure 2, page 531. J. comp. physiol. Psychol., *1956,* 49, *529–533.*

ELECTROPHYSIOLOGICAL INVESTIGATIONS OF LEARNING AND MEMORY

In recent years there have been a number of attempts to determine the neural events underlying learning and memory by recording the electrical activity of the brain during the course of learning. In these experiments, electrodes are permanently implanted in brain structures so that the electrical activity of these structures can be later recorded while the animal is awake and freely moving in a learning situation. Since the electrical activity of several brain structures can be continuously recorded during learning, one could find out with this technique what parts of the brain show changes in electrical activity when the animal is learning.

ELECTRICAL CORRELATES OF LEARNING

One problem that arises in an experiment of the kind described above is how to determine whether the electrical changes that are recorded are neural responses to an environmental stimulus that the experimenter presents or whether they are responses to some other events. John and Killam (1959) provided an ingenious solution to this problem by using as a conditioned stimulus a light that flickers on and off at a fixed rate. When such a stimulus is presented to an animal, electrical discharges of the same frequency as the flickering light are recorded in the brain. Thus, by means of this technique, it is possible to determine what brain structures show frequency-specific responses during the course of learning. In John and Killam's experiment, cats with electrodes implanted in a number of brain structures were placed in a two-compartment box and repeatedly presented with a 10/sec. flickering light. In this initial "familiarization" stage, the light was presented by itself. Initially, 10/sec. electrical responses were recorded in widespread regions of the brain when the flickering light was presented (see Figure 8.4A). After the light was presented repeatedly, however, it no longer evoked the frequency-specific response in subcortical structures, and finally the response disappeared even in the visual pathways (see Figure 8.4B). In the next stage, each presentation of the 10/sec. light was followed by electric shock to the cat's feet. The cat could avoid the shock, however, by jumping to the other compartment of the box whenever the flickering light came on. After the light and shock were paired for several trials, the cat began to show signs of fear whenever the light came on. Coincident with these first signs of conditioning, the frequency-specific electrical response reappeared in many brain structures, and it was seen most prominently in reticular structures, as seen in Figure 8.4C. These widespread changes in electrical activity accompanying learning have been found in other investigations, implying that many brain structures are involved in the formation of memory traces. After the cat learned to jump to the opposite compartment to avoid the shock, the frequency-specific response disappeared again in subcortical structures, but remained stable in the visual cortex (see Figure 8.4D).

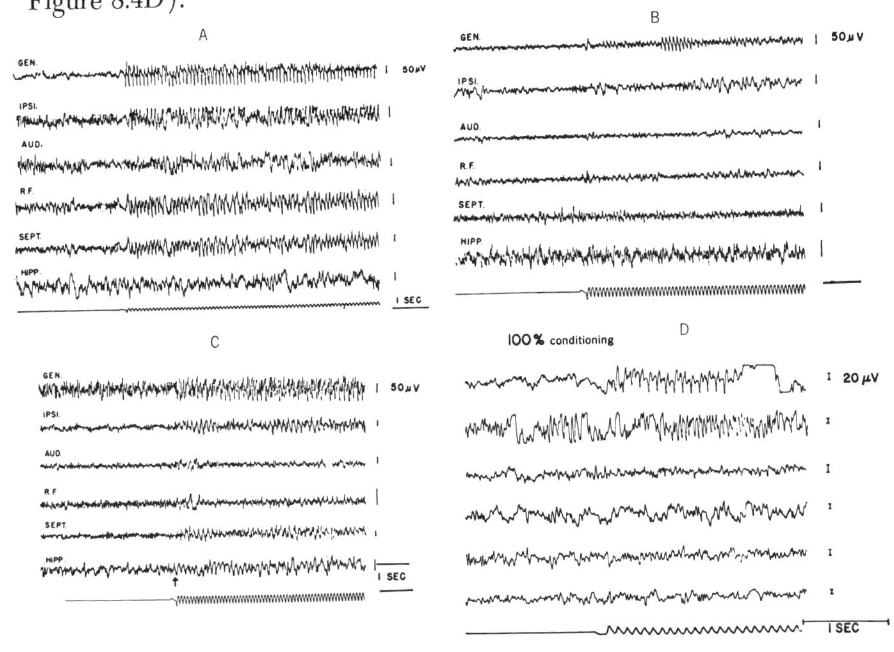

Figure 8.4

Electrographic recordings from various brain structures in cat at different stages of conditioned avoidance learning experiment. **(A)** *At the start of the experiment ("familiarization" stage).* **(B)** *After the 10/sec. light has been presented for 20 sessions, the frequency-specific response has habituated, except for its occasional appearance in the visual pathways.* **(C)** *The frequency-specific response reappears when the 10/sec. light becomes a signal for electric shock.* **(D)** *Avoidance response now fully established; the frequency-specific response is seen only in the visual pathways.* (GEN.: *lateral geniculate nucleus;* IPSI: *visual cortex;* AUD: *auditory cortex;* R.F.: *reticular formation;* SEPT.: *septum;* HIPP.: *hippocampus.) The structures from which tracings were obtained in* (D) *are in the same order as in* (A–C). *From John, E. R., and Killam, K., Electrophysiological correlates of avoidance conditioning in the cat. Figure 1A, page 255; Figure 1C, page 257; Figure 2, page 258; Figure 7, page 263.* J. Pharmacol. exp. Therap., *1959,* 125, *252–274.*

John and Killam also found that the conditioned avoidance response was occasionally elicited by flickering light of a frequency different from that of the CS; for example, a 7/sec. flickering light would sometimes elicit the avoidance response. Whenever the cat performed the avoidance response to this stimulus, 10/sec. waves were recorded from the brain. On the other hand, when the cat did not perform the avoidance response to the 7/sec. stimulus, the frequency of the brain waves closely matched that of the stimulus. In other words, the frequency of the electrical response was appropriate to the animal's reaction to the stimulus rather than the frequency of the stimulus itself. This finding indicates that the nervous system can generate electrical activity related to a particular stimulus even when this stimulus is not present. Thus, the frequency-specific response appears to reflect the neural representation or memory trace of the original stimulating event. If such a neural trace can be evoked by a new input, then it might be assumed that there is a mechanism in the brain for comparing current inputs with the stored representation in order that the current input be recognized. Such a comparator mechanism might well involve widespread neural structures, including the reticular structures from which John and Killam recorded such prominent responses, as well as structures in the visual system.

While the frequency-specific responses observed by John and Killam correlate closely with the animal's behavior in the conditioning situation, they do not necessarily reflect the memory trace directly. The memory trace underlying a learned response is apparently quite stable and resistant to change. For example, if failure to perform the CR is no longer followed by shock in the conditioned avoidance situation, the CR will extinguish. That is, the CR is elicited by the CS less and less until finally it is not elicited at all. However, this does not mean that the learned response has been erased from memory, for the response will reappear if the animal is put back in the conditioning situation following CR extinction. Furthermore, the CR can be reconditioned in fewer trials than were required for it to be established in initial learning. On the other hand, in John and Killam's experiment, the frequency-specific response disappeared in extinction. The electrical response, then, seems to reflect retrieval of the memory trace from storage rather than its permanent structural representation in the nervous system.

CONDITIONING OF ELECTRICAL RESPONSES IN THE CNS

The search for the neural bases of learning has also led investigators to inquire whether the electrical activity of the brain can be conditioned in the way that behavioral responses are conditioned. An analysis of the structures and pathways involved in such conditioning could provide valuable clues as to the basis of behavioral conditioning. The experimenters who have dealt with this problem have used classical conditioning as the model of learning; they have attempted to determine whether a stimulus which does not initially elicit an electrical response in the CNS can do so after being paired with another stimulus which reliably elicits the response.

The initial evidence that electrical activity can be conditioned came from studies of the human EEG. The presentation of light produces the desynchronized pattern in the EEG of a resting, awake subject. A weak tone does not elicit the desynchronized pattern, but will do so after it is paired a number of times with the light. Thus, the tone can act as a CS for cortical desynchronization (Jasper and Shagass, 1941). This electrical conditioning phenomenon has been described in more detail by Morrell and Jasper (1956). Using animals as subjects, these investigators employed a light to evoke cortical desynchronization and a tone as a CS, as in the earlier experiments with human subjects. As shown in Figure 8.5C and D, after the tone is paired a number of times with the light, the tone itself produces the desynchronized EEG pattern, as though it were "anticipating" the light. Furthermore, early in conditioning, desynchronization is found in many cortical areas; but, as conditioning proceeds, the conditioned desynchronization "contracts" and finally is found primarily in the visual areas of the occipital lobes (see Figure 8.5E). It will be recalled that similar changes in electrical responses were found by John and Killam. Thus, it appears that, in classical as well as in instrumental conditioning, many brain structures participate in the development of the memory trace. Morrell and Jasper also found that after the conditioned desynchronization becomes stable, it can be selectively evoked by the particular tone used as a CS. If the same-tone CS continues to be paired with light while another tone of a different frequency is presented alone, the conditioned desynchronization will be elicited only by the former and not by the latter tone—that is, discrimination takes place. Furthermore, if the CS is unaccompanied by light for a number of trials, it will no longer elicit the electrical response—in other words, the CR extinguishes. Thus, it seems that the conditioning of electrical activity follows the same rules that govern behavioral conditioning.

In some of their experiments Morrell and Jasper used a bright, flickering light to evoke electrical discharges. This stimulus caused the animals to wince, as though the light were unpleasant. By recording contractions of the animals' facial muscles, the experimenters found that these movements, as well as the electrical discharges, could be conditioned to a stimulus paired with the flickering light. Interestingly, the electrical signs of conditioning always appeared before this behavioral reaction became conditioned.

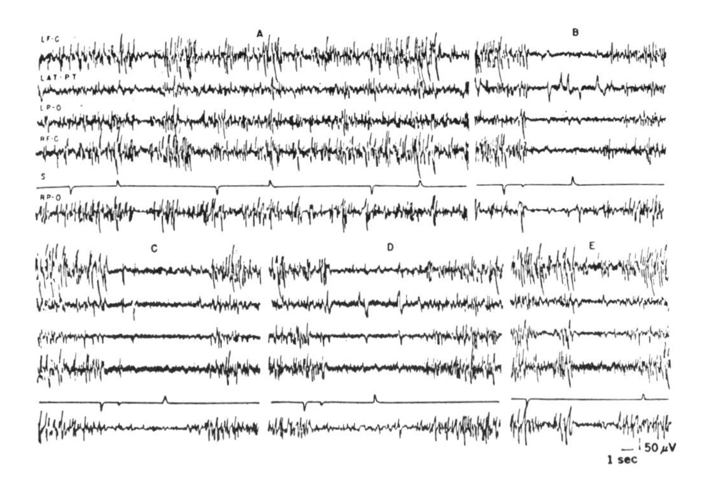

Figure 8.5

Conditioning of EEG desychronization in monkey. In **(A)**, *note the absence of arousal response to onset of a tone, marked by displacement of signal marker* (S) *below horizontal line. In* **(B)**, *the tone is followed by a flickering light (short displacement of signal marker) for the first time. Note that light, but not tone, produces EEG desynchronization. Conditioned desynchronization is seen to the tone in* **(C)** *and in* **(D)**. *In* **(E)**, *conditioned desynchronization appears most clearly in the occipital region when the light is omitted.* (LF-C: *left fronto-central;* LAT-PT: *left anterior-posterior temporal;* LP-O: *left parieto-occipital;* RF-C: *right fronto-central;* RP-O: *right parieto-occipital.) From Morrell, F., and Jasper, H. H., Electrographic studies of the formation of temporary connections in the brain, Figure 1, page 203.* Electroencephalog. clin. Neurophysiol., *1956, 8, 201–215.*

An important question raised by the findings described in this section is: What neural structures are involved in classical conditioning? It is known that classical conditioning can take place in the absence of any cortex, although the ability to discriminate between different CSs is lost (Girden, Mettler, Finch, and Culler, 1936). This finding suggests that while the cerebral cortex is necessary for many discriminative processes, subcortical structures might mediate associational processes underlying conditioning. As mentioned in Chapter 7, ablations of the limbic system produce impairments in behavior that seem to reflect a loss of associations between external events and emotional responses. Thus, the limbic system might participate in associational mechanisms underlying conditioning. There is also evidence that another subcortical structure—the reticular formation—is involved in conditioning. As seen in Figure 8.6, conditioned frequency-specific responses (similar to those described by John and Killam) are seen in the reticular formation prior to their appearance in other structures, including the cortex. This finding implies that associative connections underlying conditioning might be formed in the reticular formation. On the basis of findings such as these, it has been proposed that the reticular formation provides the neural linkages between different sensory messages which converge on this structure from various afferent pathways (Gastaut, 1958). However, one should be cautious in accepting these conclusions, because investigators have been unable to replicate the finding that frequency-specific responses are first seen in the reticular system.

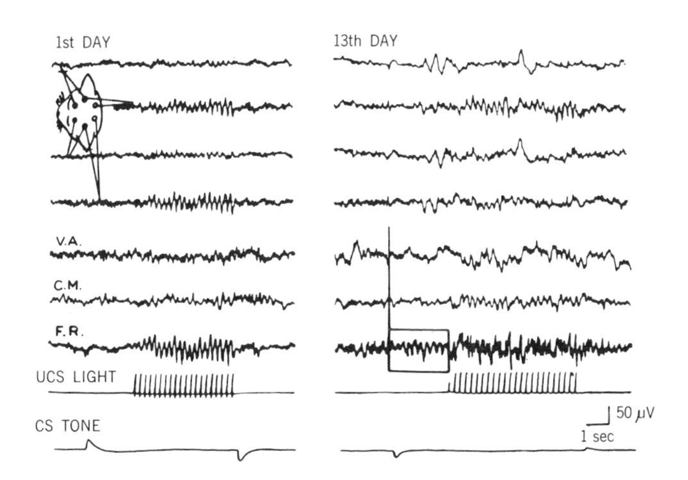

Figure 8.6

Conditioning of the frequency-specific electrical response of various brain structures to a tone. On the first day of conditioning (left side), the CS, a tone, does not yet elicit the frequency-specific response. However, after 13 days of conditioning, in which the tone is paired with the flickering light (right side), the frequency-specific response is elicited by the tone in the reticular formation (boxed-in area), but not in other brain structures. (Top four rows: Cortical EEGs.; V.A.: *nucleus ventralis anterior (thalamus);* C.M.: *nucleus centrum medianum (thalamus);* F.R.: *reticular formation of the mesencephalon.) From Yoshii, N., Pruvot, P., and Gastaut, H., Electrographic activity of the mesencephalic reticular formation during conditioning in the cat, Figure 1, page 596.* Electroencephalog. clin. Neurophysiol., *1957*, 9, *595–608.*

THE ORIENTING RESPONSE AND LEARNING

Traditionally, investigators of learning have been concerned primarily with conditioned responses when they observe the behavior of subjects in a learning situation. However, there is another kind of response, referred to as the orienting response, which seems to play an important role in the learning process. Behaviorally, this response consists of orienting or investigatory movements to stimuli that are novel or that signal a biologically important event (such as food). Thus, a CS frequently evokes orienting movements when it is acquiring significance for the animal. These investigatory movements provide the organism with more information about the stimulus and thus tend to facilitate learning. If a stimulus is repeatedly presented and unaccompanied by a biologically significant event, the orienting response habituates—that is, it is evoked by the stimulus less and less. Furthermore, orienting reactions are accompanied by signs of sympathetic activation, such as rapid respiration and increased muscle tension. The orienting response thus not only aids in focussing the organism's attention on the stimulus, it also prepares the organism for appropriate reactions to a potentially significant stimulus. A number of experimental findings suggest that the reticular formation of the brain stem and thalamus mediate the orienting response.

Electrophysiological investigations indicate that a part of the limbic system referred to as the hippocampus plays an important role in the control of the orienting response. In an experiment similar to that of John and Killam's, Grastyan, Lissak, Madarasz, and Donhoffer (1959) recorded the electrical activity of the hippocampus and of other brain structures in cats during the course of learning. In one of their learning situations, the cat learned to jump to a platform in order to obtain food whenever a sound occurred. In the first part of the experiment, after the sound had been paired with the presentation of food several times, the cat began to show orienting responses to the sound. Coincidental with the development of this orienting response to the CS, slow, rhythmic waves, referred to as the theta rhythm, appeared in the hippocampus. As the instrumental response of approaching the feeding platform became established, however, this theta rhythm was replaced by low-voltage desynchronized activity and the orienting response disappeared (see Figure 8.7). If the significance of the CS was changed (for example, when it was no longer associated with food), the theta rhythm reappeared in the hippocampus and the animal showed orienting responses. On the basis of these findings, Grastyan infers that the hippocampus modulates the orienting response in different phases of learning. According to this view, the hippocampus actively suppresses the excitatory influences of the reticular formation, and so prevents the orienting response from occurring. Inactivation of the

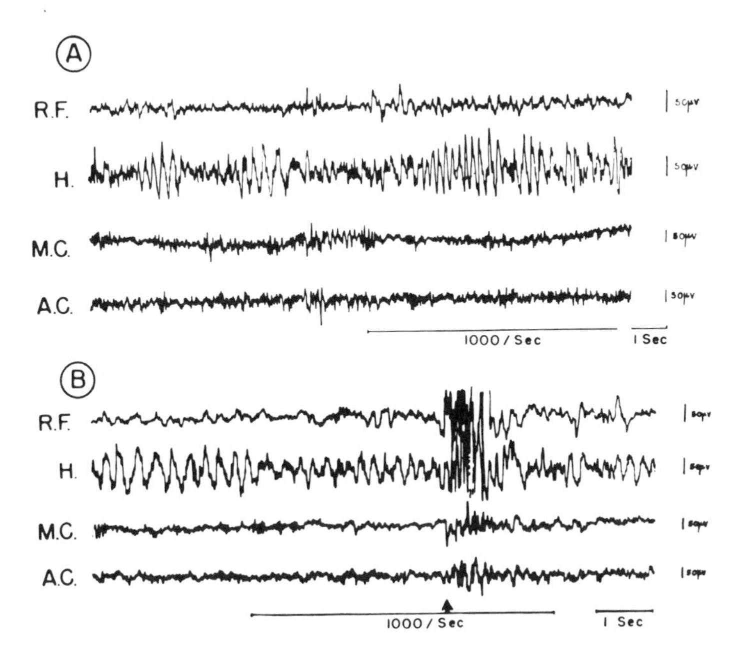

Figure 8.7

Electrographic correlates of orienting behavior from the hippocampus of cat. In **(A)**, *the sound stimulus (a 1000/sec tone), which has just recently become a signal for the presentation of food, evokes an orienting response and slow synchronous waves from the hippocampus* (H). *However, when the animal begins to make the instrumental response* **(B)**, *the synchronous waves are replaced by desynchronized waves, especially noticeable when the CR is performed* (arrow). (R.F.: *reticular formation;* M.C.: *motor cortex;* A.C.: *auditory cortex.) From Grastyan, E., Lissak, K., Madarasz, I., and Donhoffer, H., Hippocampal electrical activity during the development of conditioned reflexes, Figure 3, page 413.* Electroencephalog. clin. Neurophysiol., *1959,* 11, *409–430.*

hippocampus releases the reticular formation from this inhibitory control and thus allows the orienting response to take place. The slow, theta rhythm recorded from the hippocampus indicates an inactive state of this structure, according to Grastyan, just as the slow waves in the cortex seem to reflect deactivation of that structure, as described in Chapter 6. The theta rhythm is found early in learning, at a time when orienting responses tend to facilitate the conditioning process by providing more information about the CS. However, as learning proceeds and the stimulus acquires meaning, the orienting response is no longer necessary and may actually interfere with the rapid execution of the CR. It is during this stage of learning that the hippocampus shows the desynchronized pattern indicative of an activated state and may suppress reticular mechanisms controlling the orienting response.

BIOCHEMICAL ASPECTS OF MEMORY

So far we have been concerned with the role of various brain structures in learning and memory. Another related problem that has attracted wide attention concerns the physical change that takes place in the nervous system when learning occurs. As mentioned previously, this physical change is referred to as the memory trace. In the past, theories of the physical basis of the memory trace have assumed that some structural change occurs in neurons when learning takes place. Thus, for example, it has been speculated that repeated synaptic activity produces an enlarged area of synaptic contact between neurons, so that a neuron fires impulses more readily when its inputs are active than it did prior to synaptic growth. While notions of this sort have been attractive, there is no direct evidence to support them.

Recently it has been suggested that biochemical processes may be involved in memory formation and storage. Of course, even a neuronal theory of memory would assume that biochemical events are of importance, insofar as they determine the structural and functional properties of neurons. However, on the basis of recent developments in molecular genetics, it has been proposed that particular chemical substances are directly responsible for memory coding and storage. More specifically, it has been suggested that ribonucleic acid (RNA) participates in these functions. Before presenting the evidence for this hypothesis, we first will briefly describe some of the properties of RNA and its role in protein synthesis.

THE ROLE OF RNA AND DNA IN PROTEIN SYNTHESIS

Proteins are complex molecules which are essential constituents of all living cells. There are many different kinds of proteins; all, however, are comprised of smaller molecules—the amino acids. Cells are continuously in need of various proteins, which they must manufacture from simpler components. It appears that protein synthesis is guided by RNA, the structure of which is determined by another substance called DNA (deoxyribonucleic acid). DNA, like RNA, is a nucleic acid, a large and complex molecule composed of nucleotides. Nucleotides consist of a sugar (ribose in RNA, deoxyribose in DNA), phosphoric acid, and structures called bases (see Figure 8.8A). In nucleic acids these nucleotides are linked together to form a long chain; in the DNA molecule the nucleotide chain forms a double helix, as shown in

Figure 8.8. It will be noted that along the double helix of the DNA molecule the four bases form paired sequences. DNA molecules differ in the particular sequence of their bases along the double helix, and it is thought that the particular sequence of bases determines the type of protein that is manufactured in the cell. DNA is found only in the cell nucleus, where it is concentrated in the chromosomes. RNA molecules, which like DNA molecules differ in their base sequence, are also found in the nucleus, but much larger amounts of RNA are present in the cytoplasm of the cell. Furthermore, DNA is a highly stable structure and is present in a constant amount in body cells; RNA, on the other hand, is much less stable and its concentration varies widely in different cells.

It appears that one kind of RNA, called messenger RNA, is synthesized in the nucleus out of components according to a "set of rules" determined by the base sequence of DNA. In other words, DNA serves as a kind of template for the formation of messenger RNA. Messenger RNA then travels to the cytoplasm where it serves as a template for the construction of specific proteins from amino acids, brought to it by another kind of RNA, transfer RNA (see Figure 8.8B). It is thought that the particular base sequence on an RNA molecule determines the structure of the protein it synthesizes, just as the base sequence of DNA determines the structure of RNA.

Since the kind of protein that is manufactured by a cell determines the cell's structure and functions, the base sequence of DNA, which is genetically fixed, constitutes a genetic code. When a cell divides, its DNA molecule also divides lengthwise, so that the base sequence on DNA in the parent cell is passed along in the DNA of the daughter cell, where the other half of the DNA molecule is synthesized. In this way, the daughter cell's instructions for protein manufacture (and thus its structure) are an exact duplicate of the parent cell's.

RNA—A POSSIBLE CARRIER OF THE MEMORY CODE

Since DNA carries the genetic code, it is conceivable that it might also carry a memory code—that is, it might code neural signals that impinge on the cell in the form of some permanent change in the sequence of bases along its helical structure. The changed structure of the DNA molecule would then cause changes in protein structure of the cell, so that it would in the future react differently to neural inputs. However, as mentioned previously, DNA appears to be a very stable molecule, and its structure is not readily altered by external events. RNA, on the other hand, is a more likely candidate for a possible molecular memory coder, since it is more readily altered in amount and in structure. Moreover, neurons in the CNS have a very high RNA content. While this intriguing notion is still highly speculative, there are several findings which lend support to the view that RNA may be intimately involved in memory processes.

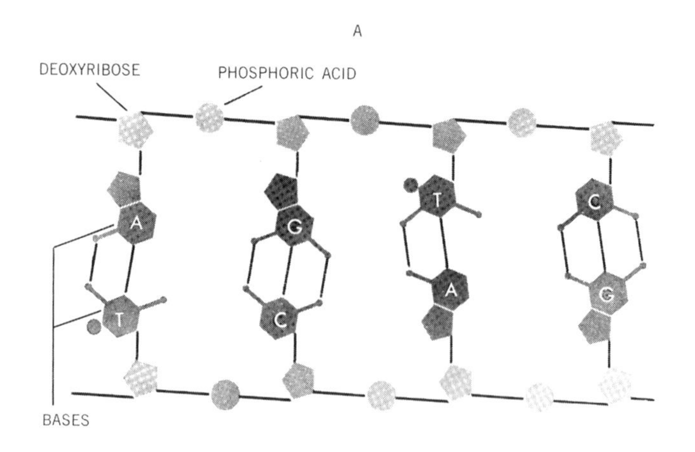

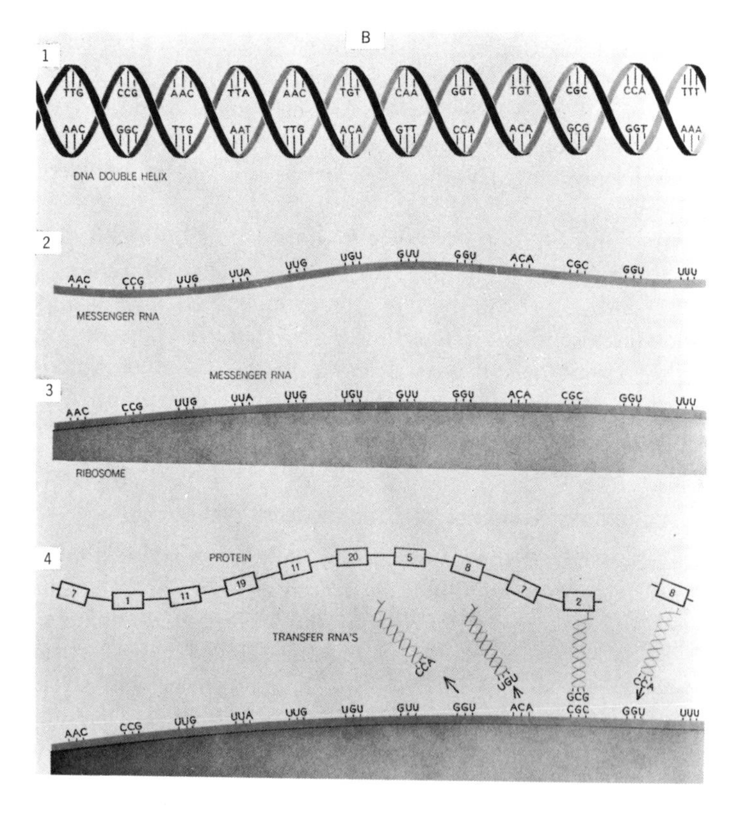

Figure 8.8

The role of DNA and RNA in protein synthesis. **(A)** *A short segment of the DNA molecule, showing how the two linear chains are constructed of deoxyribose and phosphate, linked together by pairs of*

Hydén and his colleagues (Hydén, 1959) have reported several findings which indicate that following stimulation, neurons show an increase in their RNA content and in protein synthesis, whereas disuse of neurons leads to a depletion of their RNA and lowers protein synthesis. Of more relevance to the possible role of RNA in memory is the following finding reported by Hydén and Egyhazi (1962). In this experiment, rats learned to walk up a thin wire in order to obtain food, a task which was designed to produce stimulation of the vestibular nuclei. Control rats were rotated so that they also received vestibular stimulation, but presumably not the same pattern of excitation as the experimental rats received. Subsequent biochemical analysis indicated that vestibular stimulation, both in the experimental and control animals, increased the RNA content of vestibular neurons. However, only the rats that learned to walk the wire showed a change in the relative proportion of two bases (adenine and uricil) of nuclear RNA.

On the basis of these and similar findings, Hydén has proposed that a given pattern of nerve impulses impinging on a neuron might produce a slight but permanent change in the ratio of bases in its RNA molecules, which would then synthesize proteins differing in some way from those it previously synthesized. As a result, there would be a change in the cell's structure which, in turn, would lead to a change in the cell's electrochemical reaction when it is stimulated by the same pattern of nerve impulses in the future.

Presumably, if new patterns of electrical stimulation produce permanent changes in RNA structure, it might be possible to transfer memories from one animal to another by transferring RNA from neurons of an animal that has had a particular learning experience to the brain

---

bases. The four bases are adenine (A), *thyamine* (T), *cytosine* (C), *and guanine* (G). **(B)** *A portion of a DNA molecule, forming a double helix, is shown at the top* (1). *The four bases form complementary pairs across each strand of the helix: adenine is joined to thyamine, and guanine is joined to cytosine. The coded sequence of bases is transcribed into messenger RNA* (2). *The bases in messenger RNA are complementary to those in one strand of DNA;* U *(uracil) appears in the RNA chain wherever adenine is present on the complementary site on the DNA chain. Messenger RNA then reaches a ribosome* (3), *the site of protein synthesis. Amino acids, indicated by the numbered rectangles, are carried to their proper place on the messenger RNA by transfer RNA* (4), *a helical form of RNA, to form a protein molecule. From Nirenberg, M. W., The genetic code: II.* Sci. Amer., *March 1963.*

of a naive animal. In fact, several studies have reported such transfer effects (e.g., Jacobson, Babich, Bubash, and Jacobson, 1965). While the implications of these findings are fascinating, it should be pointed out that other investigators have not been able to replicate these results, and there is at present a good deal of controversy in this area of research.

On the other hand, it has been demonstrated that some substances which interfere with protein synthesis produce constistent effects on memory. One of these substances, puromycin, was injected into the temporal areas of the brains of mice at various times after thèy learned an avoidance response in a Y-maze (Flexner, Flexner, and Stellar, 1963). The mice were then tested for retention of the avoidance response three days following puromycin injection. When puromycin was injected six days or more following initial learning, it had no effect on performance in the retention test. However, when puromycin injections were given two days or less following initial learning, the mice showed no retention of the avoidance response. Apparently, then, interference with protein synthesis in certain brain regions blocks short-term memory, but not long-term memory.

The selective effects of puromycin on short-term memory have also been demonstrated by Davis, Bright, and Agranoff (1965). These investigators trained goldfish to avoid electric shock by swimming from an illuminated to a darkened compartment of a tank. Puromycin was then injected over the fishes' brains at various times following learning of the avoidance response, and the fish were tested for retention of the avoidance responses four days later. The most severe retention deficits were shown when puromycin was administered immediately following learning, and smaller deficits were found when puromycin was administered thirty minutes following learning; there were no significant retention deficits when puromycin administration was delayed one hour or more following learning. Furthermore, in a subsequent experiment, Agranoff, Davis, and Brink (1965) showed that puromycin injected prior to initial avoidance training did not impair avoidance learning, but did interfere with subsequent retention. These findings, then, like those of Flexner and his colleagues, suggest that puromycin selectively interferes with short-term memory processes. However, the time course of the effect is much shorter in the goldfish study than in the former experiment; this suggests that the consolidation of memory may be more rapid under the conditions of the latter experiment than under those of the former experiment.

Dingman and Sporn (1961) obtained rather different effects on behavior using another substance, 8-azaguanine. This substance is incorporated into RNA in the brain and interferes with the formation of enzymes which determine the rate at which proteins are synthesized. Dingman and Sporn first trained rats to swim through a water maze and then administered 8-azaguanine shortly before retention testing. The animals were not significantly impaired in retention compared to their controls. However, when 8-azaguanine was administered to rats before initial training, they were retarded in learning.

It is thus apparent that different substances which inhibit protein synthesis do not necessarily produce similar effects on learned behavior. Furthermore, it should be pointed out that even the results of the experiments using puromycin do not directly demonstrate that RNA acts as a "memory molecule." While the hypothesis that biochemical substances like RNA play a role in memory has attracted a good deal of attention, a great deal of research remains to be done before the role of such substances in memory becomes clarified.

SUGGESTED READINGS

Alfrey, V. G., and Mirskey, A. E. How cells make molecules. *Sci. Amer.*, September 1961.

Boycott, B. B. Learning in the octopus. *Sci. Amer.*, March 1965.

Hurvitz, J., and Furth, J. J. Messenger RNA. *Sci. Amer.*, February 1962.

Lashley, K. S. In search of the engram. In *Soc. exp. Biol. Symp. No. 4: Physiological mechanisms in animal behavior.* Cambridge University Press, 1950, 454–482.

Nirenberg, M. W. The genetic code: II. *Sci. Amer.*, March 1963.

Penfield, W. The permanent record of the stream of consciousness. In T. K. Landauer (Ed.), *Readings in physiological psychology.* New York: Mc-graw-Hill Co., 1967, 352–373.

Pribram, K. H. Neurocortical function in behavior. H. F. Harlow and C. N. Woolsey (Eds.), *Biological and biochemical bases of behavior.* Madison, Wisc.: University of Wisconsin Press, 1958, 151–172.

Sperry, R. W. The great cerebral commissure. *Sci. Amer.*, January 1964.

REFERENCES*

CHAPTER 2

Bodian, D. The generalized vertebrate neuron. *Science*, 1962, *137*, 323–326.

CHAPTER 4

VISION

Arden, G. B., and Soderberg, U. The transfer of optic information through the lateral geniculate body of the rabbit. In W. Rosenblith (Ed.), *Sensory communication.* New York: Wiley, 1961.

Blake, L. The effect of lesions of the superior colliculus on brightness and pattern discrimination in the cat. *J. comp. physiol. Psychol.*, 1959, *52*, 272–278.

Brindley, G. S., and Merton, P. A. The absence of position sense in the human eye. *J. Physiol.*, 1960, *153*, 127–130.

Brown, P. K., and Wald, G. Visual pigments in the human and monkey retinas. *Nature*, 1963, *200*, 37–43.

*Gibson, J. J. The useful dimensions of sensitivity. *Amer. Psychologist*, 1963, *18*, 1–15.

*Granit, R. *Sensory mechanisms of the retina.* London: Oxford University Press, 1947.

*________. *Receptors and sensory perception.* New Haven: Yale University Press, 1955.

Holst, E. von, and Mittelstaedt, H. Das Reafferenzprinzip. *Naturwissen.*, 1950, *37*, 464–476.

Hubel, D. H., and Wiesel, T. N. Integrative action in the cat's lateral geniculate body. *J. Physiol.*, 1961, *155*, 385–398.

________, and Wiesel, T. N. Receptive fields, binocular interaction, and functional architecture in the cat's visual cortex. *J. Physiol.*, 1962, *160*, 106–154.

________, and Wiesel, T. N. Receptive fields and functional architecture in the nonstriate visual areas (18 and 19) of the cat. *J. Neurophysiol.*, 1965, *28*, 229–289.

Kuffler, S. W. Discharge patterns and functional organization of mammalian retina. *J. Neurophysiol.*, 1953, *16*, 37–68.

MacNichol, E. F., and Svaetichin, G. Electrical responses from the isolated retinas of fishes. *Amer. J. Ophthamol.*, 1958, *46*, 26–39.

Marks, W. B., Dobelle, W. H., and MacNichol, E. F. Visual pigments of single primate cones. *Science*, 1964, *143*, 1181–1183.

Maturana, H. R., Lettvin, J. Y., McCulloch, W. S., and Pitts, W. H. Anatomy and physiology of vision in the frog *(Rana pipiens). J. gen. Physiol.*, 1960, *43*, 2nd suppl., 129–175.

*References that are marked by asterisks are suggested readings.

Mishkin, M. Visual mechanisms beyond the striate cortex. In R. W. Russell (Ed.), *Frontiers in physiological psychology.* New York: Academic Press, 1966, 93–116.

———, and Pribram, K. H. Visual discrimination performance following partial ablations of the temporal lobe: I. Ventral vs. lateral. *J. comp. physiol. Psychol.*, 1954, *47*, 14–20.

Riopelle, A. J., and Ades, H. W. Visual discrimination performance in rhesus monkeys following extirpation of prestriate and temporal cortex. *J. genet. Psychol.*, 1953, *83*, 63–77.

Sprague, J. J., and Meikle, T. H., Jr. The role of the superior colliculus in visually guided behavior. *Exp. Neurol.*, 1965, *11*, 115–146.

*Teuber, H. L. Perception. In J. Field (Ed.), *Handbook of physiology.* Vol. III. Washington: Amer. Physiol. Soc., 1960, 1595–1668.

Tomita, T. Electrical activity in the vertebrate retina. *J. Opt. Soc. Amer.*, 1963, *53*, 49–57.

Wagner, H. G., MacNichol, E. F., and Wolbarsht, M. L. The response properties of single ganglion cells in the goldfish retina. *J. gen. Physiol.*, 1960, *43*, 2nd suppl., 45-62.

Widen, L., and Ajmone-Marsan, C. Effects of corticopetal and cortifugal impulses upon single elements of the dorsolateral geniculate nucleus. (1) Proceedings of American Electroencephalographic Soc. 14th Annual Meet., June 10–11, 1960. (2) *Electroencephalog. clin. Neurophysiol.*, 1961, *13*, 304.

Wiesel, T. N., and Hubel, D. H. Spatial and chromatic interactions in the lateral geniculate body of the rhesus monkey. *J. Neurophysiol.*, 1966, *29*, 1115–1156.

AUDITORY SYSTEM

Butler, R. A., Diamond, I. T., and Neff, W. D. Role of auditory cortex in discrimination of changes in frequency. *J. Neurophysiol.*, 1957, *20*, 108–120.

Chow, K. L. Numerical estimates of the auditory central nervous system of the monkey. *J. comp. Neurol.*, 1951, *95*, 159–175.

Desmedt, J. E. Neurophysiological mechanisms controlling acoustic input. In G. L. Rasmussen and W. F. Windle (Eds.), *Neural mechanisms of the auditory and vestibular systems.* Springfield, Ill.: C. C. Thomas, 1960.

Dewson, J. H., III, Nobel, ___, and Pribram, K. H. Unpublished experiments cited in Spinelli, D. N., and Pribram, K. H. Changes in visual recovery functions produced by temporal lobe stimulation in monkeys. *Electroencephal. clin. Neurophysiol.*, 1966, *20*, 44–49.

Diamond, I. T., and Neff, W. T. Ablation of temporal cortex and discrimination of auditory patterns. *J. Neurophysiol.*, 1957, *20*, 300–315.

Galambos, R. Suppression of auditory nerve activity by stimulation of efferent fibers to the cochlea. *J. Neurophysiol.*, 1956, *19*, 424–437.

———, and Davis, H. The response of single auditory nerve fibers to acoustic stimulation. *J. Neurophysiol.*, 1943, *6*, 39–57.

Katsuki, Y. Neural mechanism of auditory sensation in cats. In W. Rosenblith (Ed.), *Sensory communication.* New York: Wiley, 1961.

———, Suga, N., and Kanno, Y. Neural mechanism of the peripheral and central auditory system in monkey. *J. acoust. Soc. Amer.*, 1962, *34*, 1396–1410.

Luria, A. R. *Higher cortical functions in man.* Translated from the Russian by B. Haigh. New York: Basic Books, 1966.

Masterson, B., Jane, J. A., and Diamond, I. T. Role of brainstem auditory structures in sound localization: I. Trapezoid body, superior olive, and lateral lemniscus. *J. Neurophysiol.*, 1967, *30*, 341–359.
Milner, B. Laterality effects in audition. In V. B. Mountcastle (Ed.), *Interhemispheric relations and cerebral dominance.* Baltimore: Johns Hopkins Press, 1962.
Neff, W. D. Neural mechanisms of auditory discrimination. In W. Rosenblith (Ed.), *Sensory communication.* New York: Wiley, 1961, 259–278.
Nobel, K. W., Dewson, J. H., III, and Pribram, K. H. Cortifugal influence at cochlea nucleus of the cat: Some effects of ablation of insular-temporal cortex. *Brain research,* 1966, *2,* 151–159.
Oonishi, S., and Katsuki, Y. Functional organization and integrative mechanism of the auditory cortex of the cat. *Jap. J. Physiol.*, 1965, *15,* 342–365.
*Oswald, I., Taylor, A. M., and Treisman, M. Cortical function during human sleep. In G. E. W. Wolstenholme and C. M. O'Conner (Eds.), *The nature of sleep.* CIBA Foundation Symposium. Boston: Little, Brown, 1961, 343–347.

SOMATIC SENSORY SYSTEMS

Adkins, R. J., Morse, R. W., and Towe, A. L. Control of somatosensory input by cerebral cortex. *Science,* 1966, *153,* 1020–1022.
Adrian, E. D., and Zotterman, Y. The impulses produced by sensory nerve endings. Part 3: Impulses set up by touch and pressure. *J. Physiol.*, 1926, *61,* 464–483.
Bazett, H. C., McGlone, B., Williams, R. G., and Lufkin, M. H. Studies in sensation: I. Depth, distribution and probable identification in the prepuce of sensory end organs in sensations of temperature and touch. Thermometric conductivity. *Arch. neurol. Psychiat.* (Chicago), 1932, *27,* 489–517.
Casey, K. L. Unit analysis of nociceptive mechanisms in the thalamus of the awake squirrel monkey. *J. Neurophysiol.*, 1966, *29,* 727–750.
Critchley, M. *The parietal lobes.* London: Edward Arnold Ltd., 1953.
Delgado, J. M. R. Cerebral structures involved in transmission of noxious stimulation. *J. Neurophysiol.*, 1955, *18,* 261–275.
*Gibson, J. J. Observations on active touch. *Psychol. Rev.*, 1962, *69,* 477–491.
Gray, J. A. B., and Sato, M. Properties of the receptor potential in Pacinian corpuscles. *J. Physiol.*, 1953, *122,* 610–636.
Hensel, H., and Zotterman, Y. Quantitative Beziehungen zwischen der Entladung einzelner Kaeltenfasern und der Temperatur. *Acta Physiol. Scand.*, 1951, *23,* 291–319.
Iggo, A. New specific sensory structures in hairy skin. *Acta Neuroveg.*, 1963, *24,* 175–180.
Lele, P. P., and Weddell, G. The relationship between neurohistology and corneal sensibility. *Brain,* 1956, *79,* 119–154.
Malis, L. I., Pribram, K. H., and Kruger, L. Action potentials in motor cortex evoked by peripheral nerve stimulation. *J. Neurophysiol.*, 1953, *16,* 161–167.
Maruhashi, J., Mizuguchi, K., and Tasaki, I. Action currents in single afferent nerve fibers elicited by stimulation of the skin of the toad and of the cat. *J. Physiol.*, 1952, *117,* 129–151.
Mendelson, M., and Loewenstein, W. R. Mechanisms of receptor adaptation. *Science,* 1964, *144,* 554–555.

*Mountcastle, V. B. Some functional properties of the somatic afferent system. In W. Rosenblith (Ed.), *Sensory communication.* New York: Wiley, 1961, 403–436.

Penfield, W., and Jasper, H. H. *Epilepsy and functional anatomy of the human brain.* Boston: Little, Brown, 1954.

Poggio, G. F., and Mountcastle, V. B. The functional properties of ventrobasal thalamic neurons studied in unanesthetized monkeys. *J. Neurophysiol.,* 1963, *26,* 775–786.

Stevens, S. S. On the psychophysical law. *Psychol. Rev.,* 1957, *64,* 153–181.

Sweet, W. H. Pain. In J. Field (Ed.), *Handbook of physiology.* Vol. I. Washington: Amer. Physiol. Soc., 1959, 459–506.

Terzuolo, C. A., and Adey, W. R. Sensorimotor cortical activities. In J. Field (Ed.), *Handbook of physiology.* Vol. II. Washington: Amer. Physiol. Soc., 1960, 797–836.

Weddell, G. Receptors for somatic sensation. In M. A. B. Brazier (Ed.), *Brain and behavior.* Vol. I. New York: Stechert, 1961, 13–45.

———, Palmer, E., and Pallie, W. Nerve endings in mammalian skin. *Biol. Rev.,* 1955, *30,* 159–193.

Werner, G., and Mountcastle, V. B. Neural activity in mechanoreceptive cutaneous afferents: Stimulus-response relations, Weber functions, and information transmission. *J. Neurophysiol.,* 1965, *28,* 359–397.

Zotterman, Y. Specific action potentials in the lingual nerve of the cat. *Scand. Arch. Physiol.,* 1936, *75,* 105–119.

———. Special senses: Thermal receptors. *Ann. Rev. Physiol.,* 1953, *15,* 357–372.

———. Thermal sensations. In J. Field (Ed.), *Handbook of physiology.* Vol. I. Washington: Amer. Physiol. Soc., 1959, 431–458.

SMELL AND TASTE

Allen, W. F. Effect of ablating the pyriform-amygdaloid areas and hippocampi on positive and negative conditioned reflexes and on conditioned olfactory differentiation. *Amer. J. Physiol.,* 1941, *132,* 81–92.

Brown, T. C., and Mishkin, M. Olfactory and visual discrimination in the monkey after selective lesions of the temporal lobe. *J. comp. physiol. Psychol.,* 1963, *56,* 764–768.

DeVries, H., and Stuiver, M. The absolute sensitivity of the human sense of smell. In W. Rosenblith (Ed.), *Sensory communication.* New York: Wiley, 1961, 159–168.

Esakov, A. I. The efferent control of receptors. *Bull. Expl. Biol. Med.* (USSR), 1961, *51,* 257–262. Cited in B. Oakley, and R. M. Benjamin. Neural mechanisms of taste. *Physiol. Rev.,* 1966, *46,* 173–211.

Gesteland, R. C., Lettvin, J. Y., Pitts, W. H., and Rojas, A. Odor specificities of the frog's olfactory receptors. In Y. Zotterman (Ed.), *Olfaction and taste.* New York: MacMillan, 1963, 19–34.

Henning, H. *Der Geruch.* Leipzig: Barth, 1924.

Kaada, B. R. Cingulate, posterior orbital, anterior insula and temporal pole cortex. In J. Field (Ed.), *Handbook of physiology.* Vol. II. Washington: Amer. Physiol. Soc., 1960, 1345–1372.

Kimura, K., and Beidler, L. M. Microelectrode study of taste receptors of rat and hamster. *J. comp. physiol. Psychol.,* 1961, *58,* 213–218.

*Klüver, H., and Bucy, P. Preliminary analysis of functions of the temporal lobes in monkeys. *A. M. A. Arch. Neurol. Psychiat.,* 1939, *42,* 979–1000.

Lettvin, J. Y., and Gesteland, R. C. Speculations on smell. In *Cold Spring Harbor Symposia on quantitative Biology.* Vol. 30. 1965, 217–225.

Oakley, B., and Benjamin, R. M. Neural mechanisms of taste. *Physiol. Rev.*, 1966, *46*, 173–211.

Olds, J. Hypothalamic substrates of reward. *Physiol. Rev.*, 1962, *42*, 554–604.

Ottoson, D. Analysis of the electrical activity of the olfactory epithelium. *Acta Physiol. Scand.*, 1956, *35*, Suppl. 122, 209–230.

Pfaffmann, C. Gustatory afferent impulses. *J. cell. comp. Physiol.*, 1941, *17*, 243–258.

———. Gustatory nerve impulses in rat, cat, and rabbit. *J. Neurophysiol.*, 1955, *18*, 429–440.

———, Erickson, R. P., Frommer, G. P., and Halpern, B. P. Gustatory discharges in the rat medulla and thalamus. In W. Rosenblith (Ed.), *Sensory communication*. New York: Wiley, 1961, 455–474.

Sheffield, F. D., and Roby, T. B. Reward value of a non-nutritive sweet taste. *J. comp. physiol. Psychol.*, 1950, *43*, 471–481.

Shibuya, T. Dissociation of olfactory neural response and mucosal potential. *Science*, 1964, *143*, 1338–1339.

Warren, R. P., and Pfaffmann, C. Early experience and taste aversion. *J. comp. physiol. Psychol.*, 1959, *52*, 263–266.

Weiskrantz, L. Effects of medial temporal lesions on taste preference in the monkey. *Nature*, 1960, *187*, 879–880.

CHAPTER 5

Battig, K., Rosvold, H. E., and Mishkin, M. Comparison of the effects of frontal and caudate lesions on discrimination learning in monkeys. *J. comp. physiol.. Psychol.*, 1962, *55*, 458–463.

Delgado, J. M. R. Sequential behavior induced repeatedly by stimulation of the red nucleus in free monkeys. *Science*, 1965, *148*, 1361–1363.

Denny-Brown, D. *The basal ganglia and their relation to disorders of movement*. London: Oxford University Press, 1962.

Eldred, E., Granit, R., and Merton, P. A. Supraspinal control of the muscle spindles and its significance. *J. Physiol.*, 1953, *122*, 498–523.

Granit, R., Holmgren, B., and Merton, P. A. The two routes for excitation of muscle and their subservience to the cerebellum. *J. Physiol.*, 1955, *130*, 213–224.

Hess, W. R. *The functional organization of the diencephalon*. New York: Grune and Stratton, 1957.

Hunter, J., and Jasper, H. H. Effect of thalamic stimulation in unanesthetized animals. *Electroencephalog. clin. Neurophysiol.*, 1949, *1*, 305–324.

Jasper, H. H., Ricci, G. F., and Doane, B. Patterns of cortical neuronal discharge during conditioned responses in monkeys. In G. E. W. Wolstenholme and C. M. O'Connor (Eds.), *Neurological basis of behavior*. CIBA Foundation Symposium. London: Churchill, 1958, 277–289.

Jung, R., and Hassler, R. The extrapyramidal system. In J. Field (Ed.), *Handbook of physiology*. Vol. I. Washington: Amer. Physiol. Soc., 1960, 863–928.

Mettler, F. A. Fiber connections of the corpus striatum of the monkey and baboon. *J. comp. Neurol.*, 1954, *82*, 169–204.

———, Ades, H. W., Lipman, E., and Culler, E. A. The extrapyramidal system. *A.M.A. Arch. Neurol. Psychiat.*, 1939, *41*, 984–995.

———, and Mettler, C. C. The effects of striatal injury. *Brain*, 1942, *65*, 242–255.

Moruzzi, G. *Problems in cerebellar physiology.* Springfield, Ill.: C. C. Thomas, 1950.

Pribram, K. H., Kruger, L., Robinson, F., and Berman, A. J. The effects of precentral lesions on the behavior of monkeys. *Yale J. Biol. Med.,* 1955, *28,* 428–443.

Sperry, R. Cerebral regulation of motor coordination in monkeys following multiple transection of sensorimotor cortex. *J. Neurophysiol.,* 1947, *10,* 275–294.

CHAPTER 6

Amassian, V.E., and Waller, H. J. Spatiotemporal patterns in individual reticular neurons. In H. H. Jasper (Ed.), *Reticular formation of the brain.* Boston: Little, Brown, 1958, 69–108.

Aserinksky, E., and Kleitman, N. A motility cycle in sleeping infants as manifested by ocular and gross bodily activity. *J. appl. Physiol.,* 1955, *8,* 1–10.

Batini, C., Moruzzi, G., Palestini, M., Rossi, G. F., and Zanchetti, A. Effects of complete pontine transections on the sleep-wakefulness rhythm: The midpontine pretrigeminal preparation. *Arch. Ital. Biol.,* 1959, *97,* 1–12.

Bonvallet, M., and Allen, M. B. Prolonged spontaneous and evoked reticular activity following discrete bulbar lesions. *Electroencephalog. clin. Neurophysiol.,* 1963, *15,* 969–988.

Bremer, F. L'activité cérébrale au cours du sommeil et de la narcose. Contribution a l'étude du mechanisme du sommeil. *Bull. Acad. Roy. Med. Belgique,* 1937, *2,* (6th Series), 68–86.

———, and Terzuolo, C. Nouvelles recherches sur le processus physiologique du reveil. *Arch. internat. Physiol.,* 1953, *61,* 86–90. Cited in Magoun, H. W. *The waking brain,* 2nd ed. Springfield, Ill.: C. C. Thomas, 1963, 98.

*Dement, W. The effect of dream deprivation. *Science,* 1960, *131,* 1705–1708.

*———. An essay on dreams: The role of physiology in understanding their nature. In *New directions in psychology.* Vol. II. New York: Holt, 1965, 135–257.

———, and Kleitman, N. Cyclic variations in EEG during sleep and their relation to eye movements, body motility and dreaming. *Electroencephalog. clin. Neurophysiol.,* 1957a, *9,* 673–690.

———, and Kleitman, N. The relation of eye movements during sleep to dream activity: An objective method for the study of dreaming. *J. exp. Psychol.,* 1957b, *53,* 339–346.

Evarts, E. V. Activity of neurons in visual cortex of cat during sleep with low voltage fast EEG activity. *J. Neurophysiol.,* 1962, *25,* 812–816.

French, J. D., Hernández-Péon, R., and Livingston, R. B. Projections from cortex to cephalic brain stem (reticular formation) in monkey. *J. Neurophysiol.,* 1955, *18,* 74–95.

———, and Magoun, H. W. Effects of chronic lesions in the central cephalic brain stem of monkeys. *A.M.A. Arch. Neurol. and Psychiat.,* 1952, *68,* 591–604.

———, Verzeano, M., and Magoun, H. W. Extralemniscal sensory system in the brain. *A.M.A. Arch. Neurol. Psychiat.,* 1953, *69,* 505–518.

Fuster, J. M. Effects of stimulation of brain stem on tachistoscopic perception. *Science,* 1958, *127,* 150.

Haider, M., Spong, P., and Lindsley, D. B. Attention, vigilance and cortical evoked potentials in humans. *Science,* 1964, *145,* 180–182.

*Hebb, D. O. Drives and the C.N.S. (Conceptual Nervous System). *Psychol. Rev.,* 1955, *62,* 243–254.

*Hess, W. R. The functional organization of the diencephalon. New York: Grune and Stratton, 1957.

Hernández-Péon, R. Central neuro-humoral transmission in sleep and wakefulness. In Akert, K., Bally, C., and Schade, J. P. (Eds.), *Progress in brain research.* Amsterdam: Elsevier, 1965, 96–117.

Hugelin, A., and Bonvallet, M. Tonus cortical et controle de la facilitation motrice d'origine reticulaire. *J. Physiologie,* 1957a, *49,* 1171–1200.

________, and Bonvallet, M. Etude experimentale des interrelations reticulo-corticales. Proposition d'une theorie de l'avertissement reticulaire a une systeme diffus cortical. *J. Physiologie,* 1957b, *49,* 1201–1223.

*Jouvet, M. Telencephalic and rhombencephalic sleep in the cat. In: G. E. W. Wolstenholme and C. M. O'Connor (Eds.), *The nature of sleep.* Boston: Little, Brown, 1961, 188–206.

________. Paradoxical sleep: A study of its nature and mechanisms. In Akert, K., Bally, C., and Schade, J. P. (Eds.), *Progress in brain research.* Amsterdam: Elsevier, 1965, 20–62.

________. Neurophysiology of the state of sleep. *Physiol. Rev.,* 1967, *47,* 117–177.

Lindsley, D. B., Schreiner, L. H., Knowles, W. B., and Magoun, H. W. Behavioral and EEG changes following chronic brain stem lesions in the cat. *Electroencephalog. clin. Neurophysiol.,* 1950, *2,* 483–498.

Magnes, J., Moruzzi, G., and Pompeiano, O. Electroencephalogram-synchronizing structures in the lower brain stem. In: G. E. W. Wolstenholme and C. M. O'Connor (Eds.), *The nature of sleep.* Boston: Little, Brown, 1961, 57–78.

Magni, F., Moruzzi, G., Rossi, G. F., and Zanchetti, A. EEG arousal following inactivation of the lower brain stem by selective injection of barbiturate into the vertebral circulation. *Arch. Ital. Biol.,* 1959, *97,* 33–46.

*Magoun, H. W. *The waking brain,* 2nd ed., Springfield, Ill.: C. C. Thomas, 1963.

Moruzzi, G., and Magoun, H. W. Brain stem reticular formation and activation of the EEG. *Electroencephalog. clin. Neurophysiol.,* 1949, *1,* 455–473.

*Murray, E. J. *Sleep, dreams, and arousal.* New York: Appleton-Century-Crofts, 1965.

Roffwarg, H. P., Muzio, J. N., and Dement, W. Ontogenetic development of the human dream cycle. *Science,* 1966, *152,* 604–619.

Segundo, J. P., Araña-Iniquez, R., and French, J. D. Behavioral arousal by stimulation of the brain in the monkey. *J. Neurosurg.,* 1955, *12,* 601–613.

Sharpless, S., and Jasper, H. H. Habituation of the arousal reaction. *Brain,* 1956, *79,* 655–680.

Sprague, J. M., Chambers, W. W., and Stellar, E. Attentive, affective, and adaptive behavior in the cat. *Science,* 1961, *133,* 165–173.

CHAPTER 7

Adolph, E. F. Measurements of water drinking in dogs. *Amer. J. Physiol.,* 1939, *125,* 75–86.

Anand, B. K. Nervous regulation of food intake. *Physiol. Rev.,* 1961, *41,* 677–708.

_______, and Brobeck, J. R. Localization of "feeding center" in hypothalamus of rat. *Proc. Soc. exp. Biol. Med.*, 1951, *77*, 323–324.

_______, Chhina, G. S., and Singh, B. Effect of glucose on the activity of hypothalamic "feeding centers." *Science*, 1962, *138*, 597–598.

Andersson, B. The effect of injections of hypertonic NaCl solution into different parts of the hypothalamus of goats. *Acta Physiol. Scand.*, 1953, *28*, 188–201.

_______, and McCann, S. M. A further study of polydipsia evoked by hypothalamic stimulation in the goat. *Acta Physiol. Scand.*, 1955, *33*, 333–346.

_______, and Wyrwicka, W. The elicitation of a drinking motor conditioned reaction by electrical stimulation of the hypothalamic "drinking area" in the goat. *Acta Physiol. Scand.*, 1957, *41*, 194–198.

*Bard, P., and Mountcastle, V. B. Some forebrain mechanisms involved in expression of rage with special reference to suppression of angry behavior. Research Publication Association for Research in Nervous and Mental Disease, 1948, *27*, 362–404.

Beach, F. A. Effects of cortical lesions upon the copulatory behavior of male rats. *J. comp. Psychol.*, 1940, *29*, 193–239.

*_______. *Hormones and behavior.* New York: Hoeber, 1948.

Brady, J. V., and Nauta, W. J. H. Subcortical mechanisms in emotional behavior: Affective changes following septal forebrain lesions in the albino rat. *J. comp. physiol. Psychol.*, 1953, *46*, 339–346.

Carlisle, H. J. Heat intake and hypothalamic temperature during behavioral temperature regulation. *J. comp. physiol. Psychol.*, 1966a, *61*, 388–397.

_______. Behavioral significance of hypothalamic temperature sensitive cells. *Nature*, 1966b, *209*, 1324–1325.

Davidson, J. M., and Sawyer, C. H. Effects of localized intracerebral implantation of estrogen in reproductive function in the female rat. *Acta Endocrinol.*, 1961, *37*, 385–393.

Egger, M., and Flynn, J. P. Amygdaloid suppression of hypothalamically elicited attack behavior. *Science*, 1962, *136*, 43–44.

Harris, G. W., Michael, R. P., and Scott, P. P. Neurological site of action of stilbesterol in eliciting sexual behavior. In G. E. W. Wolstenholme, and C. M. O'Connor (Eds.), *Neurological basis of behavior.* London: Churchill, 1958, 236–251.

Hetherington, A. W., and Ranson, S. W. Hypothalamic lesions and adiposity in rat. *Anat. Rec.*, 1942, *78*, 149–172.

*Hoebel, B. G., and Teitelbaum, P. Hypothalamic control of feeding and self-stimulation. *Science*, 1962, *135*, 375–376.

Isaacson, R. L., and Wickelgren, W. O. Hippocampal ablation and passive avoidance. *Science*, 1962, *138*, 1104–1106.

Janowitz, H. D., and Grossman, M. I. Some factors affecting the food intake of normal dogs and dogs with esophogostomy and gastric fistula. *Amer. J. Physiol.*, 1949, *159*, 143–148.

Keller, A. D. The role of circulation in the physiology of heat regulation. *Phys. Therap. Rev.*, 1950, *30*, 511–519.

*Klüver, H., and Bucy, P. C. Preliminary analysis of the functions of the temporal lobes in monkeys. *Arch. Neurol. Psychiat.*, 1939, *42*, 979–1000.

Larsson, K. Mating behavior in male rats after cerebral cortex ablation. II: Effects of lesions in the frontal lobes compared to lesions in the posterior half of the hemispheres. *J. exp. Zool.*, 1964, *155*, 203–214.

Magoun, H. W., Harrison, F., Brobeck, J. R., and Ranson, S. W. Activation of heat loss mechanism by local heating of the brain. *J. Neurophysiol.*, 1938, *1*, 101–114.

*Margules, D. L., and Olds, J. Identical "feeding" and "rewarding" systems in the lateral hypothalamus of rats. *Science,* 1962, *135*, 374–375.

Mayer, J. Glucostatic mechanisms of regulation of food intake. *N. Engl. J. Med.*, 1953, *249,* 13–16.

McCleary, R. A. Response specificity in the behavioral effects of limbic system lesions in the cat. *J. comp. physiol. Psychol.*, 1961, *54,* 605–613.

*Miller N. E. Analytical studies of drive and reward. *Amer. Psychologist,* 1961, *16,* 739–754.

Mirsky, A. F. Studies of the effects of brain lesions on social behavior in *Macaca Mulatta*: Methodological and theoretical considerations. *Ann. N. Y. Acad. Sci.*, 1960, *85*, 785–794.

Nakayama, T., Hammel, H. T., Hardy, J. D., and Eisenman, J. S. Thermal stimulation of electrical activity of single units of the preoptic region. *Amer. J. Physiol.*, 1963, *204,* 1122–1126.

Olds, J. Hypothalamic substrates of reward. *Physiol. Rev.*, 1962, *42,* 554–604.

Pribram, K. H., and Bagshaw, M. Further analysis of the temporal lobe syndrome utilizing fronto-temporal ablations. *J. comp. Neurol.*, 1959, *99*, 347–375.

Rosvold, H. E., Mirsky, A. F., and Pribram, K. H. Influence of amygdalectomy on social behavior in monkeys. *J. comp. physiol. Psychol.*, 1954, *47*, 173–178.

Satinoff, E. Behavioral thermoregulation in response to local heating of the rat brain. *Amer. J. Physiol.*, 1964, *206,* 1389–1394.

Sawyer, C. H. Reproductive behavior. In J. Field (Ed.), *Handbook of physiology*. Vol. II. Washington: Amer. Physiol. Soc., 1960, 1225–1240.

_______, and Kawakami, M. Interactions between the central nervous system and hormones influencing ovulation. In C. A. Villé (Ed.), *Control of ovulation.* New York: Pergamon Press, 1961.

Sheffield, F. D., and Roby, T. B. Reward value of a non-nutritive sweet taste. *J. comp. physiol. Psychol.*, 1950, *43,* 471–481.

_______, Wulff, J. J., and Backer, R. Reward value of copulation without sex drive reduction. *J. comp. physiol. Psychol.*, 1951, *44,* 3–8.

*Smith, O. A. Physiological basis of motivation. In Ruch, T. C., Patton, H. D., Woodbury, J. W., and Towe, A. L. *Neurophysiology.* Philadelphia: Saunders, 1965, 494–505.

Teitelbaum, P. Sensory control of hypothalamic hyperphagia. *J. comp. physiol. Psychol.*, 1955, *48,* 156–163.

_______, and Campbell, B. A. Ingestion patterns in hyperphagic and normal rats. *J. comp. physiol. Psychol.*, 1958, *57,* 135–141.

_______, and Epstein, A. N. The lateral hypothalamic syndrome: Recovery of feeding and drinking after lateral hypothalamic lesions. *Psychol. Rev.*, 1962, *69,* 74–90.

Verney, E. B. The antidiuretic hormone and the factors which determine its release. *Proc. Roy. Soc.*, 1947, *B 135,* 25–105.

Wasman, M., and Flynn, J. P. Direct attack elicited from hypothalamus. *Arch. Neurol.*, 1962, *6,* 220–227.

Weiskrantz, L. Behavioral changes associated with ablation of the amygdaloid complex in monkeys. *J. comp. physiol. Psychol.*, 1956, *49,* 381–391.

CHAPTER 8

Agranoff, B. W., Davis, R. E., and Brink, J. J. Memory fixation in the goldfish. *Proc. Nat. Acad. Sci.*, 1965, *54*, 788–793.

Davis, R. E., Bright, P. J., and Agranoff, B. W. Effect of ECS and puromycin on memory in fish. *J. comp. physiol. Psychol.*, 1965, *60*, 162–166.

Dingman, W., and Sporn, M. B. The incorporation of 8-azaquanine into rat brain RNA and its effect on maze-learning by the rat: An inquiry into the biochemical bases of memory. *J. psychiat. Res.*, 1961, *1*, 1–11.

Fitts, P. M., and Posner, M. I. *Human performance*. Belmont, Calif.: Brooks/Cole, 1967.

Flexner, J. B., Flexner, L. B., and Stellar, E. Memory in mice as affected by intracerebral puromycin. *Science*, 1963, *141*, 57–59.

Gastaut, H. The role of the reticular formation in establishing conditioned reactions. In H. H. Jasper, L. D. Proctor, R. S. Knighton, W. C. Noshay, and R. T. Costello (Eds.), *Reticular formation of the brain*. Boston: Little, Brown, 1958, 561–579.

Girden, E., Mettler, F. A., Finch, C., and Culler, E. Conditioned responses in decorticate dog to acoustic, thermal and tactile stimulation. *J. comp. Psychol.*, 1936, *21*, 367–385.

Grastyan, E., Lissak, K., Madarasz, I., and Donhoffer, H. Hippocampal electrical activity during the development of conditioned reflexes. *Electroencephalog. clin. Neurophysiol.*, 1959, *11*, 409–430.

Gross, C. G., Chorover, S. L., and Cohen, S. M. Caudate, cortical, hippocampal, and dorsal thalamic lesions in rats: Alternation and Hebb-Williams maze performance. *Neuropsychol.*, 1965, *3*, 53–68.

Hydén, H. Biochemical changes in glial cells and nerve cells at varying activity. In O. Hoffmann-Ostenhoff (Ed.), *Biochemistry of the central nervous system*. Vol. III. *Proc. of the Fourth Intern. Congr. of Biochem.* London: Pergamon Press, 1959, 64–89.

———, and Egyhazi, H. Nuclear RNA changes of nerve cells during a learning experience in rats. *Proc. Nat. Acad. Sci.*, 1962, *48*, 1366–1375.

Jacobson, A. L., Babich, F. R., Bubash, S., and Jacobson, A. Differential approach tendencies produced by injections of RNA from trained rats. *Science*, 1965, *150*, 636–637.

Jasper, H. H., and Shagass, C. Conditioning the alpha occipital rhythm in man. *J. exp. Psychol.*, 1941, *28*, 373–388.

John, E. R., and Killam, K. F. Electrophysiological correlates of avoidance conditioning in the cat. *J. pharmacol. exp. Therap.*, 1959, *125*, 252–274.

Lashley, K. S. In search of the engram. In F. A. Beach, D. O. Hebb, C. T. Morgan, and W. W. Nissen (Eds.), *The neuropsychology of Lashley*. New York: McGraw-Hill, 1960.

———. *Brain mechanisms and intelligence*. Chicago: University of Chicago Press, 1929.

———. The mechanism of vision: XVII. Autonomy of the visual cortex. *J. genet. Psychol.*, 1942, *60*, 197–221.

Meikle, T. H., and Sechzer, J. A. Interocular transfer of brightness discrimination in "split-brain" cats. *Science*, 1960, *132*, 734–735.

Milner, B. Some effects of frontal lobectomy in man. In J. M. Warren and K. Akert (Eds.), *Frontal granular cortex and behavior*. New York: McGraw-Hill, 1964, 313–334.

Mishkin, M. Perseveration of central sets after frontal lesions in monkeys. In J. M. Warren and K. Akert (Eds.), *Frontal granular cortex and behavior.* New York: McGraw-Hill, 1964, 219–241.

Morrell, F., and Jasper, H. H. Electrographic studies of the formation of temporary connections in the brain. *Electroencephalog. clin. Neurophysiol.*, 1956, *8*, 201–215.

Myers, R. E. Interocular transfer of pattern discrimination in cats following section of crossed optic fibers. *J. comp. physiol. Psychol.*, 1955, *48*, 470–473.

________. Function of corpus callosum in interocular transfer. *Brain*, 1956, *79*, 358–363.

________. Transmission of visual information within and between the hemispheres: A behavioral study. In V. B. Mountcastle (Ed.), *Interhemispheric relations and cerebral dominance.* Baltimore: Johns Hopkins University Press, 1962, 51–74.

________, and Sperry, R. W. Interocular transfer of a visual form discrimination habit in cats after section of the optic chiasma and corpus callosum. *Anat. Rec.*, 1953, *115*, 351–352.

*Sperry, R. W. Cerebral organization and behavior. *Science*, 1961, *133*, 1749–1757.

Stamm, J. S., and Sperry, R. W. Functions of corpus callosum in contralateral transfer of somesthetic discrimination in cats. *J. comp. physiol. Psychol.*, 1957, *50*, 138–143.

Walker, E. L. *Conditioning and instrumental learning.* Belmont, Calif.: Brooks/Cole, 1967.

Weintraub, D. J., and Walker, E. L. *Perception.* Belmont, Calif.: Brooks/Cole, 1966.

NAME INDEX

SUBJECT INDEX